Technological Forecasting

edited by R. V. ARNFIELD

---

at the University Press
Edinburgh

22 George Square, Edinburgh
85224 069 4
North America
Aldine Publishing Company
529 South Wabash Avenue, Chicago
Library of Congress Catalog
Card Number 71-77158
Printed in Great Britain by
T. & A. Constable Ltd, Edinburgh

Preface

Within the last decade government departments and private corporations have come more fully to realize that the expensive and far reaching decisions they are called upon to make involve a number of factors, all interrelated. To evaluate each of these and their impact on the possible variations in a decision normally requires consideration and coordination of a number of economic, technical and social elements. It requires these to be projected into the future, in so far as this can be done. Too often, the old empirical method involved dams which had no water to catch, roads which led nowhere or railroads devoid of goods or passengers.

The sum of this process is known variously as total systems analysis, technological forecasting or long-range economic planning. The University of Strathclyde, through its European Conference on Technological Forecasting, held in Glasgow in June of 1968, has rendered a great service to this art by assembling a group of the foremost thinkers in the field. Anyone interested in this vital type of planning will be well repaid by a careful reading of the papers assembled in this volume.

As one convinced of the need and value of the type of planning described, I would like at the same time to urge all planners to keep the implementation stage in mind while doing their work. There are too many file cabinets and bottom drawers filled with 'plans' which never see the light of day. A filed plan is no plan. It is the proper balance between the carefully thought out plan and the will and ability to implement it which give the economy the lift desired, which is, after all, 'the object of the exercise'.

Admiral Elliott B. Strauss

Contents

Part 1

General

ROBERT JUNGK

Technological Forecasting as a Tool of Social Strategy

The recent student revolts in the Western world have in my opinion a strong bearing on technological forecasting and its role in society. One of the outstanding targets of protest was 'the wrong use of technology'. The young men and women who took this stand were no Luddites. They did not propose to do away with all machinery. They want to change technology by directing it toward different goals. Many of them feel that such a mutation of mankind's most important material base will only be possible after a radical political reversal has taken place. Others hope that a gradual transformation towards a more human technology might be possible if the aims of a comprehensive social strategy could be made as clear and urgent as the objectives of the military and the industrial establishments.

This discontent cannot be ignored by those who make it their business to look into the future. It is one of the most serious consequences of the rapid industrialization we have experienced in the last twenty years, spelling out the growing alienation between modern man and the world he created for himself. Technological forecasting has greatly helped to bring this kind of world about. It played an important part in the creation of modern weapons systems and product lines. It might now help to clear the path for a helpful and protective technology, serving, instead of subjugating, man and his environment.

Discussing the growing impact of technological forecasting on society, Erich Jantsch warned:

> 'There can be no doubt that, with the full integration of exploratory and normative technological forecasting in a feedback scheme, man is developing a powerful means of directing and concentrating human energy and of interfering with the movement of history. He will have to guard against consequences of the sort Goethe's *sorcerer's apprentice* experienced.'

The fact that technological forecasting is not 'hardware', neither a machine nor a bomb, has made it appear as something rather innocuous not only in the eyes of the public but even in the judgment of many of its practitioners. It is high time that we begin to see it as a *most potent intellectual instrument* with possible and probable decisive impact on things and events to come. Therefore it will certainly have to be handled less secretively, more diligently and in more democratic ways than hitherto. For, if we spoil the future as we have spoiled our environment, through avidity and narrowmindedness, hoping to gain power for partial interests by control and manipulation of human development, we are in for an epoch of despotism and desperation, of tyranny and revolt.

So far, disciplined technological forecasting has not only been created but also dominated by the military. And quite rightly so. They had the foresight to start the first groups dedicated to the systematic study of long-range developments. They created the type of intellectual interdisciplinary institution which has been dubbed *think factory*, and they were tolerant enough to let the people working there devote a considerable part of their energy to the study and development of new methods.

But now many scientists and engineers employed by these establishments see themselves saddled with a dilemma rather similar to the one which confronted physicists and technicians in wartime Los Alamos. A number of them at least are aware that they have helped to develop important know-how, which might be used for the preparation of war as well as for the preparation of a more livable, more civilized future. They feel that the social and societal problems and possibilities which could and should be tackled by the use of these new tools have had a relatively low priority. Partly as a result of that 'inside pressure' some of the *think tanks* working for the US Armed Forces have – as you know – recently increased the number of studies devoted to civilian problems as a kind of benign sideline. But even now – quite understandably if one takes into account who after all pays the piper – the bulk of the intellectually brilliant work in these institutions is dedicated to subjects which are directly or indirectly related to the task of military posture and future strategic contingencies.

The recent emergence of organizations devoted almost entirely to *Social engineering* in the US as well as in Europe and Asia seems to be more promising than the partial reconversion of the old military *think tanks*. Not only because they will at last focus all efforts on such urgent problems as famine, urban renewal, pollution, medicine, and education, but even more, because they may be able to develop mental attitudes and styles of thinking, approaches, methods and correspondingly, forms of internal organization, which will have to differ considerably from the concepts and procedures of the first – shall we now call it *historic*? – phase of forecasting.

There is one passage in the rightly famous survey by Jantsch which has worried me ever since I read it. Here it is:

'It should be clearly understood that normative technological forecasting is meaningful only if two conditions obtain: If the levels to which it is applied are characterized by constraints; normative forecasting can be applied to the impact levels (goals, objectives, missions) only if these levels are sufficiently "closed" by natural or artificial forces, or by consensus (for example an agreed set of values or ethical directives, etc.; *fully integrated normative forecasting is applicable only to a "closed" society*;

'If more opportunities exist and are recognized on these levels than can be exploited under given constraints; normative forecasting is essentially an attempt to optimize, *which implies selection.*'

Don't these passages point to a kind of society whose ideal model would be an army or another kind of military organization? These closed societies can define their strategic goals and tactical targets more clearly than other more complex and contradictory social units. Their linear autocratic command structure is built to assure the fast, smooth, undisputed execution of planned objectives.

The suspicion that technological forecasting as conceived by Jantsch might be used to pave the way for an authoritarian, totalitarian technocracy is strengthened by the fact that, quoting Salvador de Madariaga, he tries to support his position by elevating social compulsion to the rank of a natural force comparable to Gravity in the Universe.

If we look at *technological forecasting* as it is used today we find – with very few exceptions – precisely the style of decision-making at work, which is typical for closed societies. Small managerial groups helped by the staff work of scientific and technological experts invent and prepare strategies without ever consulting those who will simply have to accept the social consequences of ideas, concepts and plans – conceived without their participation and in most cases without their knowledge.

An interdisciplinary approach, the widening of the data bases by the inclusion of social and political, biological and psychological parameters will by itself alone not be sufficient to assure the right use of technological forecasting, because it will only assure a more sophisticated style of manipulating society towards goals which have been chosen by the power elite.

Are these groups interested in a radically new technology? Are they inclined to work for the common good? Are they really innovation minded? Donald A. Schon, Director of OSTI, who has worked and is still working as consultant to major industrial companies, thinks there exists in the corporate society an *unofficial view* which runs like this:

'Technical innovation is dangerous, disruptive and uncertain. It is the enemy of orderly, planned activity. It changes everything about the business we are in. It hurts. Let us talk about it, study it, praise it, espouse it – anything but do it.' In his searing indictment of this mentality he cuts even deeper: 'Technological innovation attacks the corporate society on all levels. The corporate society is built to function on the model of the production process – that is to say, in a manner that is rational, orderly, uniform and predictable.'

The lack of action on the transportation crises in the highly industrial regions of the Western world seems to confirm this diagnosis. Far too many and powerful interests are afraid of radical technological innovations which might endanger the 'civilization of the motor car' and have not yet fully understood that their functional role – to provide transportation – should in the interest of society have precedence over the particular product they hope to sell.

The suspicion that *technological forecasting* is nowadays sometimes really used more to prevent a new and different future being born than to help that to happen, stems from developments like the Supersonic Transport Plane which is fostered on society by an industry afraid of the saturation of its markets and subsequent cutbacks. In this case 'prognosis' is used as propaganda which tries to persuade the public that such a development is necessary or even inevitable for a technically advanced nation. The existence of such a plane becomes a fixed item in more and more published anticipations to such a degree that opposing it means one is opposing 'the future'. Thus an interested forecast of tomorrow is used to justify a bad decision of today.

If we want to create a technology dedicated to goals which may be unprofitable in terms of money and power, but important for the 'quality of life' rather than the 'quantity of goods' at our disposal, then the people should have more opportunities to be consulted about the future technology they want and the future technology they would rather reject.

How could this be done? The first most obvious model of forecasting in a democratic framework has been clearly described by Nigel Calder, who thinks that each political party should have its portfolio of favoured technical trends which match its political intentions. Bertrand de Jouvenel in proposing his 'surmising forum' conceives a public institution even larger than Parliament for the discussion of 'possible and desirable futures' by qualified people from the most differing spheres of interest.

The opening up of a sphere which was up to now the exclusive domain of the scientific and technical expert must evoke objections and raise doubts reminiscent of the debates which raged in the transition period from feudal to parliamentarian forms of government. The 'aristocrats of knowledge' will be afraid that barbarian laymen might vulgarize and destroy what they have created. The level of discourse, they will let us know, would suffer; crude manners, cross words become the rule. Now such fears are not quite unjustified. Along with some overprecious rococo mannerisms developed in the oligarchy of expertize whose knocking is not really regrettable, other more valuable refinements would be endangered – at least in the beginning.

But, despite all that, the doors of the lecture halls, seminars, institutes, and laboratories will have to be opened much wider despite the initial difficulties to be expected. Otherwise it might become true, what the son of the German Nobel prize physicist Max von Laue once anticipated in an article published by the *Bulletin of the Atomic Scientists*: the popular outcry 'Hang all scientists on the lamp-posts' (or something more handy in an age of neon street lighting).

How will such a *democratization* be made to work? I see three main avenues:

(1) a continuous mutual learning process

(2) the education of sufficient intermediaries and 'interpreters'

(3) the creation of institutions, where experts and laymen meet and co-operate.

The learning process will have to be instituted on two levels:

(*a*) the interaction between experts and politicians

(*b*) the permanent conversation between experts and the larger public.

There are by now quite a few examples of the successful co-operation of scientific and political representatives. The French nuclear physicist Lew Kowarski has described how the diplomatic and scientific members of the Committee on nuclear controls, which met in Lake Success and Manhattan right after World War II, learned in many months of protracted and in the end unsuccessful debates to understand their necessary differences of approach to the same subject. In the end new species emerged – M. Zweginstew might classify them as *straddlers* – 'the scientific statesman' and the 'political-minded scientist'.

The reason why, in that case, the symbiosis worked to a certain degree might be discovered in the fact that the negotiations were protracted over years. The great number of meetings, certainly a source of unhappiness to most of the participants, had at least one advantage: they had time to study each other, to learn from each other.

The same cannot be said of most other meetings between the men whose discoveries have such decisive impact on society and those who are supposed to govern and control it. They tend to be much too short to be of an educational value. Far too often the administrators in government and business reject or – what may be even worse! – uncritically accept the conclusions of the experts, because they have not really understood them and are reluctant to say so. The German sociologist Hans Paul Bahrdt has pointed out that the scientists and technicians play in this context a role similar to that of the shamans, the holy magicians in primitive societies, and he is very sceptical if it will ever be possible to really bridge that educational gap. Here indeed exists a challenge which might be taken up by forecasters, who specialize in the technologies of learning and information.

But short of new devices, be they chemical, biological, or physical, which might increase the human capability to perceive and assimilate new knowledge, we will probably have to train thousands of human translators who will interpret and explain at meetings which bring experts together with political or industrial managers; and we will get used to them as we got used to the skilful and indispensable men and women who are helping us to overcome our language barriers.

In a society of the near future, where interaction between expert and layman is accepted as an indispensable foundation of democracy, education by schools, universities, training centres for adults, and the mass media will not only have to be greatly intensified, but must also adopt a different attitude towards innovation and change. Nowadays almost exclusive stress is laid on learning what has happened and has been done. Tomorrow we will have to draw attention to what will happen and might or should be done. At least one-third of all lectures and exercises ought to be concerned with scientific, technical, artistic, and philosophical work in progress, anticipated crises and possible future answers to these challenges. Pupils of all ages and all classes might be trained, in special courses, how to limber up their rusted imagination, just as they are taught to reuse their physical abilities in gymnastic classes. An exercise like the Glideway Project at MIT, under the guidance of Dean William Saifert, where students developed, with the help of eminent consulting experts, precise plans for a much needed future public transportation system in the crowded triangle of Boston, New York, and Washington, has not only created an advanced socio-technological proposal but, in the same time, a model for future-oriented engineering education.

The men and women brought up that way will have learned incentives to view technological innovation as something normal rather than as a kind of magic. They will no longer be overwhelmed by 'miracles' coming out of our laboratories, and will look at them in a less emotional, more critical way. Even the creators of that ever-changing environment, the researchers and engineers, will then no longer feel compelled to translate every possibility into reality. The seduction exercised by projects which are 'technically sweet', but 'socially monstrous' (such as ever more advanced weapons) may then begin to wane.

All these developments will seem less Utopian if we take into consideration the trend to ever more automation. The time saved in the production process might usefully be transferred at least partly to the understanding, discussion, and preparation of these processes. In his very impressive analysis of the recent social upheaval in France the well-known sociologist Georges Friedmann has pointed out that the strikes were only incidentally connected with economic aims. The deeper reason seems to stem from the malaise felt by millions of industrial employees who are no longer satisfied to work without participating in the creative process underlying it. The technical environment, as we know it today, uses only a part of the human capabilities which exist either dormant or crippled in the 'working force'. There goes right through our industrial work a new division of haves and have-nots along psychological rather than economic lines. The 'affluent' are those who are employed in positions where they can develop initiative, creativity and responsibility, while the 'poor' are those millions of (materially sometimes quite well off) men and women who waste a large part of their life in tasks which are dull, repetitive, outlined by others than themselves.

The democratization of technological forecasting will probably lengthen the process of deliberation and decision, but it will be time well employed and worth it. Not only because these decisions, which will have an impact on almost everybody's life, will then have been taken by a more representative sample of the population than so far, but also because it might restore in millions the feeling that the industrial civilization growing out of such debates is their work, is a creation they have been able or at least been asked to contribute to.

Another more serious objection against such a fundamental extension of public rights, which almost certainly will be heard, concerns the adaptability of planning and production processes which nowadays tend to be rather inelastic and are therefore best served by plans with as few disturbing factors as possible. Will it be possible to develop industrial systems which would respond faster and more willingly than the present ones to demands for changes emerging from democratic debates? With how much 'feedback' could more elastic technologies cope? A different evaluation of the economic side, which might no longer be so much constrained by considerations of rentability, might help. But even more important would be the design of new planning and production devices of greatly increased plasticity and openness to perpetual change.

Pierre Naville of the Conseil National de la Recherche in France has compared thinkable machines of the future to words of our language which can be combined into an immense variety of different sentences. And there will be in addition new words or changed words or words taken from one language into the other one. The possibility of such a supermobile technology should at least be envisaged.

The democratization of the forecasting activities implies a pluralism of forecasting institutions. Every social organization from the largest to the smallest should be able to see the way ahead of it. Therefore, a 'look out department' or 'prognostic cell' will be an essential part of every collective structure just as important as eyes and ears are to an individual. There will be large institutes on a planetary, continental, and national level, medium ones dedicated to regions, urban areas, and small ones to neighbourhood groups.

Different political associations, different productive enterprises and different professions will all have their own forecasting units differing to a certain extent in their functions, methods, and features, but probably (or at least desirably) linked to each other in a vast network. The quality of such a 'world brain' will probably increase with its ability to develop a very high degree of differentiation and variety. In order to assure the survival of humanity it will have to acquire heuristic functions plus the ability to grow and correct itself by experience.

In this family of 'lookout institutions' there should also be a number of experimental units trying continually to re-examine, change and possibly improve the styles and methods of forecasting. They might for instance devise 'prognostic cells' which are:

(1) More open to the unpredictable, more flexible, readier to update, correct and give up earlier assumptions. One of the devices to escape the 'jail of the present', which confines all men trying to look into the future might be the deliberate use of paradoxes, the effort to formulate the opposite to every thinkable concept, to test anticipations by standing them on their heads or enriching them with 'impossible' and 'foolish' parameters. The study of mental illness and the way the deranged mind deforms reality could perhaps be used for the willed production of 'crazy ideas'. Experimentation with chemical imagination helps (drugs) should not be excluded. This would simply be in line with tradition of the Greek oracles.

(2) These experimental forecasting laboratories should certainly try to get a mental grip on qualitative phenomena, which cannot be quantified or – what is more common – are harmed, even killed by quantification. They might study the nature and role of processes, images, perspectives, 'wholes' (which implies more than systems), e.g. properties, which can be felt, but not yet expressed in any existing form of language.

(3) They would be ready to use and to develop intuitive, imaginative, and visionary approaches.

(4) They will try to follow up not only direct and secondary possible consequences of innovation, but also tertiary and even further implications. This will almost certainly not lead to even remotely reliable forecasts, but prove to be an interesting technique for the deepening of imagination.

An important function of these 'Institutes' for Advanced Forecasting will be the 'invention of futures'. Dennis Gabor, who coined this inspiring notion, has spoken about a possible 'Mozartian future'. If one conceives a model in which the quality of an artist is the decisive feature, why should not composers, painters, poets help the forecasters in their creation of 'possible' and 'desirable futures'? Already, today, a number of artists are using technology not for production but for play. The machines of Schoeffer, of Tinguely and Rauschenberg, the mobiles of Malina and Duchamp may be important forerunners of future apparatus, because they have been liberated from their selfdom of speed and efficiency. Could we not conceive rolling mills, which produce fewer goods at a slower pace, because the employment they give may at a certain point of history be more desirable than the amount of things they might produce? Is it not thinkable that the artist in man will be inspired by the artificial world around him as he was before by the natural world? That would be the moment when we really will have lost our fear of the robots, because we will assign them as one of their functions the task to give us aesthetic thrills and make us laugh.

While I am writing this I can imagine the kind of faces some of you may make perhaps, when I will be reading this in Glasgow. After all, here we have come together for rather serious purposes and that fellow talks about mechanical play-things. Quite. But is not that kind of reaction indication to the limitation of our own, our very special human qualities we all have learned to accept almost without realizing it? We have become beasts of burden, and of prey, the exemplary mass producers, the exemplary mass killers. What a fall from the ideal of the Greek citizen, of the English Gentleman. True – a world afraid of the most terrible of all wars, a world overshadowed by the much too long neglected danger of mass-starvation is no playground, is no place where one could really enjoy the less material, the so-called 'useless' joys and sorrows human life has to offer. Yet precisely by our fixation on the goals of necessity and the most efficient means to reach them we may have created that nightmare against which more and more people – not only the hippies – revolt by open withdrawal or by meaningful and meaningless acts of destruction.

Therefore I consider it to be useful to discuss the powerful new intellectual instrument that is *technological forecasting* in the context of larger not specifically technical goals. Technology and technological forecasting will have to become tools of man and his society. This has been said quite often. But when we conceived man mainly as *homo economicus* and *man, the warrior*, maybe we should add *human forecasting* to technological forecasting and try to draw an envelope curve of man. This would lead us straight into biology, psychology, philosophy, possibly to the frontiers of metaphysics. Quite a task, quite an adventure, quite a challenge!

HENRI AUJAC

Technical Progress and French National Planning

If one had to illustrate to what degree technical progress plays a decisive part in the economic as well as in the social and political development of a society, and if as a consequence one wished to demonstrate just how important it is that forecasts of technical evolution should be available, no better example could be found than the crisis which has just shaken French society to its very foundations. This crisis had indeed many causes: one, however, does not seem to have been sufficiently stressed, although its importance was decisive: the acceleration of technical progress in the French economy in recent years. This acceleration has caused or strengthened certain maladjustments such as: stagnation or decline of certain traditional industries and fast growth of new techniques and activities, brutal inequality of treatment of the professional qualifications of workers, technicians, and executives, accentuation of the conflict between the old and the young generation, the latter technically better qualified to serve the new expanding industries, sudden evidence of the obsolete character of much of the teaching in the Universities, etc. . . . The conscious realization of these maladjustments by the various social groups concerned resulted in a generalized fear of the future: more or less consciously, workers, students, and executives suddenly found themselves afraid of being rejected by a society which was, according to a widespread myth, to lead them to the Golden Age. . . .

How has this technical progress, which so deeply perturbs the whole of French society, been accounted for in the effort towards national planning?

We can distinguish two periods. In the first, technical progress was considered as an autonomous growth factor. There was no specific planning policy, but only forecasts concerning technical progress: and technical progress was left outside the field of planning. In the second period, the attitude of the French planners radically changed: technical progress has progressively become one of the fundamental objects of the planning policy.

It is indeed difficult to put a precise date on this change in outlook, which, at first, was a hardly perceptible movement, gradually becoming stronger and stronger. Nevertheless 1965, the year of the beginning of the Fifth Plan, can be considered as the turning point. It was during the Fourth Plan that the Centre National d'Etudes Spatiales was created and the construction of the uranium enrichment plant at Pierrelatte was begun. It was at the end of 1964 that the first research concerning a new series of entirely French computers was started. And in 1966, the post of Délégué á l'Informatique was created and the 'Plan Calcul' was launched.

We shall now examine the practical problems which the planners were faced with in each period, the policy they adopted to try to solve the problems, the difficulties they met with, concerning the policy adopted or the methods of planning. This analysis should contribute to define the relations between technical progress and national planning.

The First Phase

The French economy, after rebuilding the ruins of war, grew at a rate rarely attained in French history. Although certain social categories or geographical regions were left behind, the country as a whole was getting much richer. Global productivity increased by 4·5 per cent per annum on average, and, most important, this progress was realized by relatively traditional techniques. New industries, new products, and new techniques indeed appeared and were developed, but these industries, products, and techniques apparently integrated into national production with no difficulty and seemed to create no particular problem.

The French planners then set themselves the following problem: how could one make it possible for the French people to enjoy greater and greater quantities of the goods and services they already had? Or, in other words, what policy should be adopted in order that the annual growth rate of the GNP should be as high as possible under two constraints: high employment and no inflation?

The content of the policy to be adopted to achieve these ends was easy to define: in the short term, control the growth of final demand, by alternatively or simultaneously acting on consumer and investment demand; keep an eye on the growth of productivity in order to see whether final demand was reaching a sufficient level to use the manpower liberated by progress in productivity; and lastly, encourage, through long-term economic information concerning first the four- and then the five-year span covered by the Plan, a harmonious growth of the various sectors of the economy: industry, agriculture, services.

Clearly a preferential method for implementing such a policy was National Accounting. With the balance sheets drawn up each year to define the *economic budget* of the country, it was possible to set final demand at a suitable level to avoid unemployment and inflation: and indeed, save for some rare incidents, this objective was remarkably well fulfilled during this first period. As for the long term, the inter-industrial input-output tables made it possible to determine growth rates for the various sectors which would be compatible with each other and compatible also with the consumption and investment objectives corresponding to the terminal year of the Plan. As we can see, during this period, technical progress was not generally an object of planning policy, but it had nevertheless to be taken into account in the methods of planning. We shall now examine how this was done.

Technical progress must necessarily be taken into account when an inter-industrial input-output table is projected, to enable the production objectives for industry, agriculture, and service employment to be equated with the consumption objectives. In fact, this amounts to forecasting the evolution of capital ratios, input-output ratios, productivity ratios, for a table with about a hundred lines and columns (and it is important to keep this number in mind).

How can one forecast the evolution of these various ratios? The French Plan has constituted 'vertical' committees responsible for each of the main sectors of the economy. These committees bring together managers of firms in the industry concerned, technicians specialized in the economic and technical evolution of the industry in question, civil servants from the ministries concerned, and of course representatives from the Plan. These committees must supply information on the evolution of capital, input-output, and productivity ratios. The information thus made available varies in significance from committee to committee, but is always of interest. However, the procedure is not without difficulties.

A first difficulty is caused by the vocabulary of products and techniques under about a hundred headings, used in the input-output tables: this vocabulary is much too condensed for a dialogue to be possible between the national accountants responsible for the input-output tables and the technicians from the industries, for the simple reason that they do not speak the same language. The national accountants describe the whole of the production process with the hundred words of their input-output classification; the company managers use a few thousand words to describe their industry; these correspond more or less with the classifications the various professional organizations use to gather the information concerning the activity of the various sectors of the French economy. As for the engineers in R&D laboratories and agencies, who are specialized in new techniques, their vocabulary is different still. They express themselves in an extremely detailed manner, and their language has little in common with that of the national accountants, or even with that of the managers of industrial companies.

A second difficulty arises when one tries to integrate technical progress into input-output tables: the period for which one can forecast with any reasonable conviction varies from industry to industry. For some industries, in which technical progress is very fast (electronic computers or lasers for instance) a four- or five-year forecast is relatively long-term; for other industries, where technical progress is more or less stabilized, a ten-year forecast seems possible without too great a risk. Now the projection of the input-output table is made for a given year, which is the terminal year of the Plan, generally five years away. Consequently, the forecasts for each activity of the national economy must be made for that year without considering, or insufficiently considering, the fact that probable forecasting errors differ according to the various activities; this in a way amounts to considering that technical progress develops in a comparable manner in the various sectors of the economy; and this we know to be wrong.

For all these reasons, and others still, it proves extremely difficult to integrate all the technical information supplied by the industry committees of the Plan into modifications of the various ratios used for projecting the input-output table and forecasting the terminal year of the Plan. It is, besides, significant that the Bureau d'Informations et de Prévisions Economiques (BIPE) was created some ten years ago by the French administration, in particular the Commissariat Général au Plan, precisely in order to gain a better knowledge of the evolution of these ratios. This organization brings together the administration, the professional organizations, and about sixty of the larger French companies. One of its main objects is to facilitate the dialogue between those responsible for economic policy and planning and the sector of private enterprise, precisely in the field of expected or desired technical evolution.

The various efforts in this direction can be briefly summarized as follows. A first line of approach was to try to draw up input-output tables in very precise language which would be easy for industrial executives to read. The relatively good triangulation of the French tables made it possible to consider groups of industries which were very tightly interrelated. This permitted a certain degree of liberty in the description of the production processes, as it was possible, in describing each group, to use a specific terminology, as used by the profession in question. This description was attempted both in values and, whenever possible, in quantities. Then, on this new basis, the dialogue was resumed with the industrial executives, in their own language, and it was found in fact that a satisfactory dialogue could be established, in certain sectors of activity. But unfortunately this language proved insufficient to open a dialogue with the engineers and scientists engaged in research and development.

In order precisely to take into account the information supplied by the people responsible for research and development, the BIPE attempted to list the main inventions and innovations concerning a given industry. Then, for each of these products and techniques, situated at different stages of the 'research, development, prototype, small-scale production' chain, the BIPE tried to determine the possible diffusion of the new product or technique and the consequences of this diffusion on the economy as a whole. With this aim in view, information was gathered on each of these actual or potential innovations, on points such as its nature, the technical difficulties still to be overcome, the knowledge of the technical and socio-economic characteristics of the product or process, the expected advantage over the rival products or techniques presently in use, the probable main direct consequences on rival industries as well as on the industries which supply the materials or on those which use the product or process. The BIPE had also set itself the task of determining which industries would suffer and which would benefit by the industrialization of the innovation, what consequences were to be expected as to quantity and qualification of labour, how much and what type of machinery should be installed, at what date the first industrial applications could be expected, in which countries and which firms research was being carried out and how this research was financed (public or private funds), etc.

It is of course necessary to define the main factors which command the passage from invention to innovation. Some are of a political order, such as large public investment programmes or the research expenditures on public funds; others are of an economic order, such as the possible evolution of the various elements of the cost of the new product or the growth rate of the economy: it is obvious, for instance, that a high growth rate encourages the replacement of capital goods and consequently the diffusion of new products and techniques.

As one can see, the method rests on the following simple idea: around each actual or potential major innovation an attempt is made to build up a portion of input-output table, based on the analysis of possible outlets, uses of materials and labour qualifications, and especially (this is most important) described, not in the language of the existing techniques as used in the input-output table of the national accounts, but in a nomenclature which takes precisely into account the new products and techniques. It is no doubt unnecessary to insist on the importance and nature of the difficulties of such an approach: the extraordinary multitude and diversity of technical progress which might cause one to be smothered under the excess of materials, the difficulty of defining the future technical and economic environment in which the new products and processes will have to take their place, and consequently of selecting the techniques which will be viable and will be adopted in the future. This approach has however the advantage of enabling one to consider the forecasting 'horizon' specific to each innovation, in as much as such a forecast has still any guarantee of solidity!

We have tried to use both approaches simultaneously: on one hand the approach through relatively detailed input-output tables concerning strongly interrelated groups of industries in the traditional nomenclature corresponding to the techniques presently in use; and on the other hand the approach through the construction, around each innovation, of a portion of input-output table in new nomenclatures expressly referring to the new techniques which will or may be used in the future. We hoped that sooner or later these two approaches would meet and that a synthesis would then be possible; we took encouragement from the touching story of the blind man and the paralytic who, in spite of their infirmities, managed to move forward. But we must admit that the junction between these two methods has not yet occurred, and there are probably fundamental reasons why this junction can only be very superficial.

To conclude, during the first period which we have just described, French Planning has taken technical progress very much into account, but this progress has been considered as an autonomous variable whose evolution it was necessary to forecast, but which was not, in general rule, itself an object of planning.

The Second Phase

During the second period, which began only a few years ago, the attitude of the government towards the relation between planning and technical progress has been very different: now, one is trying to plan technical progress itself. We shall see how this change took place.

The French economy had rebuilt itself. The various colonial wars, fought with conventional weapons in Indochina and Algeria, had come to an end. The government then decided to equip the country with a modern armament, which meant the thermo-nuclear bomb, with aeroplanes and missiles capable of carrying it. The elaboration and application of this programme showed that the various French industries were not, as they stood, capable of fulfilling it; it showed that they had to develop a whole series of products and techniques which were quite new for them, and that, in any case, it was necessary to resort widely to foreign techniques, especially American techniques. Out of political considerations such as independence and national sovereignty, it appeared dangerous for French industry, and especially its advanced sectors, to be so dependent on foreign technology.

Besides, the economic authorities, particularly in the Délégation à la Recherche Scientifique et Technique, had strongly stressed the point

B

that the technological gap was widening between Europe and the United States, and that it had already and would have in the future a greater and greater influence on the evolution of the structure of exchanges between the United States and Europe, the United States supplying the products and processes incorporating much intellectual added value, whereas Europe would seem condemned to supply only traditional products requiring little intellectual value in their elaboration.

The French economists pointed out that although foreign investment in France was still relatively low, compared with the mass of new investment each year, it would be a great mistake to infer that its influence was slight. This investment is concentrated in advanced sectors and is thus placed in strategic positions; moreover, it is often made by multinational companies which are able to elude the control of any particular government, and consequently seem difficult to integrate into national planning.

For all these reasons, and others also, the French planners rediscovered a truth too often forgotten by the national accountants: the evaluation of the growth rate through GNP at constant prices can lead to serious errors in diagnosis concerning the state of health of an economy. Economic growth must be considered from at least two angles: quantity and quality. The evaluation of growth in terms of gross national production at constant prices can, under certain conditions, give a correct view of the quantitative aspect of growth; but it gives a very imperfect view of the qualitative difference implied by growth, qualitative difference which is precisely caused by technical progress.

With the qualitative aspect of growth more present to the mind, and having set themselves the objective of building up a modern army and reducing the gap between France and foreign countries, what policy should the Government logically try to follow? The Government, directly or through the agency of the Commissariat à l'Energie Atomique or the nationalized firms, launched a series of great programmes in the military, aeronautical, atomic, and spatial fields. The main effort was made in this direction, but the Government also put research and development funds at the disposal of the private companies; aid to industrial development of the results of research amounted to about twenty million dollars for 1966, the year in which this form of aid was started. During the Fifth Plan, this aid should amount to more than one hundred and twenty million dollars. It concerns a great variety of sectors, and is given with the object of aiding the development of new products and techniques. Quite recently, the Government has put into operation a *Plan Calcul* for the electronic industry, and has fostered the creation of a private firm capable of fulfilling it.

Thus, the effort of the French planners is now turned towards the implantation and development in France of a series of new and advanced industries, with the object of preserving the opportunity of the French economy developing in a relatively independent manner, and escaping from the domination of foreign technology. Besides, in the more traditional sectors, some relatively important actions have been started in order to encourage private firms to develop their effort in the field of research and development.

Such is, briefly summed up, the content of the present planning effort which aims to control and direct technical progress. What are the methods which enabled the elaboration of this policy? To tell the truth, this planning of scientific and technological progress is very recent, and was started and developed in a most empirical manner. We are only just beginning to be able to state clearly a certain number of problems posed by this new fashion of considering the relation between planning and technical progress, and we have only a glimpse of some of the principles underlying the methods which should enable the introduction of greater rationality in the definition of this policy.

The implementation of this new policy gives rise to a number of theoretical but also very practical problems, and we shall mention only a few, such as, for instance:

(1) From the point of view of general interest, is it possible to choose from amongst the new industries or the traditional industries those which it is specially significant to help, and upon what criteria should this selection be based?

(2) Is there a way of defining the nature and importance of the research and development effort necessary for aiding the fulfilment of any given programme?

(3) What should the behaviour of the Government and the nationalized firms be in order to efficiently help private companies to obtain desired results as concerns quality of products and techniques? The answer to this must obviously vary according to the strength and dynamism of the private firms considered; thus in the initial phase of the great atomic, military, and aerospatial programmes the public authorities found it necessary to assume responsibility for the general design of the equipment, restricting the private companies to the part of sub-contractors. We think this is not a good solution.

(4) Which leading company responsible for the design and direction of a large project should the authorities choose as contractor, with the object that this leader should be able to ensure the transfer to the private sector of the results of the research it will have to carry out on this occasion?

(5) What mechanism can be set up to control the use the authorities make of the exorbitant power they have of making the fortune, or

causing the ruin, of such and such a private firm when they give out contracts?

(6) In order to attain a certain independence in the technological field, is it necessary to promote all new and advanced techniques, or is it possible to develop only some of them, and if so, which ones?

(7) Is the scope the French economy offers not too narrow to justify the creation of advanced industries, and is it not essential to build a technological Europe as soon as possible?

These are but a few of the difficulties caused by the new attitude of the Government towards technical progress. The efforts undertaken in this direction had only just begun when new problems sprang up; we shall only mention two of them. The first concerns the relationship between new and traditional industries, the second concerns the rapid obsolescence of the national accounting methods as privileged instruments of national planning. This rapid obsolescence is precisely caused by the acceleration of technical progress.

The first problem we would like to evoke is the relationship between the traditional industries and the advanced industries which the Government is trying to implant in France. The implantation of these new industries corresponds to a double objective: diversification of French production so that the French economy should have at its disposal all that is necessary to enable its autonomous development; and assistance to the traditional industries in changing their technique of production by using the most advanced products and the most modern processes.

In fact, we can see that the advanced industries seem very tightly interrelated and that their interdependence is very strong. On the other hand these industries seem only to have very occasional and superficial relations with the traditional industries. For the time being, the advanced industries seem to develop independently from the traditional industries, without bringing them any significant help.

Some remarks should be made concerning the future of the relationship between the advanced industries on one hand and the traditional industries on the other. If the gap widens between the advanced industries and the consumer and capital goods industries, all the effort presently expended in France in the field of research and development will be vain. What is the present situation, from this point of view?

In every industry, and even inside a single company, two sectors coexist, one which may be considered as a prefiguration of the future, the other being sometimes prematurely considered as condemned. In an extremely simplified picture, one could distinguish, in the evolution of the production process, on one side new activities which require very qualified men capable of designing and working with very advanced techniques, products and equipment, and which must pay a high price for these men, equipment and techniques, because of their high cost at the present point of development; on the other side, traditional activities which are satisfied with men, equipment, and techniques of a more modest technical level, providing they can get them at as low a price as possible, the cost level being decisive for ensuring a satisfactory growth level for these activities. At present, the gap between these two groups of activities seems to be growing. From this point, several evolutions are possible, two of which we shall briefly outline: if the advanced activities continue together to grow at a sufficient rate to offer a large and stable market for the firms which supply them, a fall in the cost of the highly technically qualified men, equipment and techniques will probably follow, making them less inaccessible to the traditional industries. Besides, these traditional industries will certainly in the future become year by year more demanding on a technical plane. So it is possible that these two groups of activities, the advanced and the traditional, are destined sooner or later efficiently to help one another. This will happen when the advanced industries, in order to satisfy their technical needs, will have obtained costs economically interesting for the traditional industries. The symbiosis will then be total, and it will be true to say that industries today considered as advanced will have played a decisive part in the growth of the economy as a whole.

But things may happen differently. The success of the whole affair rests on the comparison of two rates: the rise of the technical requirements of the traditional industries, and the fall in price of the advanced technicians and equipment. All that encourages the acceleration of these two trends contributes to make the optimistic version of our forecast more likely: all that slows it down contributes to make it more like wishful thinking.

Now, for obvious reasons, the Government has the main responsibility for the evolution of the advanced sectors, as it is the main client. If Government demand has neither the necessary volume nor the necessary continuity, if the policy of the public authorities leads to the dispersion instead of the concentration of the production of advanced products and techniques, if the producers are confined to, accept or even demand, the part of mere sub-contractors and mere executants, only working for and only wishing to work for the public programmes, then the gap will remain and may even widen between advanced technical requirements and traditional economic requirements. All the potential wealth represented for the whole economy by the experience of the teams of scientists, engineers, architects, and companies, brought together by the great programmes for launching new industries, would then be irreparably lost. And in this case, the traditional industries would have to look abroad to satisfy their growing requirements for technical progress.

A Look Ahead

The second problem I would like to discuss is the following: the acceleration of technical progress and the opening of foreign markets impose a radical change in the rhythm and the quality of the development of the French economy, and consequently a reconversion of the French planning methods, the main directions of which can be summarized as follows.

The gradual opening of foreign markets makes the medium- and long-term forecast of foreign outlets impossible; the acceleration of technical progress makes the forecast of intermediate demand through the inter-industry input-output tables more and more uncertain. Up to now, the global optimum rate of growth, without unemployment or inflation, was determined on the basis of an evaluation of the supply and demand of labour, this evaluation itself resulting from the forecast of the evolution of the various activities and of their respective productivities by the mean of an input-output table. This method will prove less and less efficient, as it becomes less realistic; and, in the future, the uncertainty caused by the difficulty to integrate, in forecasting the evolution of the activity of each industrial or agricultural sector, the information concerning technical progress and international trade, will impose a complete reversal of the method: it will be necessary to take as a starting point the forecast of labour supply, defined by number and professional qualification, and to try to find out into what activities this labour power should be oriented in order that the French economy can continue to develop and to stay competitive on an international plane.

A change in methods must follow this change in the situation. Two instruments of planning will now prove indispensable:

The first instrument would be a systematic and permanent analysis of the main directions which technical progress seems to be taking in the various main activities. This analysis should enable companies not to stray towards technically obsolete directions of technological development. And it should enable the Government to elaborate a policy aiming, day after day, to reinforce the firms and the national industrial structures and to guide them steadily in the direction of realistic technical progress, and, for example, to orient the qualification of labour in consequence.

The second instrument would be a periodical technical survey which should show to what degree, considering the policy of foreign companies and governments, the policy followed both by French companies and by the French Government has improved or deteriorated

France's international position. This survey should be made at two levels: that of equipment, techniques, and services, where the existing situation should simply be described, and that of the companies and technical, industrial, and commercial structures, where one should look for elements of explanation of the situation previously described. International comparisons of the structures of the various rival industries and of the most dynamic companies would be a useful contribution to this line of research.

To define the new situation in which planning is placed as a consequence of the lowering of tariff barriers and the increasing importance of technical progress, we can perhaps use an analogy. The preparation of the Plan, in other words the industrial policy put forward by the Government and the instructions given to the various industries, can be likened to the preparation of the athletes which a country intends to enter for the Olympic Games. Each country prepares its own champions for this contest, and amongst these, several have serious chances of winning. It is impossible to foresee before each contest the nationality of the winner, in the same way as in the future it will be more and more difficult to forecast the evolution of the activity of a given industry. On the other hand, after the Games, it is very easy to see if a given country has won an honourable position in the international competition by counting up its gold, silver, and bronze medals. The periodical technical survey will make it possible to judge the competitive position of a given economy. The new conditions of economic development will impose a change in the methods of planning which will bring them rather close to those used for preparing athletes for the Olympic Games. The object will no longer be to try to tell the various industries what their level of production should be in five years if their growth rate is to remain sufficient to be compatible with the targets set by the Plan, in particular with the targets set for the level of consumption and employment. Nor will it be to use these forecasts of levels of production as reference figures for writing, five years later, the report on the execution of the Plan. The object will be to try to forecast, for the private companies, the level of introduction of new techniques and the level of prices which should be reached by the French companies who wish to occupy an honourable international position.

And then, one must see whether these technical forecasts were correct, and how far the policy of the French companies and public authorities has succeeded in keeping work on a level of professional qualification consistent with international standards.

Of these two planning instruments, one seems relatively easy to set up: the periodical technical survey. What about the other one, the forecast of the main technical trends which should appear in a given industry? Is such a forecast possible? That is what the Commissariat

Général au Plan asked the BIPE to find out, taking the textile industry as an example.

In a few words, this is what was done. An important quantity of national and international information was gathered concerning all the new products and techniques which are used or which stand some chance of being used sooner or later in the various sectors of the textile industry. After having in this manner defined and analyzed as completely as possible the economic and technical advantages of the present or future production techniques, the BIPE tried to forecast the relative importance of each of these techniques at different times in the future, until practically the year 2000. Then it tried to gain a synthetic view of the whole of the technical processes which the textile industries could use and of the whole of the products which they could make. Conclusions were also drawn in the field of employment, professional qualification, and also geographical location. Such a forecast is obviously difficult to make. Its quality depends on the quality of the information it was possible to use and, of course, on the quality of the team whose job it was to make it. In the example studied, it seems to have been proved that such a forecast was possible and could be made in sufficient detail to be directly usable by private firms, professional organizations or the Government.

To give only one result, the consequences on the level of employment are the following: the 350,000 unskilled workers of the textile industry may soon be unemployed if a considerable effort is not made to give them a qualification sufficient for their reconversion. If, in the same manner, we consider the other sectors of the French economy using much labour, we must conclude that technical progress will, very soon, upset the situation of employment and professional qualification. Today about four million workers earn less than 130 dollars per month; they are under-qualified workers. It is very likely that, before long, all these workers will be unemployed. As can be seen, the French economy is on the eve of feeling the full impact of the acceleration of technical progress; the economic political and social consequences may well be incommensurably greater than the trouble France only recently lived through.

The problems of all kinds created by the acceleration of technical progress, their frequently dramatic nature, the necessity of foreseeing this progress in order to analyze its consequences, to try to gain as much benefit as possible from it and to correct its harmful effects, do not concern France alone. For instance, technical progress should normally make the situation of insufficiently qualified workers worse everywhere in the world, in the same way as it widens the gap between the underdeveloped countries and the industrial countries.

For technical progress to become what it should be by nature: the source of welfare for the people of all countries and not a source of misery for insufficiently qualified labour and underdeveloped countries, studies should be undertaken now, on an international plane. These studies should concern the evolution of techniques, in the long and even very long term, and the consequences of this evolution on the relative situation of the various social groups in a given country and on the relationships of all kinds between technically developed countries and underdeveloped countries. Solutions must be looked for and proposed which may help to avoid widening the gap between the more and more miserable situation of others. And, lastly, these studies must be given the widest possible diffusion, as these problems directly concern all men of good will, in all countries of the world.

E. FONTELA

Technological Forecasting and Corporate Strategy

In recent years, European business firms have shown increasing interest in forecasting and planning the future. Motives vary from firm to firm and country to country, but it can be said that they have a common basis: while business expansion in the immediate post-war reconstruction period was a fairly straightforward matter, the mechanisms of economic growth became increasingly complex in succeeding years, making business opportunities harder to identify. Furthermore, the past twenty years have seen a continuing acceleration of produce and market change. The successful firm now needs to be able not only to perceive opportunities but also to know how to anticipate them. Thus management has arrived at the conclusion that anticipation of future changes and the introduction in due time of innovations which will best respond to them are a necessary pre-requisite of healthy corporate growth.

This more-or-less-consciously expressed need for crystal gazing has led to the development of a wide range of forecasting and planning techniques and exercises of varied sophistication. Two of the most notable elements have been the development of information (especially by means of direct surveys) and the building of quantitative mathematical models. However, it is by no means clear how far management decisions have in fact been made easier. In many cases it would seem that management is unable to clarify what type of changes it would like to anticipate; in others, the economic staffs of companies have not been in a position to develop methods of translating information on future changes into practical suggestions for management decisions, despite the fact that in a private corporation the improvement of decision-making processes is the only justification for forecasting studies, and consequently 'art for art' studies should be left to other institutions.

Management decisions can be broadly divided into two categories:

Actions, i.e. decisions under the direct control of the company policy-maker; and

Reactions, i.e. where many factors are outside his control.

As regards 'action' decisions, forecasting and planning can be said to be deterministic, and the use of optimization techniques is quite widespread. This of course is fairly well known. 'Reaction' decisions are basically concerned with market changes and thus market 'sense', i.e. ability to evaluate the effects of *social*, *technological*, and *political* changes as well as *financial/psychological*, or *price* changes. So-called technological forecasting should aim at improving the quality of this latter type of 'reaction' decision. If it could arrive at a nearly deterministic forecast, it could even change 'reaction' decisions into real 'action' decisions.

The definition of technological forecasting, seen from the point of view of the business firm, is (or should be) restricted to the anticipation of only such changes in technology as could have an impact on the future economy; in other words, forecasting future innovations on a time scale, and not only outlining some possible new fields for technical discoveries. It should also provide ways of achieving these innovations (objectives) using the optimum technical paths.

A distinction has been made, between 'exploratory' and 'normative' technological forecasting, which is extremely useful for our purposes. Simply stated, 'exploratory' forecasting consists in using our present knowledge of the potentialities and technical trends of Science for projection purposes under a *ceteris paribus* assumption, which generally neglects all other possible structural changes. 'Normative' forecasting, on the other hand, works backwards from future to present; it implies a coherent examination of future needs in a future society which helps to define, first, socio-economic objectives, and then purely technical research objectives; and the best way to achieve them. Obviously, techniques are never as distinctly different as that, and in general a feedback process is introduced which links the two.

Exploratory technological forecasting requires a good understanding of technological trends, gaps, and scientific possibilities. Good technical researchers, able to move above their single field of specialization, can interpret the progressive movement of the different disciplines and pinpoint the places where progress becomes possible. Consistency and coherence are not merely characteristic of an economic system; they are also fundamental to the development of the technical system.

We construct our technical knowledge much as a spider constructs its web. Let me briefly present an example of technological forecasting with a simple procedure, which gives surprisingly interesting results. This procedure has been developed at Battelle-Geneva by G. Bouladon for outlining 'transport gaps'.

The graph illustrated is, so to speak, three-dimensional, since the top line of the triangle formed by the figure represents optimum use; that is to say, it indicates maximum satisfaction to users. All along this line users would say that they were almost completely satisfied. The line below shows a lesser degree of satisfaction which is the limit

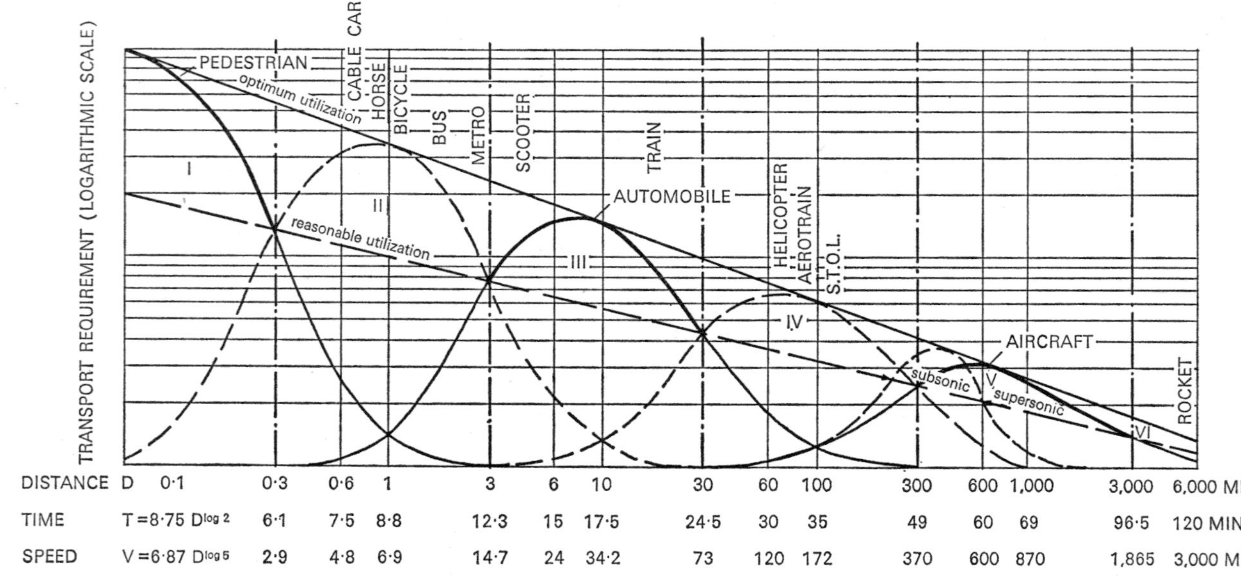
TRANSPORT REQUIREMENT (LOGARITHMIC SCALE)
PEDESTRIAN
CABLE CAR
HORSE
BICYCLE
BUS
METRO
SCOOTER
TRAIN
AUTOMOBILE
HELICOPTER
AEROTRAIN
S.T.O.L.
AIRCRAFT
ROCKET
optimum utilization
reasonable utilization
subsonic
supersonic
I
II
III
IV
V
VI
DISTANCE D 0·1 0·3 0·6 1 3 6 10 30 60 100 300 600 1,000 3,000 6,000 MILES
TIME T =8·75 D^log 2 6·1 7·5 8·8 12·3 15 17·5 24·5 30 35 49 60 69 96·5 120 MINUTES
SPEED V =6·87 D^log 5 2·9 4·8 6·9 14·7 24 34·2 73 120 172 370 600 870 1,865 3,000 M.P.H.

for reasonable use, as it represents the point at which 50 per cent of the users would be satisfied but the remainder would be dissatisfied. The figure is divided along the abscissa into five areas: (1) from 0 to 0·3 mile, (2) from 0·3 to 3 miles, and so on up to 3,000 miles. Beyond area 6 the distances are really related only to space travel. In each area, there should be an optimum means of transport; in fact these exist solely in areas 1, 3, and 5. They are: pedestrian, car, and air transport, which, to all intents and purposes, dominate the whole hierarchy of transport. Between these three curves there are obviously many other methods of transport which are used, such as the subway in large towns, but these do not provide the satisfaction of the first three. It can be seen that there is a gap in area 2, Transfer Systems, and also in area 4, corresponding to the aerotrain or to convertible aircraft.

In a recent OECD report there are a number of other procedures of exploratory technological forecasting, more or less sophisticated. Normally those based on visual appraisal (like envelope curves) seem more attractive. This or other kinds of exploratory forecasting furnish inputs for the decision maker; the limitation of the value of these inputs should, however, be clear; the possibility of filling up the first 'transport gap' (by Transfer systems) has been well known for many years, but what actually seems to interest the decision maker is at what moment this 'anticipation' will open or close business opportunities.

The question that now faces the decision maker is how to act correctly while waiting for the anticipation to become a reality. What is essential is to develop a strategy and to derive from it technical objectives, in order to be able to optimize the use of R&D funds and the policies of acquisition of techniques or firms. What is often said of a country, applies equally to a firm: 'a company has the future it deserves', and in the case of well-planned firms, 'a company has the future for which it is looking'.

The importance given to the question of planning for the future is increasing every day. For long-term planning purposes, the pinpointing of possible future innovations is insufficient. The future is not something entirely different from today: there is a future for existing polymers as well as for new polymers. What is more, the future is not 'one particular technology', just as transistors are not *all* the present: the future will be a system with a coherent equilibrium at any time period. Consequently, there is a need for looking into the future social, economic, and technical environment in a coherent way, and this is very difficult, as our own coherent appraisal of the present is very poor.

The environment in which companies will be operating will be affected by structural changes. In order to give to the decision makers ways of appreciating these changes better, *Battelle* has in the past five years been developing a programme to forecast the future of the United

States and Europe (this programme is called ACT = *A*ids to *C*orporate *T*hinking).

At the present moment, a complete circular model, programmed for use on a computer, is available for all the EEC countries, Great Britain and the United States.

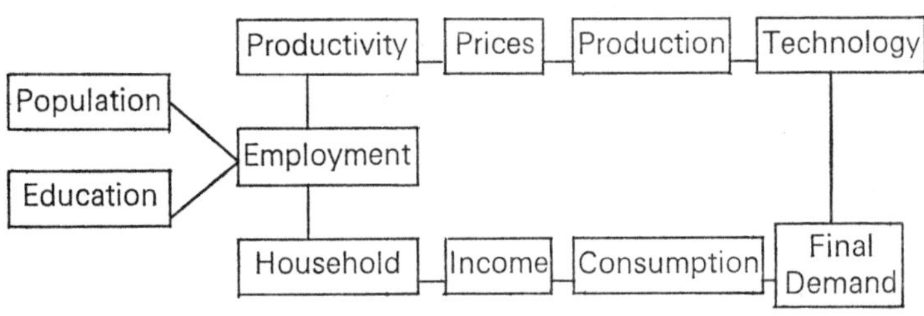

The model starts by building a socio-economic picture of the future, forecasting the education and the occupation of the members of the working population; it then groups individuals into households and distributes total income between them. Detailed consumer expenditure patterns, according to the occupation of the head of the household and its total income, are next used in order to estimate the future level of private demand for given products. Hypotheses and forecasts are then made as to the future structure of Government spending, of corporate investment and of foreign trade, in order to obtain a total picture of the final demand for commodities.

The second part of the model consists of input-output analysis, that is, the study of inter-industry relationships and of what raw materials, semi-finished goods, and machinery will be necessary to meet the requirements of final demand. This involves developing technical coefficients which give a quantitative relation between two industrial sectors and are modified by forecasts of technological change. The final result of this part of the research is an estimate of the total output of each commodity sector together with its participation in the formation of GNP; that is, its contribution to the value added of the economy.

The third stage of the model involves projections of wages and profits, and of prices of final commodities and introduced changes in relative prices. A forecast of average productivity rates by sectors has permitted a new estimation of the employment patterns and has led to a revision of initial assumptions and in this way has introduced a mechanism of overall iteration of the model. It can be easily seen that the main advantage of the model is its coherence which is assumed by its circularity: thus the industrial employment structure has enabled us to elaborate household consumption, and this final consumption gives rise to a demand for industrial production which subsequently requires a given employment. This global approach furnishes other elements for the elaboration of a corporate strategy; for instance, the question of the change of income distribution.

The concept of *mass market* is expected to change substantially in Europe during the next ten years. This can be seen clearly by looking at the distribution of households according to their global income (after tax).

The projection shows that European countries are rapidly moving into what could be called an open society.

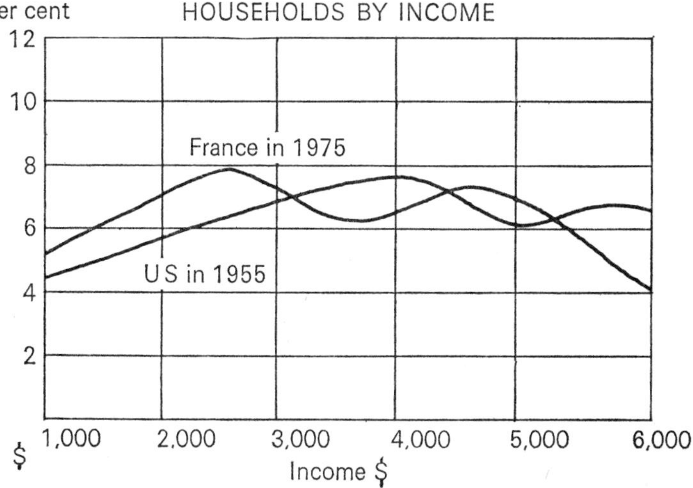

This is a society in which disparities between incomes are large: for in fact the only societies in which everyone has more or less the same are the least developed ones where there is general poverty. However, it is in these same societies that income disparities seem greatest, owing to the fact that rich households, though an infinite minority, are very visible. To take an extreme example, we could say that, in proportion to the population, there are more fortunes over 100 million dollars in the US than in Italy. France will be the first to arrive at an open society, and strikingly enough, its distribution will quite closely resemble present American distribution.

In an open society, doubling a salary is a socially easy operation. The group with £1,000 is identical in size to that which will have £2,000. There will be no social resistance. However, in Italy, while 10 per cent of households will have £1,000 only 5 per cent will have twice this sum.

Planning for an open society is quite different from planning for a concentrated society; the economy must produce not for one mass but for several masses, and manufacturers must aim at several markets. United, integrated Europe will provide the big mass.

When a manufacturer wants to produce a TV set aimed at a mass with an income of between £1,500 and £2,000 he will find that in 1975 this represents 20 per cent of British households, 16 per cent of Italian and German households, and 14 per cent of French households, which taken together will represent a larger market than the whole British market today.

The open society calls for large areas and for the integration of Europe, and in fact the Common Market is an essential pre-condition of the open society. Great Britain, which has the most dispersed income distribution in Europe and which does not have a large enough single market, urgently needs a unified market.

If we combine this kind of economic and social forecasting with pure exploratory technological forecasting, we may reach already some interesting conclusions: the flattening of the curves in the US has led to a higher uneconomic use of private cars for shorter distances: traditional public service systems (like buses, undergrounds, ...) have all seen their activity decrease in absolute terms since 1950. A part of the gap (shown by G. Bouladon) may very well be covered by an expensive semi-public system reserved at the beginning for the future very large group of the top level incomers,

Here we have improved the vision of the potential market, combining technical and economic information. But the strategy is not yet there because strategy is an essential *internal* company affair combining the risky and the sure.

The economist and the technical man have today a number of instruments which – if properly used – can positively provide fields for future development with fairly high possibilities of success. They can also evaluate with appropriate techniques the potential of the markets of existing products of the company, outline optimum fields of diversification in products of techniques already available. But in the end, choices have to be made by the decision makers, and these choices have to be made taking into consideration clear long term objectives.

Objectives can be expressed quantitatively (future level of sales, share of a market, number of employees) or in terms of performance criteria (profitability, capital value) or even in terms of rather abstract preferences of the firm ('the firm has to satisfy in the best way the need for communications of mankind'). These general objectives can be clearly expressed by the policy maker only if he is fully aware of the assets and constraints of the company.

If this is so, he can really fix an optimum strategy using the data from the forecasters concerning future markets and their costs in terms of *investments*:

(1) investments for the expansion of the capacity for producing existing products;

(2) investments for diversification of the present production lines by: acquiring new techniques; acquiring other companies;

(3) investments for R & D for innovations at different time periods, and of the possible returns on these investments.

If quantitative estimates can be given to all these parameters and to the risks involved, even at this final stage of the decision-making procedure mathematical models can be used with great advantages.

At certain points during this presentation I may have appeared to depart from the initial subject of 'technological forecasting and corporate strategy'. This has been quite deliberate since I felt that it was necessary to situate technological forecasting in the framework of all forecasting procedures. I then tried to make what is a very important point for us, that technological forecasting, to be close to the process of elaboration of a corporate strategy, should be accompanied by economic evaluations.

Nowadays, the concept of 'you can invent to order' is spreading rapidly. But only when a corporate strategy has been clearly defined can the 'orders' be made and carried out appropriately. And this strategy can be generally expressed in terms of 'products' or 'functions to be fulfilled'; that is on economic and social terms.

The need to appreciate the technical feasibility of the strategic objectives of the firm is however so important that continuous communication should be maintained between technical forecasters and long-range planners, and a great effort to improve the value of technological forecasting methods should be made.

PETER WARD AND BALINT BODROGHY

Planning in Conditions of Uncertainty

This is a joint paper. I (Peter Ward) will raise some doubts on the validity of present attempts to forecast the future of technology; my colleague (Balint Bodroghy) will put the question: 'if it were possible, would it be worth it?' Finally, I shall attempt to suggest an adaptive approach to planning (dynamic planning) suited to a highly uncertain context.

Perhaps I should try to summarize more clearly what I believe my colleague has in mind. As I understand his view, he maintains that, in financial terms, forecasting can be self-defeating, with time and expenditure building up in a cumulative way, such that the benefit will be marginal, or even negative, for any one company, as foreshortening defeats us when we endeavour to exceed the speed of light. In other words, it may eventually cost more than it is worth. Competitive forecasting is like giving trading stamps: we may have to do it to remain abreast, but in the longer term it is only a drain on our resources. More particularly, he will develop a theory of what he calls *hot and cold money*.

When the convener of the conference made his opening remarks he said very sensibly 'We cannot guarantee that nothing will go wrong, but let us know quickly if something does and we shall try to put it right.' This could be a text for dynamic planning, which is an approach to planning where everything goes wrong.

First, I would like to question some of the assumptions that we take for granted when we attempt to forecast, technologically or otherwise. 'Forecasting', a Danish economist is reported to have said, 'is very difficult – especially about the future.' In the last analysis, problems can only be solved empirically: we must observe and record what actually happens when certain steps are taken, use our good sense and apply whatever methods and techniques seem suitable.

Planning is often seen as an attempt to plot a route across the future to a predetermined destination. All we need is a satisfactory map. But, sadly, we cannot chart the future. There may be one or two uncertain points of reference, some lines of credible continuing development, branching in various directions, but mostly areas of doubt and emptiness. We are like Columbus facing the Atlantic; we do not even know that America is there. For part of our voyage we may hopefully depend on a number of recorded soundings and legendary channels, fix our position by observation of the stars, calculate wind force and direction, anticipate a hazard of advantage, but that is all. Worse, in forecasting the future, uncertainty is absolute and only probabilities having meaning.

Also, the future is inevitably abstract (we cannot see it, touch it, measure it or test it, only think about it) and we therefore tend to simplify its structure and its content in our minds. The predictables are all too clear: we know that we shall take our holiday as planned (Paris in the spring?) and that the Hanover Fair will still be held next year. Such confidence wrongly leads us to assume that a substantial sector of the future is foreseeable. Why should the future be any less complex than the geographical world with which we are so much more familiar? Descend in parts of Colorado or the Gobi Desert from another planet and you might suppose the earth was dead. We may impose a reference grid on time, but cannot say to what the grid refers.

Already I have tried to convey the indeterminate nature of the future by comparing it with a virtually uncharted sea, full of unknown or only half-anticipated currents. The comparison is only intended as a metaphor, and the future, unlike an unknown ocean, becomes continuously more indeterminate as the time scale is extended. We can be reasonably sure that a certain exhibition will be held next week. But will it be held again next year? And will it still be taking place in ten years time? Probabilities even vary for the same event. The three o'clock at Lingfield race course will almost certainly be run (weather permitting) but we are able to select the winning horse with much less confidence.

Neither is it a question of scale. The main sweep of events runs no more true to form. Perhaps in Britain and America we have been relatively sheltered, but what Central European family, corporation, government, or nation has not been shaken by some cataclysm every ten or thirty years? History cannot be conceived as built from countless tiny elements, smoothing the curves statistically as they become more numerous. Violent transitions occur throughout society and not predominantly at any level of importance.

The long-term plan that will survive its period, faced as it will be with social change, radical innovation, upheaval, and disaster, is very rare indeed. We are always surprised in the event and wisdom only teaches us that surprise is an immature emotion. Always? No, that is too certain a prediction. Perhaps we should seek some other datum line. 'If I were going to Killimore', replied an Irishman in answer to the enquiry of a motorist, 'I wouldn't start from here.'

No doubt we have a partial and imperfect chart, and that can help to some extent. But it may be the most important features that we are missing, like the outbreak of a war or the liquidation of a key supplier. What is the use of a roadmap that does not show a motorway, or shows a motorway that does not yet exist?

Causal Change. Perhaps it would be more useful to examine change. Change is more accessible to study than the world in ten years time, since it is occurring here and now, and has been taking place for all recorded history. We can therefore observe it and possibly discern its nature.

The determinist sees change as a fully interlocking system of cause and effect. Neglecting Heisenberg's uncertainty (which Einstein was unwilling to accept) and supernatural intervention, the world is reduced to primary units of energy or matter, such that their action in one moment determines their situation in the next, applying equally to brains and battles as to billiard balls. Were we able to ascertain the precise condition of the world today, we could calculate its state tomorrow and for a thousand years. But only a sublime computer could handle the necessary data: to build it we should need to duplicate the universe and stagger it in time.

Although we can conceive no analogue to represent the total pattern of experience, cause and effect remain fundamental to our thinking. Can they illuminate the processes of change at any other level than the sub-atomic? Certainly, if we wish to understand some situation, say an accident or a delinquent child, we try to identify the causes. But often it is only in retrospect that we are able to select and highlight the factors that are most significant.

Cause and effect can be regarded as a chain reaction, constantly branching and recombining, with consequences multiplied at every junction. Often it proceeds so rapidly that we cannot follow or control it, as with the complex of events, including the intermeshing timetables of military trains, that led to the European war in 1914. A man speaks harshly to his wife at breakfast and, depending on her state of mind and the pressures of her day, he may return at night to find her gone – or at her most affectionate. It is not only women who are unpredictable, but the world itself. (In *Breaking Strain*, the science-fiction writer Arthur Clarke observes that 'A single neutron begins the chain reaction that in an instant can destroy a million lives and the toil of generations. Equally insignificant and unimportant are the trigger events which can sometimes change a man's course of action and so alter the whole pattern of his future.')

If we consider cause and effect as a branching or generative sequence, it may be shown as a series of nodes, linked by lines and increasing in number over time. Take the simplest example of cause and effect: the fission reaction in nuclear physics, illustrated diagrammatically in Figure 1.

A neutron collides with the nucleus of a uranium (235) atom. The nucleus undergoes fission, producing heat (the fast-moving fragments) plus an average of rather more than two emitted neutrons. Each of these neutrons enters the nuclei of two further uranium atoms, with the same result. If the number of emitted neutrons were exactly two and each neutron always found a target nucleus, there would clearly be a doubling effect. Any physicist, biologist, or mathematician knows that a doubling process develops very rapidly indeed: take a sheet of paper, say one-hundredth of an inch thick, fold it once, then fold the double sheet, repeat the operation altogether fifty times, and the total thickness, given that the initial sheet was large enough, will amount to sixty-eight million miles – further than the distance to the sun. With a critical mass of fissile uranium, we have a devastating explosion; with virulent bacteria an epidemic.

Causes have seldom one or even two effects, but many. Each cause is a node, from which a dozen or a million consequences spring, each consequence in part conditioned by other causes too. The route becomes more complex, and very soon untraceable.

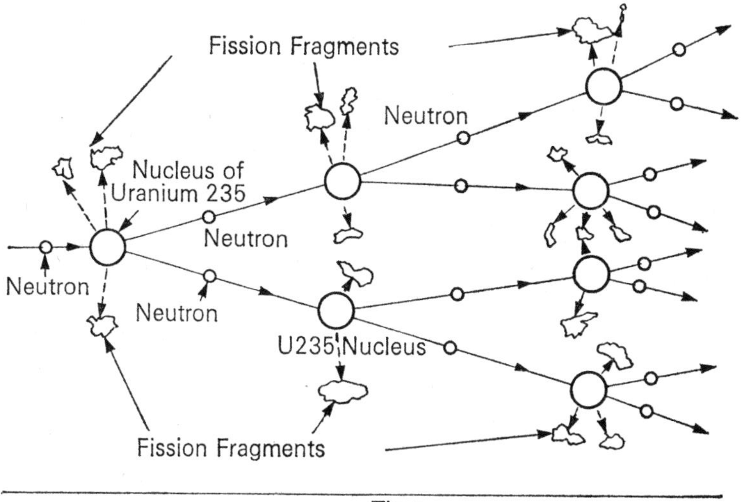

Figure 1. Simplified representation of chain reaction in nuclear fission to illustrate process of cause and effect.

Patterns in Events

Five or six years ago, when seeking staff, I designed an advertisement in the form of a stark black and white chequer board, calculated to catch the attention of casual Sunday-paper scanners. In each white square I put a question, the first being: 'Are you quick to see a pattern in events?' At that time I suffered from the hopeful belief that pattern recognition was the key to our work in forecasting and to the way in which processes occur. I note that most current attempts at forecasting are based on pattern recognition, of one kind or another. Patterns may be found by plotting points and if co-ordinates can be found (logarithmic or otherwise) such that points are seen to lie sensibly on a straight line, then a mathematical relationship may be assumed. Through long experience, engineers and even physicists have grown wary of jumping to linear conclusions.

Figure 2 shows a series of points which might have been plotted by a physicist studying reaction cross-section for fission of uranium 235 at different neutron approach energies (effectively velocities). Cross-section (in barns) is really a measure of the probability that a reaction will occur and may be visualized in terms of two cars approaching one another: the likelihood of collision depends on the frontal area that each car presents. It may also be a function of their relative speeds.

I am not sure how the unit of cross-section originated and sometimes wonder if it was chosen after one physicist had told another: 'You couldn't hit a barn with a shotgun.' Alternatively, the unit may have been chosen in honour of a friend of mine and former colleague who likewise spells his name without an 'e'. He always had a high cross-section for happenings and it was always Peter who would be in Florida when the tornado struck, whose luggage would be accidently transferred to the Karachi plane and who would arrive in Wiesbaden late at night and find that the only room available was already occupied by a large and shaggy dog. I know, I also shared the room.

The points in Figure 2 seem nicely arranged. Naturally, the co-ordinates are logarithmic, and to give a good effect I chose a mixture of inches and centimetres for the scales in preparing the original drawing.

More detailed plotting will reveal that between about one and a thousand electron volts (eV) there are violent departures from simple linearity, as seen in Figure 3. The cause is known as resonance, a phenomenon that frequently occurs, sometimes through impurities in materials, but often through the basic nature of a system.

It is not only extrapolation, therefore, that can be misleading. There are four stars in the constellation Pegasus which lie in a straight line, but no one would forecast the appearance of other stars on an extension of this line or even within its length. Again, few would argue

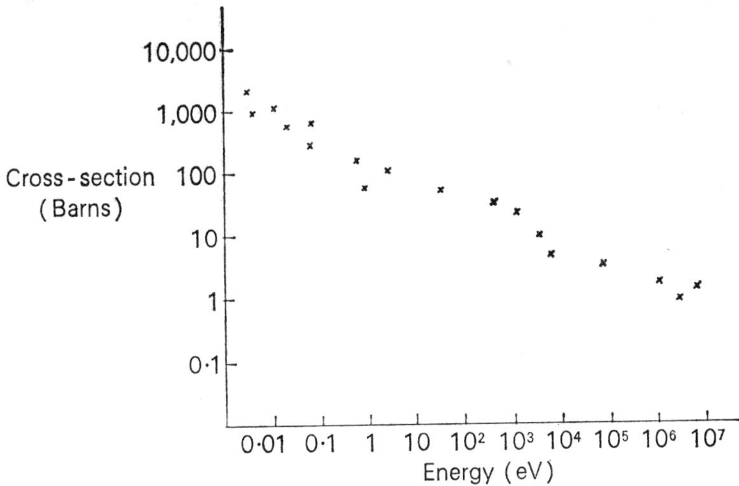

Figure 2. Reaction cross-section for fission of uranium 235 at different neutron approach energies.

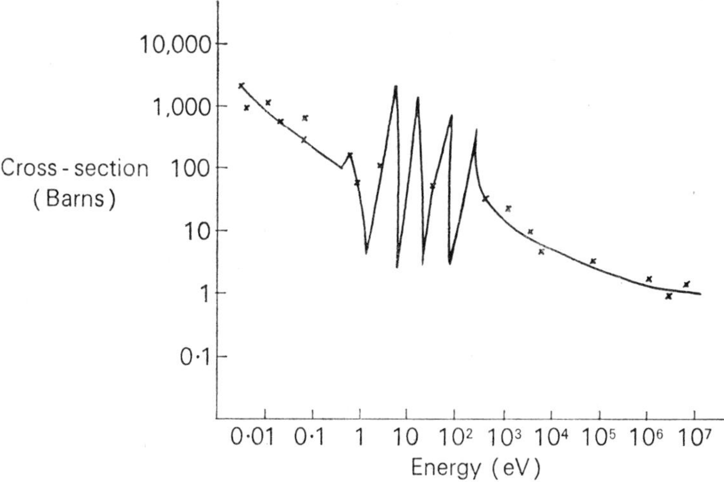

Figure 3. More detailed plotting revealing violent departures from simple linearity.

whether the three stars in Orion's Belt lie on a straight line or logistic. (But I have seen linear plots of lumens per watt against calendar year for forms of lighting, starting with a paraffin candle and spanning the period 1850 to 1990.) The sloping line is shown perfectly straight and intersecting a vertical axis, notwithstanding that before 1850 (logarithmic scale or not) the line would lie parallel to the horizontal axis for a very long time indeed. Lack of homogenity between candles, filament lamps and fluorescent tubes would raise most people's suspicions. But worse, the line is projected straight through the point where the efficiency of converting watts to lumens is 100 per cent and it appears that by 1990 lamps will be available approaching 200 per cent efficiency.

In view of the pitfalls in pattern recognition, it may be helpful to classify some of the patterns that we encounter:

(1) A pattern that appears in nature because it has a genuine underlying cause, for example a trajectory, the double helix of DNA, the gas laws and the motion of the planets (planet does of course mean wanderer and before Copernicus the essentially simple pattern of planetary movement was by no means clear).

(2) A pattern that is imposed on nature for purely subjective reasons, say as a mnemonic; thus a constellation has no reality, in astronomy, except as an aid in recognition (to me Cassiopeia looks like a 'W' lying on its side – the man who saw it as a woman could evidently think of nothing else).

(3) A pattern that is purely man-made for purpose of design, such as a jug, which is part functional and part aesthetic (if the first men on the moon discover a perfectly geometrical piece of stone, they will probably conclude that some other living thing has been there first).

(4) A pattern that appears by chance; if a coin is tossed a sufficient number of times, we can expect eventually a sequence of, say, ten heads, and if someone enters the room at the beginning of the sequence he may wrongly infer that it is a double-headed coin.

(5) A pattern that is tautological or a mathematical identity; thus rainfall on an island would no doubt show a close relationship with total river discharge to the sea (also, we should not be surprised to discover that plotting the values on two sides of a metric-English conversion table or kilowatts against horse-power would give us a perfectly straight line).

In practice, the patterns we observe tend to embrace many overlapping and interlocking component patterns of both subjective and fundamental kinds.

The key distinction is between a projection based entirely on extrapolation of historic trends and one where extrapolation is qualified by an understanding of the underlying causes. As far as possible, extrapolation should be limited to those values which in principle or practice cannot be built up from individual cases or where enquiry into cause and effect would be prohibitively expensive or time-consuming.

Morphology of Data

I have attempted to indicate the unmanageable complexity of nature at the most fundamental level of cause and effect. But there are other levels of interpretation. If we set out to understand the mind at an atomic or molecular level, human behaviour would remain a mystery. The social scientist concerns himself simply with the way that people act, being rather more humble than the physicist. He would not presume to fabricate an all-embracing and everlasting law about his subject matter. He simply watches and records: What happens if? What happens when?

Again, weather forecasting on a direct causal basis is unreliable and short term. In long-term weather forecasting, we seek to discover the sequential pattern of seasonal conditions over many years and the successful forecaster is one who, perhaps with the aid of a computer, is quick to see a pattern in events.

If we find on a substantial number of occasions that a sequence of morning mist, sunshine, frost, fog, and grey skies is followed by rain, then re-occurrence of the initial sequence may lead us to forecast rain again, though we may not know the reason. More simply, the shepherd learns from experience to welcome a 'red sky at night', though he may be ignorant of meteorology.

The approach is unrelated to the billiard-ball logic of classical mechanics: we do not need to understand the underlying mechanism – indeed we never really do, and scientific laws are at best an inspired and superbly concise, but incomplete and impermanent, description of reality; at worst a transient mnemonic. Newton's view was and remains useful in a mundane context; Einstein's picture is more helpful on a cosmic and sub-atomic scale.

The patterns we endeavour to discover in the predictive context for purposes of planning are again several planes above the fundamental level, as psychology is above the electroneural. Useful observations can be made, with practical results, but still the map can never be complete.

But patterns should be recognized with caution. On the one hand, they may be implicit in what we observe, as in the mathematical expression for a trajectory; or on the other, purely subjective, as when a constellation is remembered as a plough or bear. There may thus be an underlying reason for a pattern or it may simply be imposed as a reminder. The surprising continues to surprise. Operational research

scientists, I believe, distinguish between a model (an objective or subjective pattern?) and a metaphor by emphasizing that a model exhibits one-to-one correspondence with all significant parameters in the real system; and between models and maps by noting that a map is static and includes too many details. But what is significant? Where mathematics goes underground for any length of time, it frequently emerges blind – and pointing in the wrong direction.

Few would feel anything but sympathy for the retired forecaster who, to supplement his pension, spent his savings on an isolated country pub, dependent on the carriage trade – six months before the introduction of breathalyser tests. The house might well have yielded a comfortable income for the past 500 years, but may not last another ten.

Never can we insulate ourselves, or our affairs, from the external world. I raise my hand and, through gravity, disturb Arcturus. One factor or a thousand in combination may reverse a trend that has seemed set for centuries.

Such factors may be quite unconnected with our present interests: if I am a successful manufacturer of razor blades, familiar with developments in steel and cutting edges, I may not know that, somewhere,

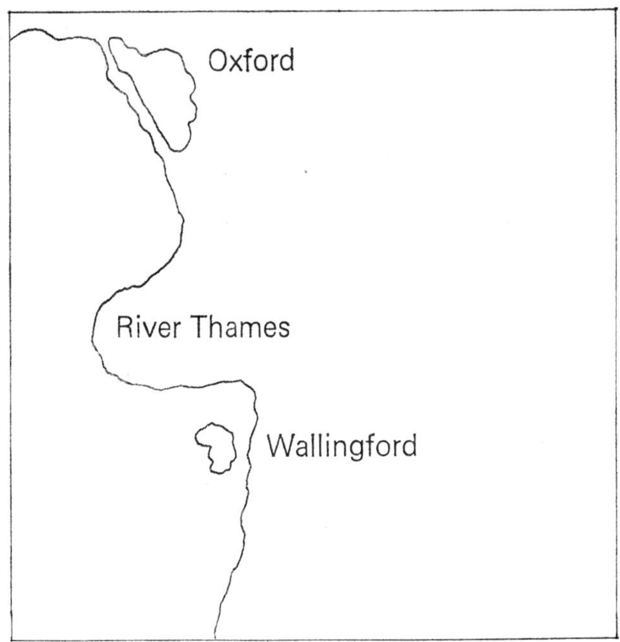

Figures 4 and 5. Left- and right-hand halves of O.S. Map 158.

a chemist has at last developed a comfortable, effective, quick-acting, odourless, cheap but virile depilatory. Yet I may be out of business overnight.

This may not be the way the operational research scientist sees his task. But take Sheet 158 of the United Kingdom Ordnance Survey and tear it in equal halves. Examine the real terrain corresponding to the left-hand half in as much or little detail as may seem desirable. It will be seen from the simple version of the map in Figure 4 that the River Thames is flowing roughly west to east.

Given only the information that could be gathered in this area, however scientifically, could anyone construct a model which would permit us to predict the River's course in the right-hand half of Sheet 158, without knowing the contours and features of the countryside through which it passes? Even the position of a single tree could change the whole direction. In fact, as will be noted from Figure 5, the River flows due south.

Are we any better able to determine the configuration of the future? Because it is unknown and hence less detailed in our minds, can we assume it is less complex and irregular than the surface of the earth?

In the case of the two adjacent sections of the map, all we can say with confidence is that the direction of flow at the right-hand edge of the first half will be the same as that at the left-hand edge of the second half.

The next minute of the future is equally predictable. No doubt a trend in time differs from a trend in space, but who can say in what manner it is different?

The analogy is fairer if we are allowed to use any information we can gather while standing in the left-hand half, including such ground in the right-hand half that we can see from vantage points. Various hills will be visible and also other evidence, distorted by perspective. The course will still be difficult to calculate, if not impossible. We are reduced to a statement beginning 'All things being equal...' – but all things never are.

The conclusion to be drawn is not that forecasting is useless, but simply that it cannot help us to plot a comprehensive future map. I am not saying that we should avoid imperfect forecasting techniques, but simply that we should be aware of their shortcomings. In most cases, the fascination of the method far exceeds its fruitfulness and many a forecaster has fallen for the attraction of a pretty curve. Still, as Professor A. N. Whitehead once remarked, 'It is the business of the future to be dangerous'. Risk and danger have a lot in common and I think this is a good opportunity to introduce my colleague, Balint Bodroghy, who has some views on financial risk, which certainly gave me a fresh view on capital investment.

[*Balint Bodroghy*]
The now familiar method of discounted cash flow is an aid to choosing between projects, bearing in mind the present value of future expenditure under the influence of such factors as interest and taxation. In other words, alternative projects are reduced to a common base for present comparison.

The net present value (NPV) of a project can be evaluated by discounting the cash flow at a predetermined rate. The difficulty of choosing the rate of return is avoided in DCF by calculating the rate of return which will reduce the net present value to nil. The rates for different projects can then be compared.

Risk and Return

There is, however, no question that increasing weight attached to more distant cash flows in any way balances the greater risk and uncertainty of the remoter future. I shall be discussing the relationship between risk and the corresponding expectation of return later. It is of course the cost of capital, not any artificial factor, that is set against the rapidly increasing risk associated with the hope of longer-term reward.

Given a cash flow approach to accounting, it is possible to structure risk by means of an option diagram as in Figure 6. Risk, as has already been amply emphasized, is difficult to calculate, but error is reduced if the options can be systematically defined.

Consider the introduction of a new capital product. Already £10,000 has been spent on preliminary studies. At the first node we have the choice of conducting further studies, requiring twelve weeks to complete and costing £10,000, or embarking on serious technical development and production planning at a cost of £120,000. If we take the second course, we have the further option of dropping the project, in which case we have lost a total of £130,000, or selling and installing the plant for say £200,000. Net positive cash flow will then be £70,000. Should we embark on further study, we may have the subsequent options indicated in the diagram, but we shall eventually come to a state when the net positive cash flow resulting from successful sale has fallen to a level where neither option is attractive. It is clear that a

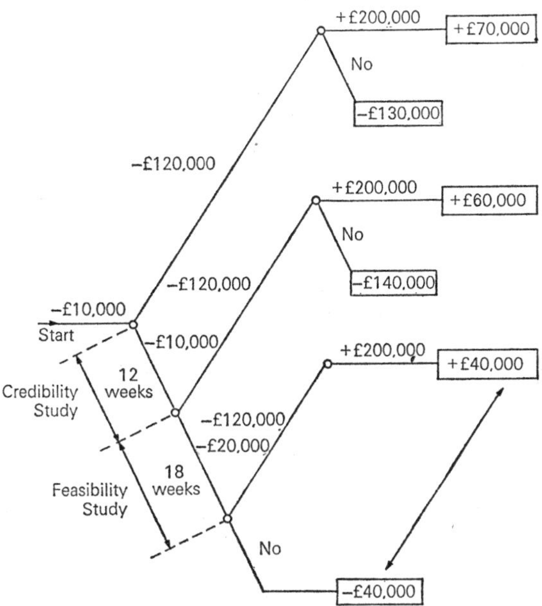

Figure 6. Option diagram for introduction of capital product. *After* R.V. Brown *et al.*

decision to proceed or abandon the project would be taken long before this point. The diagram is based on ideas developed by Rex Brown and his colleagues at the Harvard Business School.

It will be evident that the decisions taken at the various nodes will depend on a great number of objective and subjective factors. The situation of a company or individual at the time a decision is taken will have a very considerable bearing on the choice, as illustrated by the following example.

Two men are in a bar. One says to the other: 'I am feeling very generous tonight, having won a fortune on the pools, and am prepared to give you £10 if you will toss a coin and it happens to turn up heads'.

At this point a bystander joins in the conversation and says to the man who has received this somewhat surprising offer: 'I would like to buy the opportunity from you; what will you sell it for?'

If a sale is negotiated, the sum is likely to be less than £5, but the actual figure will depend on the seller's situation. If he is far from home, has missed his last bus, spent all his money and knows that the taxi fare is just £2, he may agree to sacrifice the opportunity for this low figure. If there is no such pressure on him, he may prefer to take the chance of winning the more substantial sum.

The development of market research and the proliferation of other techniques for gathering and analysing data may have reduced to some extent the risks inherent in decision making, but they have brought new dangers of their own. Quite rightly, we believe in information, but are becoming ever more reluctant to take decisions without a fully comprehensive and convincing case. But the facts can never all be known and over-dependence on processed information may lead to indecisiveness and eventually to the atrophy of our decision-making faculty. There are signs of it already.

Risk can never be quite eliminated and there is therefore scope for planning by trial and error, or rather successive adjustment – namely dynamic and catalytic planning.

Not only are decisions inhibited, but in addition, the cost of decision-making progressively increases. Time spent in seeking and reviewing information expands and diffuses like a gas to fill the space available. It is difficult to put a value on executive time. Expressed in terms of opportunity cost, the value of a middle or senior executive in industry must be somewhere between £100 and £1,000 a day. In other words, on a good day, and it is assumed that most days are good, a capable company executive should be able to undertake actions that will ultimately yield an incremental profit in that range for every day of his working life.

It is disturbing to think that members of top management from dozens of small, medium, and large companies should sit together at seminars and courses, in Europe and America, discussing management methods, corporate planning, the impact of innovation and technology on business, and how to benefit. Although the cost to industry cannot be known, it must run well into seven or eight figures per annum. Since companies act, or are expected to act, in a rational manner, we must suppose that there are sound reasons for the obvious preoccupation with management and innovation. What are the reasons and the motivation?

Primogeniture

On a human level, there is clearly an element of beauty and excitement in invention and its embodiment in practice. Indeed, there is something beautiful in doing anything for the first time, whether it is sailing round the world single-handed, climbing a mountain, or falling in love, and with certain notable exceptions, the also-ran is heavily discounted in the private and the public eye. The first man to climb Mount Everest will be remembered; but who followed in their tracks? The name of the first man to swim the English Channel is recorded in the *Guinness Book of Records*, but though it takes much the same effort to perform the feat today, no one is likely to be interested.

Undoubtedly, we attribute certain intrinsic values to primogeniture, but there must be more to it than that, and it seems probable that the key consideration is the element of risk. The second time round everybody knows that the feat can be accomplished; it may be difficult, but certainly not impossible. The reduction in risk leads to a heavy discounting in esteem.

The intellectual beauty of innovation attracts most human beings. They like to be associated with it and enjoy the experience. But the sensation is personal and on the commercial level, it would be surprising if industry consented to support such whims without good business reasons.

Innovation is more fashionable today than it has ever been. Annual reports, which become ever more image-conscious and elaborate, are no longer limited to the obligatory denunciation of national economic measures and expressions of appreciation for the loyalty of staff, but are full of fascinating facts. Certain kinds of phrase appear with growing frequency: 'Your company were pioneers in the development of left-handed screw threads in the United Kingdom' or even more often: 'More than 80 per cent of what we sell today did not exist ten years ago', – doubtless a reference, not to innovation, but to better stock control. Fashion, alone, is not a sufficient explanation. Perhaps innovation has become a weapon in the battles of corporate politics. Innovation means change and change means opportunity for junior executives not yet near the top. Those at the top no longer have ambitions to achieve, and welcome a fluid situation immediately below, since it diminishes the threat to their authority.

At the same time, without innovation, competition between companies becomes ever more sterile, like trench warfare in the years 1914 to 1918. The only weapons are more and better advertising, more and better packaging, more and better promotion; and more and better brand managers, succeeding their fallen predecessors ever more rapidly, but with diminishing returns. In such static warfare, attrition continues until the only escape is a tacit truce or accommodation.

Where innovation rules and ideas proliferate, business conditions resemble those of desert warfare. Battles are fought over ground which is precious one moment and valueless the next. The situation is fluid and exciting, because it is a war of movement and the unexpected is part of the game. As a consequence of flanking manœuvres, entrenched positions are lost overnight, almost without a struggle.

Similarly, the advent of efficient air conditioning and structural gaskets, whereby glass windows can be set directly into concrete, coupled with the need in city offices to keep out noise and dirt, may sharply cut demand for opening windows and hence for window frames. The linear progression from wooden frames to metal frames to plastics frames is outflanked and loses its meaning. Again, an air-supported bearing, a solid-state device, welded fabrication, powder metallurgy, or a plastics film on a stainless razor blade can change the whole perspective of an industry, suddenly and with very little warning.

Are we therefore to visualize the captains of modern innovative industries in dark goggles and peaked caps, standing upright in open tank turrets, like generals in a desert war? Hardly. While embracing the freedom of desert warfare, they are clearly determined to impose on it all the stability of static trenches. The programmes of management training schemes and seminars show that the prime concern today is how to avoid risk, while retaining the benefits of innovation.

Under competitive and public pressure, we have adopted innovation but not the mobility that goes with it. Rather than exploit it through adaptive management, we attempt to plot it in advance and write it in a programme. We seek stability and compromise with change by regarding it as predetermined and hence foreseeable and static.

It may be possible in some degree to underwrite the future by management research and forecasting, but the premiums are likely to be high.

Though we may be driven to innovate by force of circumstances, I am not suggesting that innovation has any virtue in itself. Indeed, many successful companies have in the past, consciously or unconsciously, deliberately or accidentally, been consistently second in the field and made substantial profits. Some of them have recently seen fit to apologize for such conservative behaviour and are now maintaining large-scale research programmes. At the same time, they are finding it necessary to explain to shareholders why pretax profits have fallen so dramatically. The problem of innovation and security is one of the great dilemmas facing modern management. It bears closely on our attitude to risk and return in capital commitment and provides one more reason for management's concern with innovation.

The point may be made clearer by considering money in terms of dimensional analysis, a method familiar in engineering. We think of money as having a single dimension, namely its face value, but this is only true in isolation from an owner. In fact, the value of money only assumes meaning when related to an owner, as purpose is meaningless divorced from personal or corporate identity.

Hot and Cold Money

As soon as a quantity of money comes under the control of somebody, be it an individual, a board of directors or a government, it acquires a second dimension, which may be conveniently called its *temperature*. As a consequence of currency crises, the phrase *hot money* has passed into the public vocabulary. We may usefully extend the idea to embrace warm, cool, and cold money, in addition.

If a quantity of money is controlled by a body, it will have the two dimensions of value and temperature distributed as shown in Figure 7, where value is given as percentages of the total sum controlled. These percentages are plotted on the vertical axis and temperature on the horizontal axis. Temperature is a measure of both risk and return in combination, when any fraction of the total sum is committed or invested.

A body or individual will normally be prepared to invest a fraction of the total sum, generally quite small, in an opportunity combining very high risk with very high return. Another fraction, usually even smaller, would be available for opportunities where risk and return are minimal, such as donations to charities of unimpeachable reputation. Slightly higher up the scale might come donations for a political cause, where both risk and return are somewhat higher. The bulk of funds would be mobilized only when opportunities offer modest returns with a relatively high measure of security.

This kind of distribution is typical of aggregate funds available on a free capital market, funds held by private individuals, funds controlled by corporations, or the budget of a nation. It is unlikely that the precise shape of such a curve has ever been defined, but its existence and approximate form seem consistent with experience. Even without numerical values, examination of the curve yields some useful and interesting conclusions.

For purposes of argument it is assumed that the curve refers to a sum of cash controlled by an individual. Deviation from the basic pattern can be anticipated. For example, the distorted curve shown in Figure 8 seems entirely feasible and would indicate the miser syndrome. Such a distribution would be typical of the pauper who dies with a few thousand pounds hidden under the newspapers and tins that litter his lodgings.

In an individual, such behaviour would be tolerated as a mild eccentricity, but in a company it would be entirely unacceptable. A company exhibiting a distribution of this kind has under-utilized financial assets and will either be overtaken by inflation or taken over by Jim Slater or a Charley Clore.

A similar anomaly at the opposite end of the scale would describe the behaviour of a compulsive gambler, as suggested in Figure 9. There is no corporate equivalent, since no company could survive reckless gambling over any period of time. On the other hand, it may be that individual entrepreneurs have founded their fortunes on a comparable pattern of investment.

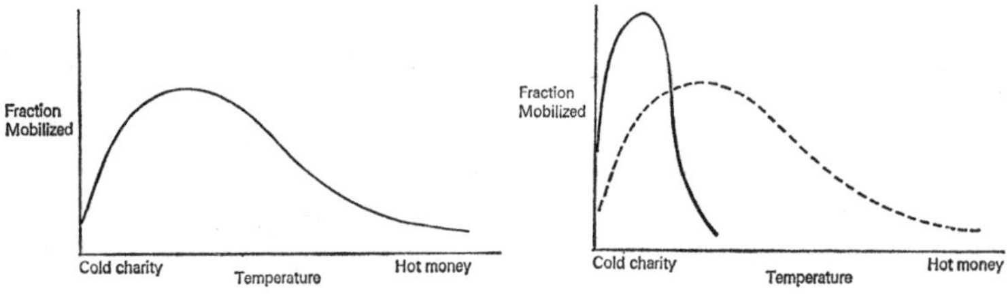

Figures 7 to 10. Attitude to risk and return illustrated by plotting the value and 'temperature' of a fund (7); distortion of pattern under the 'miser' syndrome (8); distortion by compulsive gambling (9); the influence of growth in the fund on behaviour (10).

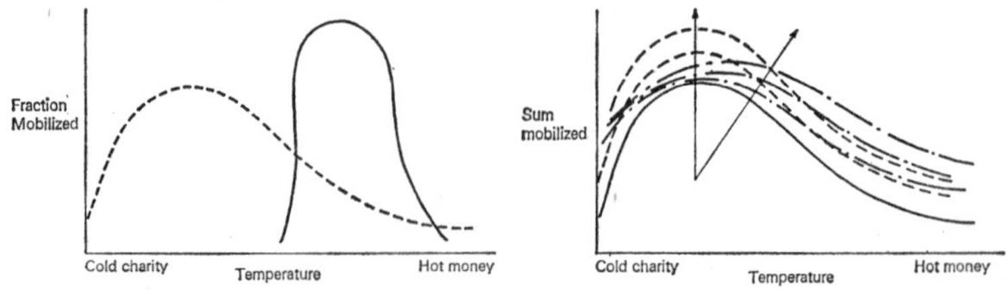

It will be evident that if all money controlled by a single body is governed by a temperature distribution such as that in Figure 7, then the sum total of all money in a national economy would show a similar distribution. The pattern will therefore represent the behaviour of the investing public, offering a small proportion of its funds for low yield quasi-charitable investments, a small proportion for a flutter on speculative investment, but the bulk being mobilized only for investments offering the normal combination of risk and return. For convenience, the large volume investment can be considered as falling in the 'six or nine per cent category'.

In summary, money, with reference to the body controlling it, has a quality in addition to its face value, which can be described as temperature, ranging, in accordance with the distribution shown, from hot money to cold charity.

So far, the vertical scale has represented percentage of the total fund examined. If instead of a percentage an absolute scale is used, it is possible to speculate on the way in which the distribution changes as the absolute size of the fund increases. It could be assumed that the relative proportions remain unaltered, with the line assembly shifting up and down the vertical scale, as suggested in Figure 10.

It is suspected, however, on the basis of personal observation, that, instead of a straight up-and-down movement, the distribution becomes gradually distorted, increasing the proportion of funds available, both at the hot and cold ends of the scale, as the absolute sum expands. Certainly on an individual level this is so. As the more immediate human needs are satisfied, extra marginal satisfaction is derived from acts of charity and from the milder forms of gambling. In other words, the attitude to risk-taking changes as more money becomes available.

It is likely that a similar development is taking place in companies. Since the war, companies have been growing bigger and richer overall. The slowly distorting distribution of hot and cold money places additional pressures on those controlling it to find suitable investments in the hot-money region. It is submitted that it is the increasing size of the hot-money portfolio which accounts in large measure for the concern, the universal concern, with innovation. This money is available and wanting to be utilized in ventures offering a high return at risks in excess of those normally accepted.

Unfortunately, this phenomenon is not sufficiently understood either by corporate investors or by the decision makers. The pressure is unconscious and the mental adjustment to accept the risk has not yet been accomplished. In consequence, the approach of companies to hot-money investment is based on the techniques and attitudes assimilated in dealing with the six per cent portion of the portfolio.

There is a constant search for certainty.

Every attempt is therefore made, using the power of modern information gathering, economic manipulation, statistical forecasting and electronic data processing, to eliminate the risk from risk investment. It is a contradiction both in terms and fact, and poses a great dilemma for the six per cent mentality.

The attempt to eliminate the risk from risk money is inherently self-defeating. The first result of any determined effort is a dramatic reduction in returns. The effort itself involves a heavy expenditure, since, in seeking certainty, a company may insist on running through the full range of management techniques. First, there may be extensive product development, followed by evaluation, using prototypes, consumer panels and elaborate physical testing programmes. Next, there will be market research on a local, national or global scale, followed by an appraisal of purchasing motivation and the decision-making process.

By this time the quantitative information is so enormous and the number of variables so large that, short of commissioning a major computer simulation, useful decisions cannot be based on the results. The outcome of the computer simulation will be predictably indecisive and a test marketing programme may then be launched. Finally, buried by information, the management may resort to probabilistic decision making, the virtually mechanistic application of hunch, to help make up its mind.

Prohibitive Expenditure

The application of these techniques costs large sums of money and in fact there are now computer programmes available such as Demon 1 and Demon 2, developed by the agency BBDO, which attempt to optimize the amount of money spent on seeking information and making decisions in relation to other variables involved in the project. A situation has now been reached in certain industries where the cost of *information*, not the cost of development, production, or distribution, is the single major dominating factor governing the profitability of projects.

But other consequences of these frantic attempts to remove risk from risk capital are much more far reaching and equally self-defeating. Assume that the attempts to eliminate uncertainty succeed beyond the wildest hopes of the decision maker; also that the cost of these attempts has not completely eradicated any hope of profitable exploitation.

Then the mere fact of converting a risk situation into one of relative certainty will suddenly shift the project from the hot end of the curve to the six per cent section. Here the funds available are much more generous within the company, but at the same time, the opportunity will now attract a far larger segment of the investing public, including competitors and their financial backers. Funds from these sources will not only be available, but will be positively chasing prospects of this kind.

It is of course the hope of all managers to eliminate risk and to be in a unique position when they do so. Unfortunately, information spreads very rapidly today and is universally available. Techniques for eliminating risk are known to all, discussed in public meetings, and the subject of extensive experiments in industry and the academic world. Any advantage will therefore be temporary and a pioneer deciding to exploit an innovation, believing he has eliminated risk may find himself in competition with a vast investing public whose reactions could not have been anticipated in the computer programmes.

Unlike the self-fulfilling prophecies of certain forecasting (such, I suppose, as the spring or autumn fashions predicted by *Vogue*), eliminating risk from risk investment is entirely self-defeating; the risk has vanished, but so has the return.

The picture is less gloomy than it seems. The point is not that the body of management techniques designed to minimize risk in decision making is a waste of time, only that it is often misapplied. When the full resources of information collection and analysis are devoted to an innovative project (and few worthwhile projects involve no innovation) it will tend to move from the hot-money to the six per cent region. In other words, the stakes have been raised all round and the new situation must be accepted as a fact of life.

But the pressure resulting from the temperature distribution of money, in particular the increasing size of the hot-money region, still remains. It will therefore become necessary to look for satisfaction further and further afield, to projects where the resources of modern management techniques cannot be applied.

There is still room for intelligent action. It is first of all important to be acquainted with all techniques at the disposal of the decision makers, with a good working understanding of their limitations. It is then essential to consider which of the techniques should be applied in any particular case, and at what cost, so as not to erode unduly the potential profitability.

Finally, the project should not be considered in isolation, but in its own particular environment. In other words, it is desirable to take up projects which, in relation to the differentiated assets of the business, provide advantages which no competitor can equal, no matter what techniques are used and at whatever cost. Differentiated assets will be discussed by Peter, who will now talk about dynamic planning.

[*Peter Ward*]
I am sure that in the end, when all the available techniques are seen in perspective and used with discretion, the benefits will be real, leading to better utilization of the available resources everywhere. It shows what a good forecaster I am: I could not even predict correctly what my own colleague would be saying.

For purposes of argument, it has been assumed that risk can be eliminated, but in practice this is very far from true. Uncertainty remains and business problems are much more complex than we habitually suppose. I would refer to the relatively simple game of chess, in which there are only thirty-two pieces (many identical), only sixty-four squares on a board, only two independent players. But what master could plan his whole game with another from the outset? It is enough to note that in chess problems, where only a few pieces are normally left on the board, the requirement is usually to mate in two. Even then, contingent moves may well be very numerous. So, how many moves ahead can we reasonably plan in business, where pieces are legion and of infinite variety; their disposition uncertain or unknown; the field limitless, ill-defined and fluid; the players countless, and the rules complex, mainly unwritten and often unobserved?

In such circumstances, it is very easy to be wrong. Scientists are often encouraged to prophesy where current discoveries may lead us, so it seems rather ungenerous to quote them when they prove to be mistaken. Yet to do so may sometimes help us to realize how capricious events can be and to recognize that what seems fanciful today may tomorrow be a commonplace. A book by a great scientist of world-wide reputation, published in 1940, contains the following passage:

> 'A few years ago we used to read sensational stories about what would happen when atoms were split. The coalminers were to be put out of work by atomic power. A single bomb would liberate enough energy to destroy a whole city. And so on. Unfortunately the prophets had forgotten to do a few little calculations. The sun turns out energy at 60 horse-power per square inch which sounds very impressive. But if we make the calculation in a rather different way, we find that it is only producing 1 horse-power for every 3,000 tons of its weight. I am an optimist, and I hope that within a century it will be possible on earth to construct a motor using atomic energy as efficient as the sun. If so, it will probably weigh a ton and develop several horse-power. It is true that it will not need refuelling for a good many thousand million years, but it will not earn a thousandth of a per cent interest per year on its cost. That figure will perhaps be exceeded later on, but the universe is pretty solidly constructed, and atoms are remarkably tough, so I think many generations will elapse before atomic power is of practical importance.'

On the other hand, had we known of Fermi's experiments with uranium and graphite piles twenty or thirty years ago, most of us would have predicted that by now our power-generating industry would have been transformed. So far, changes have come rather from the growth in unit size of plant, than from the development of nuclear power. More pessimistically, the pioneer nuclear physicist, Lord Rutherford, dismissed the possibility of extracting useful energy from the atomic nucleus, by comparing the task with hitting a fly in the Albert Hall with a pea-shooter.

It is not only the scientist who sometimes fails to see the wood for trees. Even the most imaginative prophets go astray. I gather from a recent advertisement that H. G. Wells once wrote (*Anticipations*, 1901): 'I do not think . . . aeronautics will ever come into play as a serious modification of transport and communication'.

A blinkered view along a single track may lead us to overlook developments in parallel. Most research on the control of thermonuclear reactions (the fusion of hydrogen nuclei to form helium, as in the hydrogen bomb) seems to be directed towards confining a plasma at many million degrees (Kelvin) by electromagnetic fields so that the hot ionized gas may not vaporize the walls of the material container. At high temperatures, the velocity of the ions is sufficient to overcome the resistance to fusion, by what may be figuratively called a battering-ram effect.

In 1956 I read of some modest experiments at the Universities of California and Liverpool, where fusion had been achieved in liquid hydrogen and therefore at very low temperatures. By simple mechanics, as illustrated in Figure 11, it can be seen that if a negative μ meson of roughly 200 times the mass were substituted for the orbiting electron, the orbit would be substantially reduced in size.

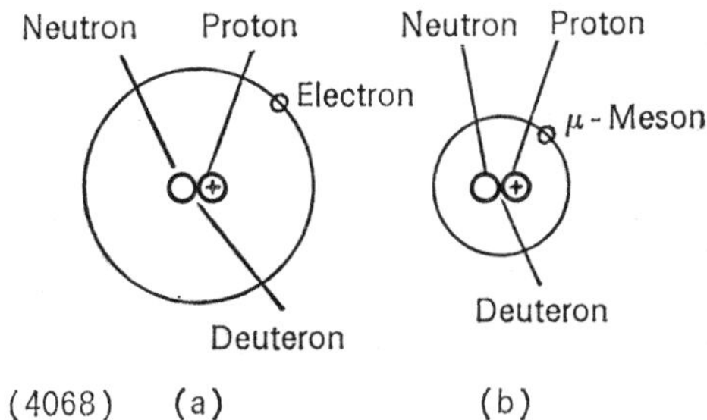

Figure 11. Size of atom as defined by the electron orbit (larger diagram) can be reduced if a negative μ meson of some 200 times the mass is substituted (smaller diagram). The energy required to achieve fusion is dramatically reduced.

Resistance to fusion becomes intense when the orbits of neighbouring atoms overlap, and the smaller the orbit, the lower the battering-ram energies needed to achieve fusion. It may be that the short life of μ mesons or other factors preclude the application of this principle, but the experiments show that there is more than one way to skin a cat.

Even our most cherished predictions may prove unfounded. The population explosion is today so taken for granted that journalists and scientists alike are prepared to be categorical in forecasting the worst. Typical of these statements was one that appeared in a Sunday paper colour supplement 'By the end of this century the world's inhabitants will have doubled to 7,000 million: well over half of them will be living in cities'. Certainty is absolute; the writer admits neither doubt nor qualification.

In fact, as long ago as 1956, at a meeting of the British Association for the Advancement of Science, Dr C. B. Goodhart explained how natural selection can sometimes operate in favour of declining population. He quoted many instances, but one, I remember, referred to the potato famine in Ireland during the last century. He noted that where two adult food gatherers supported a large family, say ten in total, it was probable that all would be undernourished and few of the children, if any, would reach child-bearing age. On the other hand, where two adult food gatherers had only themselves and two children to provide for, there was a good chance that the children would live to have offspring. In these circumstances, therefore, there would be natural selection against high fecundity. Although declining deathrate may have immediate and critical effects, it is inevitably (?) limited in time and we know today of rather more newsworthy factors applying to the birthrate which could leave the population static.

It is easy to be mistaken, however sophisticated we may be in any given field. Indeed, many good opportunities have actually been abandoned for sophisticated reasons, as might have been the case in Figure 12. We are inclined to believe anything that sounds sufficiently profound.

What we have tried to show is that the future is a risky business, to a degree of magnitude that, perhaps deliberately, we tend to overlook.

We have attempted to structure risk so that its extent may be perceived and sought to show how forecasting itself changes the situation of the forecasters. We shall never know how many elections have been won by courtesy of Dr Gallup and his colleagues.

Organic Planning

Given the changing complexity of nature, how can it best be governed to achieve our purposes? Perhaps a clue lies in a story by Isaac Asimov. At the whim of his wife, a man changes one letter in his name and

'The whole business is economically unsound, gentlemen. With a train of this length and forty miles of track, we find that only ·0568 per cent of the track will be in use at any given time, representing a constant idle investment of 99·9432 per cent.'

Figure 12. *After* an illustration by Virgil Patch, in *Dilemma; People in Motion.*

thereby alters the whole course of human history. The substituted letter catches the attention of a security officer, arouses his curiosity and sets off a quite credible sequence of events that redresses the balance of power between nations. A tenth-order cause may sponsor a first-order effect.

Is it possible that we could discern a principle in nature that will enable us to generate by modest effort major desirable results? If such a principle exists, then it is likely to possess many of the features that are associated with the word *organic.*

An organism is an entity (whether tightly knit and contained within a single envelope, like an animal or human being, or diffuse and loosely interrelated, like a society or Fred Hoyle's Black Cloud) in which the elements of a control system are present but incompletely understood or understandable. In other words, an organic situation is one in which there is a complex of interacting and perhaps conflicting parts. It is also a situation, to change the metaphor, in which the best way to reach a given destination may not be to drive straight for it but to tack against the wind and use the currents as we discover them.

When a situation, a company, a region, or a nation is very complex, it is more useful to study it as an organism, rather than a mechanism.

We may not be able to foresee precisely what a woman will do, unlike a machine, but after living with her for a few years, one comes to know her ways. Even then, it is still possible to be surprised.

The experienced manager knows that to give an instruction is not always to achieve the intended outcome, as in a control system, cumulative feedback may lead to undesirable conditions. Where many different interests are involved and direct communication is precluded by the size of an organization, management does not lie in telling people what to do, which is seldom effective even in the smallest company. It is better to establish a framework within which individuals, in seeking their own ends or pursuing paths that interest them, also serve the common purpose.

The problem is to recognize that framework or to release the self-refreshing source of energy that can generate, through doubling or multiplication, the maximum benefit from the least stimulus.

Retrospectively, it is possible to detect some examples of critical stimuli, or catalysts, in history. We are told by historians, for example, that the breeding of the warhorse and the invention of chain mail gave the Normans and the Franks that supreme self-confidence, with its concomitant energy, which sent them to conquer and administer the greater part of Europe, even to the Middle East and Antioch. But a still more important factor was the feudal system itself, in which land held in fief was the only security and second sons must needs go far afield to find it. Here, three elements in combination gave birth to a new vitality and way of life.

Nearer our own day and possibly more significant, since the consequences were at least in part intended, were the Companies Acts pertaining to limited liability. These measures created a situation in which a man might risk enough on a new venture to ensure responsibility, but not so much as to deter his enterprise, leading to a proliferation of business and to an enormous growth in wealth. It is perhaps the best example of what I call *catalytic planning*. It could be applied to the task of planning in a country or in any other complex and amorphous situation, where the boundaries are ill-defined.

Dynamic Planning

Dynamic planning, on the other hand, is planning from the viewpoint of an individual, company or other self-organizing and well-defined entity and is concerned with the changing relationship between a company and its environment and how this interplay may be exploited to the company's advantage. In other words, it is the means by which a company maintains its competitive position in a changing world and its purpose is profit, survival, and growth through systematic innovation.

Commercial benefit springs not just from innovation, but from relevant and timely innovation. Like any other creative process, innovation is a consequence of interaction, and in business the basic interaction is between a company and its commercial context. Taking this intercourse as critical and the key to corporate development, dynamic planning is conceived to focus and foster the right kind of innovative thinking.

A company is in effect an organism which adapts to its environment in order to survive. Also, like an organism, it attempts to alter its environment. Products (or services) play a central part in the adaptive process, since it is through them that change is communicated to the company – and conversely. As the market changes, so must the product portfolio; but the portfolio can only change in step with existing or accessible resources. A product (or service) is thus the consequence of interaction or tension between company or market.

The function of dynamic planning is to promote the continuous realignment of a company in the light of emerging market needs, and does so through an evolving product policy, taking available assets as the first premise. It is a view of business that strikes a satisfactory balance between immediate profit and longer-term survival. Since present or potential assets are the starting point, the first step is to identify those differentiated assets (special facilities, a favourable location, experience and market outlets) which in combination make the company unique. The company which plans solely in terms of its undifferentiated assets, particularly capital resources, will tend to innovate in competition with every other business, from ICI to Marks and Spencer.

At the same time, management proceeds by a series of decisions, each a discrete step or change in direction. The purpose of this paper, therefore, is to suggest an approach to corporate planning that will assist in decision making, while maintaining continuity, and to introduce the basic concept of dynamic corporate identity. Consciousness of its identity in relation to external change helps a company to recognize those innovative opportunities best suited to its own nature and potential.

It is a basic fact of industrial and economic life that businesses are most competitive when they do something they are well equipped to do. But the recommendation: do what you are able to do well, is not necessarily the same as do what you do already, or do what you have always done.

In a situation where the future springs on us as if from ambush and change is indeterminable, there is one well-proven planning method. It is the way in which a human being plans his own career, indeed his life.

My personal identity has evolved, in response to opportunity and circumstances, but has retained an essential continuity throughout. I am now unlikely to direct a hose through my neighbour's upstairs bedroom window, but have still a predilection for experiment and possibly for mischief. I adapt to my environment, changing it occasionally to increase my comfort, but in some basic sense remain unchanged myself. If I have a flair for mathematics, I may well become an accountant or enter operational research.

It is perhaps a poor substitute for absolute planning, where firm objectives are inflexibly pursued within a perfectly predicted world. But it is rather more practical. I find that if my wife and I deliberately go shopping for a dress, we spend a whole afternoon wandering around the shops and finish, at best, with nothing at all, at worst with something that neither of us likes. We do better (I keep my wife's parameters in my diary) if either one of us spots a really attractive dress when we are not positively looking and buys it there and then. I have made a few mistakes, but not too many. Now, to shop in this way, it is necessary to have some ready cash, which will not be available if we have already committed the bulk of our resources to next year's holiday in Zanzibar or mass bookings for Glyndebourne, a season in advance.

We can act upon our world to achieve our purposes, but never completely or with certainty. But this is precisely the situation in which any organism finds itself, whether natural or contrived, including companies. As the time scale for many industrial projects is extended and companies take more and more decisions affecting the remoter future, it is essential that they plan, but perhaps I had best say first what I mean by planning. As an initial working guide, I would define planning as the purposeful programming of action, with reference to available resources and to the predictive context in which the proposed action is likely to be taken. By predictive I mean uncertain and partially predictable; and by predictive context an indicated or anticipated future, subject to continuous reformulation.

How should we seek to understand the ecological relationship of a corporate organism within its environment? It is a matter essentially of adaptation and from the viewpoint of the organism itself, the ideal solution may be the habit of optimum adaptability, taking into account not only the present and immediate environment but also the predictive future. Dynamics is in fact adaptive planning and provides a framework within which companies can foresee their own emerging character.

Both dynamic and catalytic planning are instances of *organic planning*, which recognizes the limitations of extrapolation, forecasting and target setting, and provides a framework within which a company or country may work out its purpose progressively, by taking advantage of opportunities as they arise. I suppose it is a kind of preplanned opportunism.

Vanishing Objectives

For some, planning is little more than a statement of objectives. The chairman arrives one morning and says: 'We have not been doing very well in recent months; we must have a plan. I devised one in my bath this morning. By 1975 we shall double our turnover, maintaining or increasing the return on capital employed.' And then he walks away. Fine. Sounds an easy job. Intention is certainly important and, coupled with determination, is more than half the battle. But it is nowhere near enough. In planning, as in politics, we must reconcile the desirable with the possible, and an arbitrary aim can occasionally be worse than none. Why not treble the turnover? Why not double the return on capital employed?

In general, the only practicable long-term objectives are necessarily vague and hence not very useful. The further off they are, the vaguer they must be. Make them more specific and they become increasingly improbable. Bring them back nearer to the present and they fail to be long-term. Objectives are more elusive than we realize and become less tangible the more remote they are. Also, when they are vague or general, like increasing turnover or profit, they are seldom peculiar to any company or individual. 'We are in business to make money' is a familiar statement of objectives. But so is everybody else. There can be no genuine objectives unless there is first an identifiable person or corporate entity to have objectives.

Planning is regarded almost universally (if unconsciously) as a union of objectives and forecasting, but the link is seldom clear. For reasons that I hope will soon be evident, I prefer to see it as a fusion of purpose and anticipation. My aim in formulating this new definition is to collapse planning as far as possible into the present, as discounted cash flow analysis makes it possible to compare rival future projects in present terms. By drawing back planning to the present, we may in some degree defeat the indeterminable nature of the future.

To avoid the weaknesses of planning by *objectives*, it is better to speak of *purpose*, which is uniquely associated with a single company or individual. In this context, I would define purpose as the fusion of identity and motivation, as planning is described as the fusion of purpose and anticipation. Put as two equations, therefore:

$$\text{Planning} = \text{Purpose} + \text{Anticipation}$$
$$\text{Purpose} = \text{Identity} + \text{Motivation}$$

In this way we have placed planning, as far as we are able, in the knowable intelligible present.

Again, purpose suggested adaptability and continuing initiative, whereas objectives tend to be determinate and rigid, mechanistic rather than organic. It is as if we were setting the rudder of an unmanned vessel and launching it from Liverpool in the hope that it will reach New York. It is more realistic to think of a manned vessel, the course of which can be adjusted in the light of circumstances: the captain of a ship bound for New York, which loses its rudder in a storm, will seek to make landfall anywhere. His objective has changed, but his purpose remains constant.

Anticipation is our capacity to visualize the predictive context, but in particular to imagine and forestall the contingent alternatives that may be presented to us. It is not enough to extend a trend along a single line but to anticipate the many different paths into which it may conceivably divide. I always suspect the statement that there are only two alternatives. That is why I recommend planners to read science fiction – it is psychedelic or mind-expanding and shows how many credible futures can be projected. Also, forecasting is already associated with particular techniques, so I prefer to speak of anticipation, which also has the air of being rather less ambitious.

We must certainly endeavour to discern what lies ahead and could become deeply absorbed in this fascinating problem. But purpose is the greater part of planning. Purpose is a man's intention to live a full and fruitful life and is unique to him in that it will depend on that man's own potential and constraints and what he considers to be full and fruitful. The same is true of companies. Purpose in companies can only be meaningful in terms of present and potential assets, and in the light of opportunity. Planning could therefore be defined at greater length as continuously programming the exploitation of accessible resources in the context of a changing world with future needs or benefits in mind, through an understanding of corporate identity.

The dynamic principle of business (in which the desired things happen) is I hope becoming more apparent. It is the oldest organic principle of all – an individual seeking to survive and prosper in a partly friendly, partly indifferent, and partly hostile environment. Perhaps it is only a way of thinking, but to see a problem in intelligible terms is the first step to solving it: formulation is the key to understanding, and understanding to successful action. I should now like to examine the implications of dynamic planning.

In particular, it suggests that we should organize for adaptation to a greater degree than we have ever done before. We should have more mobile commando units and fewer massive, ponderous and inflexible armies, as Xerxes and Moltke discovered to their cost. Likewise, we might usefully redress the balance of our funding policies between long-term and comparatively liquid investment. In other words, it may be desirable to give more consideration to the proper distribution of resources between current account, deposit account and higher-return longer-term investment.

It may be better, for example, to have one power station, commissioned and operating following a single year of intensive construction, than ten, one-tenth complete, all of which will be out of date when they are finished. The application of this principle to the planning of research is particularly important.

This is not to say we should never undertake long-term projects, such as Concorde; indeed we should. Likewise, we commit ourselves to long periods of study,when we decide to become surgeons, accountants, engineers, or craftsmen. But in cases of this kind, purpose must heavily dominate the planning equation. The further-off the consequences of our planning, the more weight we have to give to purpose and the less to anticipation. Anticipation has a place, but drive will be critical. Naturally, in planning Concorde, the best possible attempts were made to foresee the requirements for communication in future years.

When I asked a friend what was the alternative to building Concorde, he said: 'Not building Concorde', no doubt deliberately misunderstanding what I meant. But the alternatives to Concorde are not just other aircraft; but the development of multi-channel visual radio or cable communication links, reducing the need for high-speed human travel; the advent of highly intensive utilization of resources that may lead individual countries to becoming more self-sufficient and less dependent on international trade and personal negotiation; changes in the social order having the same effect (I note that, following the appeals for self-government in Wales and Scotland, a militant group in East Anglia have joined the queue); the outbreak of a major war; and so on.

Having decided that these alternatives are either impracticable, improbable, irrelevant or, if relevant, so disastrous as to be ignored, made such calculations as we can, and demonstrated that we have the necessary resources, we should prosecute the project with all the force at our disposal, only reviewing it at, say, monthly or yearly intervals to see if accumulated evidence, analyzed objectively, should legitimately change our view. Having taken such a decision, we should pursue it unwaveringly, whatever debate may flash about our heads. Purpose, again, is the greater part of planning.

Determination should not be confused with inflexibility, In this world of accelerating change, a company must necessarily equip itself for optimum (not maximum) adaptability. It can then plan without being forced into a straitjacket.

Dynamic, adaptive, or creative planning provides an adequately

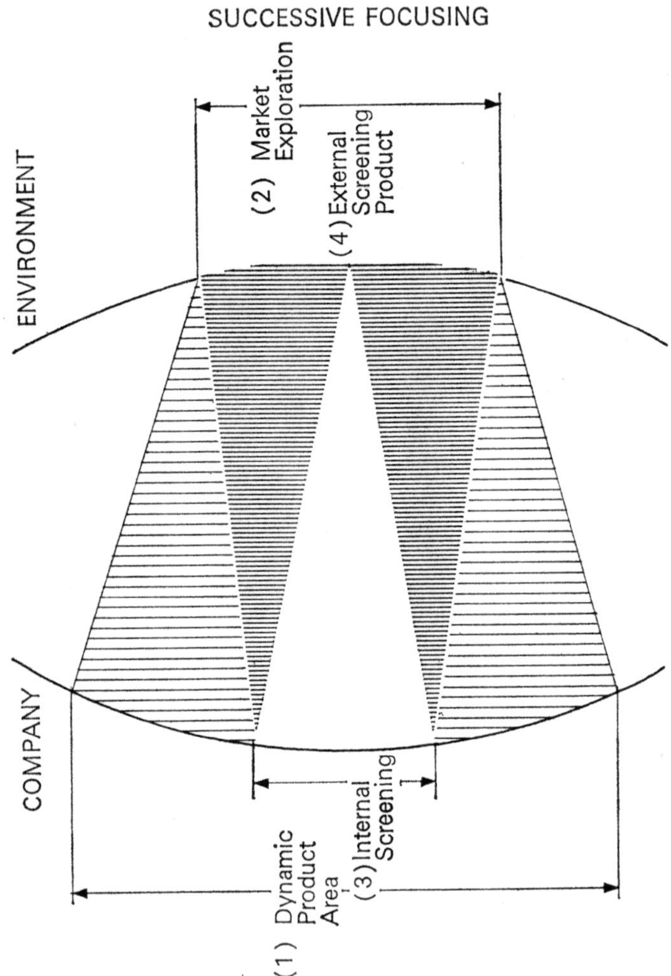

Figure 13. Simplified representation of successive focusing shown as a dialogue between a company and its environment.

flexible framework and permits the use of many methods, just as a man trying to cope with or develop his environment will draw on any tool, technique, or formula that may help him. What is important about dynamic planning is that it gives conscious direction to planning, just as awareness of his true situation enables an ambitious man to act more forcefully.

Planning in a shifting environment calls for constant adjustments to the course. The tracks of certain missiles are computed and determined before they leave the launchers; others continue to correct their paths during flight. A company whose course has been irrevocably set is unlikely to be going anywhere.

The purpose of dynamic planning is to reconcile a company with its environment and its present with its future, continuously and systematically, through a dialogue known as *successive focusing*, as shown in Figure 13. The first step is to define a dynamic corporate identity in terms of those differentiated assets (special facilities, experience, outlets, geographical and other advantages) which in combination make the company unique. The company which plans solely in terms of the overall market and undifferentiated assets, for example capital resources, will do so in competition with every other business.

Products (or services) play a central part in the adaptive process, since it is through them that change is communicated to the company. As the market changes, so must the product portfolio; but the portfolio can only change in step with the available assets and experience. Innovation is critically expressed to the outside world through product development and corporate identity is often but not always formulated in terms of product function as indicated in Figure 14. As already noted, identity must precede objectives, since nothing can have a purpose unless it first exists, or in the words of Marshall McLuhan, 'Roles are now replacing goals'.

To think usefully about its development, a company must have a recognizable identity, a role known and understood both by the company's employees and by the outside world, a lasting role that, as far as can be seen, will not be overtaken by events or changes in the market – in other words a dynamic corporate identity capable of adaptation. A suitable identity or role is the key to successful company planning, in that it extends into the future, can take account of existing potential and experience; provides a basis for a continuing market review; can simplify decision making; and offers scope for preplanned opportunism.

Bearing the company's role in mind, management is in a position to look at current news, technical innovation, commercial developments, social, political, and economic change, and ask themselves: 'What's in it for us?'

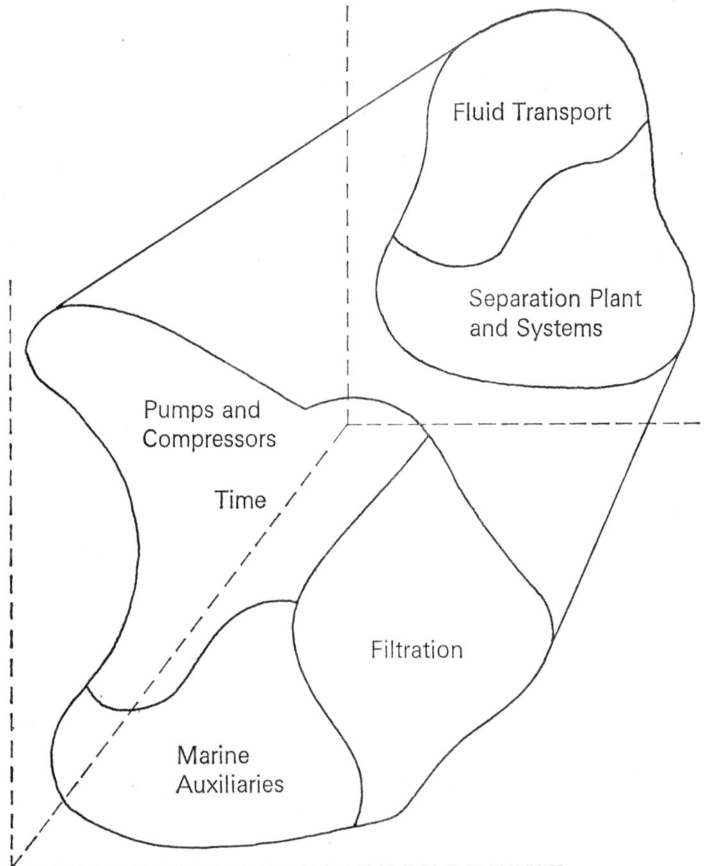

Figure 14. Identity of a company regarded as a slice from an irregular prism, the cross-section of which changes as the identity evolves.

Take, for example, a company that has traditionally supplied intrinsically safe, flame- and explosion-proof equipment for use in coal mines. Knowing that their business was threatened, in that they had a monopoly customer in the United Kingdom, which was closing pits and contracting generally, the company would be anxious to introduce new products. By adopting 'electromechanical aspects of safety' as a more general field of continuing interest, the company can conduct a regular review of product opportunities, focusing on product ideas consistent with the company's resources and experience.

The management would be aware that during recent years there has been one long succession of disasters – earthquakes, slipping coal tips, oil slicks, breached and overflowing dams, unprecedented damage due to fire, mining accidents, losses at sea and in the air, large-scale robberies, and havoc on the roads. By reviewing these events, the safety-conscious company could hardly fail to discover some product opportunities.

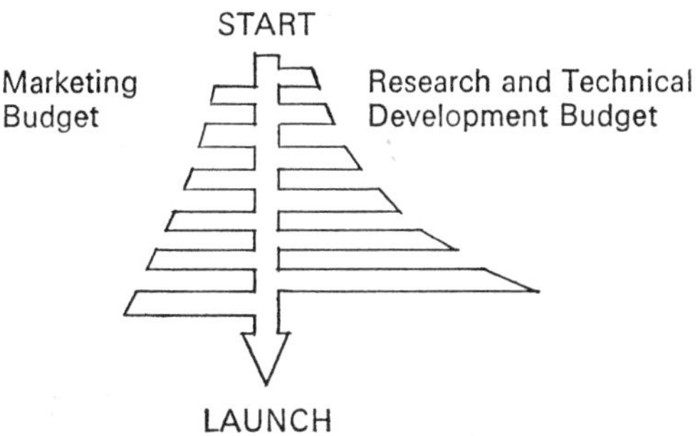

Figure 15. Research-marketing dialogue: budgeting for the development of an innovative product from idea to launch.

Market plus Technology

Strictly, there are only two sources of new products: the discovery of some property or concept for which demand might be created; and the identification of some market requirement which could be embodied in a suitable device. In either case, the ultimate product is a market plus technology.

In engineering (and no doubt also most consumer) companies, a concept will normally emerge from the technical research department, while a market need will be discovered by the marketing department. Each proposal should of course be evaluated by the other through a dialogue on the lines of Figure 15.

Technology in isolation from marketing and marketing without technology can lose touch with reality. An aircraft company developed a superbly efficient forage harvester based on aerodynamic principles, which did not sell until an agricultural-equipment company acquired it, modified the design and sold it aggressively. Shortly after the war another aircraft company introduced a photo-copying machine, only to find that there was insufficient sensitized paper in the whole world to make the machine a practical proposition. Conversely, the marketing manager who calculates the future market for stainless-steel razor blades and mounts a massive campaign to increase his company's market share might be completely foiled by the development of the depilatory which I mentioned earlier. Products have occasionally been specified through market research and proved impossible to manufacture economically.

It is evident that there must be formal channels of communication between technical and marketing staff and that these channels must become well worn. Perhaps the answer is that research and marketing staff should report to the same director and that the director should carry responsibility for the future of the company.

We can then envisage the reporting structure shown in Figure 16. Reporting to the chief executive (or possibly to a product manager in a consumer company) are two general managers of equal status (or two vice-presidents) and only two: one for the present, the other for the future. To the general manager (present) report the normal line functions of a business; to the general manager (future) report the market planning and technical research department – though we should no doubt give the two general managers rather more plausible titles.

It may be asked: where does the future begin? Performance is usually measured in terms of return on capital employed or net cash flow over a given period. But a corporation (as distinct from an individual project) does not have a predetermined life; indeed, each company expects to be immortal. Do we mean return this year? Or return over the next five, ten, or fifteen years? Where do we draw the line?

No line need in fact be drawn. The GM (present) is responsible for running present operations as efficiently as possible. The GM (future) is responsible for introducing change.

In all divisions of responsibility overlap occurs (who has ever known production and sales departments that lived in constant harmony?), but in the new concept any conflict is explicit, rather than latent or submerged.

Also, there is now a man of adequate status and authority to represent the future. Status, whether we like it or not, often depends in business on the number of staff an executive controls. Admittedly the GM (future) will normally have fewer people reporting to him than the GM (present) but they will tend to be better informed and able to provide him with convincing arguments.

Human experience shows how a case is only put effectively by a single-minded advocate, hence the political party system and the normal pattern of debate. The proposed structure might be likened to a court of law, where the chief executive is judge. Surely the future of a company is sufficiently vital to deserve its own exclusive advocate?

I would imagine that the chief executive would seldom be required to arbitrate and direct communication between the general managers would be the rule.

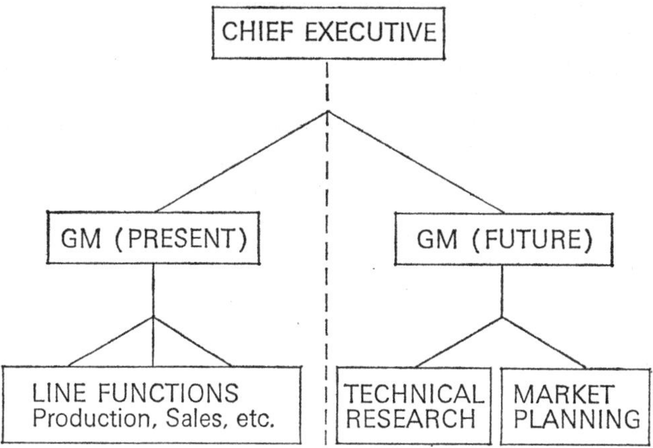

Figure 16. Company organization designed to redress the balance of corporate activity in favour of the future.

The GM (future) would also be in a position to review penumbral discoveries and decide the basis on which penumbra limitation or extension should be made, so that spin-off opportunities or research by-products are recognized and properly exploited. He should also be better equipped than the normal research director to know when projects should be terminated.

Through the closer relationship between technical research and marketing and the concept of dynamic planning, research effort may be directed towards developments and consolidate and reinforce (rather than diffuse) a company's strengths and assets. At the same time, the forward evolution of a company will be organic and self-directing. The company is organized to take advantage of its opportunities.

Only by opportunism can we hope to cope with such a situation. The pitfalls are legion and prompt adaptation the only answer. Anyone, indeed everyone, can be wrong about the future. I have here a leading Sunday newspaper, dated 13th November 1966 (the other one). A full-page article begins: 'Last week, it emerged that the Beatle phenomenon was ending'. I discovered this newspaper in our attic at the beginning of 1968. Beatles' records were at No. 1 and No. 2 in the United Kingdom charts. The titles were, I think, *Hello Goodbye* and *Fool on a Hill.*

I have also had my own embarrassing moments. As consultants, we are not allowed to advertise and it is useful, therefore, to have an occasional editorial reference in the Press. We had done quite well in the serious newspapers and technical magazines, but I was ambitious to see our company mentioned in the popular dailies, in the belief that casual reading had a greater impact on decision makers. I was puzzled for a subject. With a flash of inspiration, I realized that there was an interesting connection between our work in forecasting and the record charts. For some months I kept notes on the projections made by the various disc-jockeys on the pirate radio stations which existed at that time, measuring their success by the actual progress of records through the charts. In particular, I noted the jockeys whose recommended *climbers* went right up to the top.

I also observed that the level of musical sophistication in the more successful records was often very high and Bach, in one guise or another, frequently made the first five. I discovered that Alban Berg had composed the score for *Lulu* (first performed in Britain in 1962 by the Hamburg State Opera) and began to suspect that Benjamin Britten and Michael Tippett were ghosting for the hit parade.

Naturally, I was restricted to unknowns, since no one would think me very clever to predict success for Sandie Shaw, the Rolling Stones, Bob Dylan or the Kinks. Eventually, I completed my analysis, drafted a press release entitled *Picking Pop Records Before they Reach the Charts* and on 14th October 1965 selected my potential hit by an unknown group, The Gentrys.

It is still an unknown group. I overlooked some of the key commercial factors in the promotion of pop records, in particular those affecting the release of American records in the United Kingdom market. My record not only failed to reach the charts; it didn't even reach the shops.

References

Bodroghy, B. G., 'Risk, Return and DCF', *The Director* (July 1966).

Ward, E. P., 'The Dynamics of Business Planning', *Marketing Forum* (November/December 1967), pp. 3–33 (Institute of Marketing).

Ward, E. P., 'A Structure in Favour of the Future'. XXI Esomar Congress (September 1968).

LEONARD E. SCHWARTZ

Technological Forecasting: Another Perspective

We are gathered together in the name of technological forecasting – but what in the world is it? As one peruses the abundant literature impinging on technological forecasting, and indeed all things seem to impinge on it, and as one scans the statements of practitioners, theoreticians and scholars on what technological forecasting is, or should be, one is impressed by the enormously diverse interpretations of this term.

Varying Points of Departure

To Donald Schon, 'Technological forecasting is the forecasting of technological change'. [1] According to Ralph E. Lenz of the U S Air Force, 'Technological forecasting may be defined as the prediction of the invention, characteristics, dimensions, or performance of a machine serving some useful purpose'. [2] Robert Prehoda submits that 'technological forecasting is the description or prediction of a foreseeable invention, specific scientific refinement, or likely scientific discovery that promises to serve some useful function'. [3] To Erich C. Jantsch, 'Technological forecasting is the probabilistic assessment on a relatively high confidence level of future technology transfer'. [4]

Wary of the varying points of departure for what should be a most precise art, I selected for closer examination the work most often cited, *Technological Forecasting in Perspective* by Erich Jantsch. Reading through the 493-page volume in search of a reasonable frame of this variously-defined phenomenon, the quarry proved highly elusive. Its weightiness lay more in amassing a staggering and ill-connected assortment of diverse techniques ranging from corporate planning to the intuitive Delphi model to the trendy envelope curve to morphological structuring to relevance trees which begin with goals, set out branches representing requirements, and which are then assigned values, numerical or other. This seemingly indiscriminate selection of techniques, presented in a language that was alternatively pretentious and unoriginal, made it most difficult to discover the underlying rationale.

Planning vs. Prediction

Was technological forecasting equally operations analysis and Delphic forecasts? Is planning the same as prediction? Is not the difference between them at least an order of magnitude? Surely prediction embraces all the problems of planning, and then some. And the definition of these 'some' is what makes prediction the distinctive challenge it is.

One could postulate a progression from planning to prediction, showing in some incremental fashion how the art of anticipation can be extended. We have had a somewhat longer history of rather more serious attempts at planning, including operations analysis, systems analysis, programme analysis, and programme planning into the latest version of planned programme budget system, known among its initiates as PPBS. Planners would be enormously aided by a rigorous analysis of the comparative merits of these systems from the wider frame of systemics or cybernetics. A comparative analysis could sharpen the particular edge of each and indicate what body of decisions are best helped by which approach. Scrambling them together with a host of equally complex intuitive approaches, as Jantsch has done, advances neither our understanding of the distinctiveness of planning techniques nor their applicability towards developing the infinitely more demanding task of prediction in general or technology in a more specific sense. Crudely put, what makes technological forecasting different from systemics or cybernetics?

Mood vs Discipline

What comes out of Jantsch's work and the reception that greeted it is euphoria. This vein of technological forecasting has been more reflective of a mood than of a discipline, a mood of unmitigated confidence. If one endeavours to trace the roots of this mystique of confidence, one finds oneself harking back to World War II days. One could, I suppose, exemplify man's ingenuity in grappling with technological phenomena from the time of the wheel, to such epochal events as the plough, printing, power loom, reciprocating engines up to automation, all to the regular accompaniment of the mechanical clock.

But the more sustained, large-scale and time-compressed instances of human manipulation of technology has really come into its own only in our lifetime. While a few notable achievements in planned technology developed before World War II, such as in aviation, gas warfare and underseas sound detection, it is only since then that technological forecasting emerged from a term that one voiced inaudibly for fear of being heard, to one rife with promises of producing all sorts of radical changes. The war dramatized the partnership between technologists and government who, in concert, could produce seemingly at will inventions undreamt of – German V2 rockets spanning unprecedented distances, atomic bombs projecting mushrooming clouds. It is not for nought that ours has been dubbed the age of atoms and missiles. The development of the atomic bomb under severely compressed exigencies of time and unborn technology is most often cited in the literature, and indeed at this conference, as the instance, par excellence, of technological forecasting.

When President Roosevelt first received Albert Einstein's letter, all that could be said was that nuclear fission had been theoretically postulated. Experimental verification had yet to be fulfilled; practical demonstration lay still further in the future. Similarly, all that the German Army Board Ordnance had to go on when confronted with General Dornberger's design for a rocket missile was based on an unproven technology developed mainly by amateur enthusiasts whose verbal thrust was greater than their rocket propulsion. The exercises that followed, working from a given base of science towards desired technological ends, lent credence to the belief in technological manipulation.

This marriage of political will with technological advance encouraged a widespread belief in the rationale, in the certainty, of planning and from thence in the feasibility of prediction. Man was led to believe that where 'man wills, man will'. Concretization of this belief came in the form of ICBMs, miniaturized nuclear weapons, gigantic space vehicles, computers, supersonic airplanes. . . .

Techniques vs. Norms

But to believe is neither to predict nor to plan. One can believe that society should strive for this or that end; this neither guarantees nor even implies a prediction of things to come nor its planned realization, unless concrete plans are made. Jantsch's linking together of exploratory with normative approaches confuses techniques (exploratory) with goal-setting (normative). Moreover, certain techniques are better suited to planning; others to prediction, since the constraints on both are markedly different. Normative goal setting rests on a still different combination of skills and constraints.

I would like to see a classless society based on the triumph of the working class, said Marx normatively. *I predict it*, said Kerensky. *I shall plan it*, said Stalin.

The burden then is not to merely list techniques; this can dazzle, and also confound. The relevance of each technique has to be demonstrated in relation to the particular requirements of planning (corporate or other), prediction (short- or long-term), or goal setting (should be or could be). The difficulty was that when one finished reading the diverse offerings on technological forecasting, one did not know how to start. One gets the impression that the art of technological forecasting, at least as popularly practised or, more precisely, proclaimed, is overwhelmed by techniques which spin ever finer webs over ill-defined assumptions.

A Beginning . . .

At this point one can either abandon ship or attempt to lay a keel of some sort oneself, however modest, and hope that others of sturdier mind will build thereon. Let us then return to our original quest, thrust aside popular notions and begin anew. What is common to planning prediction, and normative thinking is a state of mind – systematization. All take their point of departure from (a) *where does one wish to go* – target; (b) *analyze resources to determine requirements*, checked by (c) *can it be done* – desirability vs. feasibility.

But what about the character of the person who innovates, i.e the inventor? Is there something distinctive about an innovator that will help us to anticipate innovations? Given a particular predisposition, technological innovations can be postulated from scientific discoveries or from already established scientific principles. One mind can deduce that an apple falling from a tree hurts, while to another the repercussions may be more significant. But what is the nature of this predisposition? In examining the wellsprings of human inventiveness, one finds that the inventor is discernible by his intellectual equipment, by his ability to analogize, by the span of his observations and contacts, and by the particular content and quality of his accumulated insights. By increasing our insight into creativity, we might be able to foster more creative environments. This then could be an attractive base for encouraging technological growth and forecasting.

But while it is difficult to define the content of technology whether in terms of tools or techniques, and equally challenging to discern the mainspring of human ingenuity, one would be additionally troubled by the change in style of technological conduct, i.e. its environment. The era of individual tinkering has become overwhelmed by the age of organized systemics. Technology, indeed society, has become systematized. 'Today we must organize' is the battle cry of IBM, ICI, Min Tech and Mao Tse Tung. This all-pervasive belief in the planning of planning persists despite sometimes shattering setbacks, some recent examples being the disappointingly slow development of nuclear electric power at economic cost in the US and Europe, *Blue Streak* in Britain, space rockets in France. . . . But ours remains an age whose faith in organization continues unimpaired. Faith in organized tinkering has even taken on new strength from the growing conviction that technology can not only be ordered but predicted as well.

Focus: Technology

What then is truly distinctive to technological forecasting? How do technical forecasts differ from economic forecasts, election forecasts, or industrial forecasts?

In bringing this 'field' into focus, the critical dimension separating it from all others is technology. Obvious. But why then, one may ask, does technology seem to receive such scant attention in the literature? By far the greatest emphasis in the reams of written material on the subject has been restricted to forecasting alone, with its relation to technology left as rather incidental. Forecasts take on particular shape and meaning only when linked; in this case, with technology. The immediate and principal burden confronting the technological forecaster then is to discern the features distinguishing this phenomenon called technology from all other species.

Whether one approaches technology from a normative point of view as to what it ought to be or prognosticates what it could be, or alternatively, plans what it should be, requires not only sensitive insights into technology but on appreciably different levels. The planner can project the next steps that technological development will or could take after a reasonable understanding of the current technological state of the art. New uses for computers and refinements in their storage capacity and speed of data transmission can be put forward by any reasonably imaginative computer engineer oriented towards computer planning.

The forecaster has a markedly more demanding task. Not only must he be *au courant* with the planner's sphere of knowledge, but if he is to prognosticate effectively, he must see behind computer engineering to computer science. Abstract mathematics and theoretical physics are stepping stones for leapfrogging to new genera of computational devices such as simulating the features of the human brain. Research at the University of Edinburgh is trying to unravel the process of human perception from observation to cognition to feedback. The magnitude of the technical challenge confronting brain simulation is exceeded only by the scale of social reaction, should the research bear fruit.

The technological eye is one capable of scanning the horizon of accumulated knowledge and theories and of discerning the connection between abstract principles and projected extensions of man's manipulative capabilities.

But what horizon does one scan? Does one proceed to abstract mathematics, physics or combinations thereof, or does one begin with fundamentals of shape and structure and proceed to postulate a theoretical profile, setting forth how different shapes could withstand different patterns of stress and strain? Since technology is often characterized as a tool, could one add the dimension of compactness as a further test of the theoretical profile and then follow with such kindred factors as malleability and tensility? Further, but undoubtedly not finally, can one correlate shape and structure and their associated characteristics of malleability and tensility against a spectrum of temperature and pressure variations.

Aside from the difficulty of determining what is more fundamental – shape, structure, temperature, etc. – and thus which is the primary point of departure, there is the corollary problem that since theoretical profiles and definition of shape and structure depend on the known state of the physical, chemical and biological sciences, the very definition of shape and structure are subject to change. But then so is the definition of technology. In the first instance, planner or prognosticator must define his technological assumptions.

The poor bloke who would go further, to postulate what technological innovations society ought to promote, requires ideally a sensitivity to development and projections in the state of the art coupled with an equal sensitivity to their meaning for man and society. The one element common to all technological definitions is the human relationship – an extension of man's elbow. Technological products are by themselves somewhat exotic; they take on meaning only when applied.

The value of technological change can be expressed in terms of greater efficiency evidenced by gain in some combination of *time*, as in pressure cookers, *space*, as in transistors, or *motion* as in motorized transportation. The human significance of technology lies in the ability of tools and techniques to make human effort more effective or harmonious, depending on one's philosophy or prejudice. But *how* applied – anti-missile-missiles? And *by whom* applied – government, pressure groups, rich men? And *when* applied – in Joseph's seven-year storage locker against famine?

This brief outline does not pretend to delineate the distinctive character of the phenomenon called technology. It simply suggests, however, that any attempt at technological forecasting which skips over the prickles of its thorny boundaries overlooks what should be its primary concern, and runs the danger of propagating pretentious nonsense.

Scientific Breakthroughs

Even a simplistic view of technology as the application of scientific breakthroughs poses problems. How does one know that a postulated scientific formula is valid and thereby susceptible to translation into engineering (and socially useful products), in other words, *when is a breakthrough a breakthrough*?

Vincent J. Schaefer, self-taught chemical engineer, tossed some dry ice into cumulus clouds off the north-east coast of the United States in December 1946, following which some snowflakes appeared. Many other enthusiasts proceeded to thrust dry ice and also silver iodide from ground generators into likely looking clouds. At first many meteorologists expressed scepticism that the breakthrough represented by cloud-seeding had actually been achieved. In its initial report issued in 1964, the US National Academy of Sciences Panel on Weather and Climate Modification concluded that 'It has not yet been demonstrated that precipitation from winter orographic storms can be increased significantly by seeding' and that 'the initiation of large scale operational weather modification programs would be premature'.

Two years later, the same august body did a turnabout and conceded that cloud-seeding might, under certain conditions, induce an increase in precipitation as high as 17 per cent. Based on statistical evidence in both cases, the Academy Panel reached two different conclusions within two years. And the character of the scientific breakthrough in artificial rainmaking was no clearer in 1966 than in 1964.

Can one then suggest applications and technique developments when the underlying scientific postulate is itself a subject of dispute? How does one verify that improving technological implements for sowing clouds with dry ice or silver iodide will truly bring about precipitation sooner, or greater than would have occurred naturally without human intervention?

When the Roosevelt Administration was first apprised of the Hahn-Strassmann recipe for splitting the atom, it was, like most governments, unable to pass judgment on the scientific proposition, let alone appreciate its ramifications, military or otherwise. A bridge had to be traversed between forecasting and commitment – experimental verification. The theoretical postulate had to be experimentally verified before thought could be given realistically to application.

And so Enrico Fermi, refugee scientist from Italy, navigated the Hahn-Straussmann theorem through the course of an experimental nuclear pile in a basement laboratory at the University of Chicago. On 2nd December 1942, Fermi wired the White House that 'the Italian navigator has landed'. Nuclear fission had passed its experimental test. Under more normal circumstances, a series of gradual steps would then have followed to translate the experimental proof into engineering models, going from mock-ups to development models, to prototypes, to field tests. But a war was on. Engineers were compelled to compress models and to project ahead to the final stage of producing a useable device and, most critically, in time.

Robert W. Prehoda, in his book, *Designing the Future*, takes the Hahn-Straussmann point in atomic theory and uses it as point of departure to search for analogous situations in other fields of science. Prehoda believes that theoretical breakthroughs constitute a demarcation at which practical applications can be articulated. But the difficulty, as Prehoda acknowledges, is to recognize when the Hahn-Straussmann level has, in fact, been reached.

As one examines events preceding 1939, one finds an array of confusing and contradictory predictions. In 1930, the Earl of Birkenhead predicted great nuclear events for the world of 2030. Three years later, in 1933, Rutherford ridiculed the idea of harnessing nuclear energy. In 1935, Joliot-Curie, in his Nobel prize address, returned to nuclear fission and its potential significance. One year later, Clifford C. Furnas, well-known American physicist, cautioned on expecting much from nuclear application. And so there are points and there are 'points'... and there are forecasts and there are 'forecasts'.

Extrapolative Technological Planning

Aware of the ambiguities of scientific technology, let us attempt to stretch the skein of technological forecasting from its planning to predictive/normative ends and reveal more clearly the distinctive shape of technology vis-à-vis human manipulation. On the planning end, we extrapolate while for forecasting we project.

Extrapolative technological planning takes its point of departure from technology-in-being. Working from the given technological state of the art, one maps out the most likely course of sequences. To take computers, the next stage seems to lie along time-shared systems. Research is proceeding on adding a variety of devices, including multi-terminals and small satellite computers to the single computer, to enable simultaneous usage of a computer by many programmers. Although some of the time-sharing devices involving programme segmentation and scheduling raise significant economic problems of cost allocation, and commercial problems of efficient production and marketing, the consensus is that, technically, they present no problems.

Extrapolative technological planning, especially of a short-term nature, has been practised on a modest and informal scale for quite some time, one might even say, from the time of the Industrial Revolution. The operations and systems research practised by a large number of firms in the US and elsewhere reveals the growing interest in developing a more formal and systematic method for technology extrapolation and for longer time periods.

Projective Technological Forecasting

Projective technological forecasting confronts all the challenges facing extrapolative technological planning, and then some – notably from the difficulty of projecting over longer periods of time. Any qualified engineer should be able to outline possible trends in the next stage of improvements in his own speciality, be it bridge building, road surfacing, or electronics. Projective technological forecasting boldly set out to project the formulation of technologies not yet in existence. Working from a given goal, either technologically or socially determined, for ten, twenty years, or more, the projective forecaster must not only review existing forms of technology but undeveloped ones as well. In this sense, projective technology anticipates building blocks of the future.

Where the technology is already there, the problem is one of management or administration or, if the situation is more serious or costly, it may mean galvanizing the political will to marshal resources. But in other situations, all the wills in the world, collective, political, or otherwise, pale before the simple but shattering judgment, *sorry, old chap, but technologically, it's just not on.* In this event, the forecaster must turn his art towards determining the technological options and the various steps along the path of feasibility.

From one to three years might not prove too put-offish and, indeed, most commercial firms limit their prognoses to this time frame. But even within this limited period, mistakes are made and prognoses proven faulty. In part, this is the normal accompaniment of those so bold as to predict. Equally relevant is the multitude of other than technical factors, including economic and political, that the forecaster must consider, which make straightforward engineering extrapolations inadequate.

Social and Political Constraints

Economic factors (such as costs and availability of land, labour, and capital) can determine which of several technological alternatives makes most sense. Each nation or company's stock of goods and services provide a kind of limit. Europe would like to pursue the same range of technological activities in electronics, computers, and aerospace that the US does, but is more constrained by her limited resources.

Using the so-called technological gap as an instance, Europe might be ill-advised to undertake further research and development in sectors such as computers, where she is critically behind, and might better concentrate on those spheres, such as new transportation and communication systems, where her position vis-à-vis the United States is more even. Indeed, innovations in the latter areas could help Europe to catapult ahead of all likely competitors, while even intensive activity in the former may, at best, lead to a reduction of the gap, without ever closing it.

Social and economic considerations are not the only constraints on technological development. Politics plays its mighty part. From its very inception, modern technological forecasting, in both its successful moments and those less so, betrayed a sensitivity to the connexion between government and technology; namely, that development of the latter was dependent on the will of the former. The German War Reich said *yes* to rockets and *no* to atoms; the American Government said *yes* to atoms and *no* to rockets.

Robert H. Goddard, the American, posthumously (and there lies the true story) acclaimed as one of the world's first rocket pioneers, found in 1941 that none of the US military services were willing to accept his rocket work. Goddard offered them the world's largest liquid-fueled rocket for its time, on which he had worked intensively over two decades gratis, but no takers. The German military command, who were not favoured by such gratuity and whose rocketeers were not as advanced, nevertheless granted rocketry topmost political priority. Ironically, America asserted political initiative in the area in which it was relatively technologically backward, i.e. atomics, and spurned the area in which it was relatively technologically advanced: with Germany doing the reverse.

On 26th September 1939, the Reich convened a secret conference of nuclear scientists. Agreed on the potential power inherent in nuclear fission, the German scientists pondered on the most effective route for achieving its practical realization. Two methods were hit upon. One would extract energy from the uranium nucleus in a controlled manner by building a uranium-fuelled reactor with a moderator, such as heavy water, to slow down the high-energy neutrons but not absorb them. The second method involved the extraction of the rare isotope, U-235, from the more common forms of uranium.

Following Germany's occupation of Norway, where she seized numerous heavy-water plants, Germany found her moderator. Stockpiles of uranium were located in occupied Belgium, and an American cyclotron was taken when Paris fell. Germany may also have had the scientists required, despite large numbers having fled the country. She clearly had one of the most impressive chemical engineering industries in the world.

But unfortunately, as it turned out for her, Germany was winning the war, at least at that moment. Her lightning invasions of her smaller, weaker neighbours overwhelmed them. Since conventional arms had proven themselves, why invest in nuclear chimeras?

Not only do social factors refuse to wither away but they present ever more complex problems as the time frame is stretched from three to five to ten and beyond years. Being somewhat more intangible than inventions or techniques, social and economic processes are not only more elusive of definition in the first instance, but even more so over time. And regrettably, the technological forecaster cannot ignore society, else he runs the risk that society will ignore his forecasts. Indeed, social pressures may override clear-cut technological recommendations, such as bacteriological warfare, in favour of those more socially acceptable. Technology might not always do well by society, but whenever a technical invention crosses the societal threshold, it can only do so at the bidding of its human manipulator.

Building Block Technology

Once the scientific postulate is stated, ideally in clear and reasonable detail – no mean accomplishment in itself – the search for appropriate technological profiles may commence. The diverse fields of engineering can then be queried for the best available engineering art forms. Appraisals may have to be made of the limits of structures, qualities of materials, and stress profiles in relation to pressure and temperature, and the other dimensions previously discussed. Should the review of the engineering state of the art reveal that the desired art form has yet to be created, engineering art must turn to engineering science.

The scale of the technology required to separate the uranium isotope essential to the atomic explosive was nowhere available; it had to be invented. Here was a true test for developing a building-block technology. How to proceed? In its review of processes for uranium isotope separation, the US came up with several processes which seemed to promise fulfilment of the technical requirement of success, the economic one of absorbable cost, and the political one of timeliness. All three processes not only produced the world's first atomic bomb, but demonstrated a significant advance in building-block technology.

In the case of *Project Mohole*, a drill was required capable of piercing the earth's mantle, hopefully to lay bare its origins and composition. This drill had to be capable of sustaining enormous friction and strain without breaking and without exhibiting undue whip. In the belief that these requirements transcended the given state of technology, a 'super drill' and hence a superior form of technology was deemed necessary, and its technological profile drawn up.

Where the scientific base is laid, as in the case of liquid-fuelled rocket motors, technical demands can still be formidable. Both the American Robert H. Gooddard and the German rocketeers articulated a technical profile of a rocket engine based on scientific and engineering principles, separating out those components derivable from the prevailing state of the art and those not so. But to attain the high propulsion required, new fields had to be created – cryogenics.

Twilight Zone . . .

If the foregoing analysis has raised more questions than answers, one should not find this unusual in a field that is still in the process of unfolding. Technological forecasting is in a twilight zone between hope and development. The euphoric reaction to atomic and space building-block technology should not be allowed to run rampant and mask the conceptual wrenching that must first take place before the science of forecasting, if it is to become such, can begin to take real shape.

To become such, technological forecasting must search for its distinctive characteristics . . . the first distinction going to technology. Articulation of technology is the substratum of all technological forecasting. It is not only the first step; it is indispensable. Once a methodology for articulating technological profiles is achieved, which take into account the variety of individual and organized tinkering, and the character of human innovation, then one can work towards the next critical phase of placing technology within its social, economic, and political context.

When one achieves some understanding of the interaction between technology and society, then perhaps one can scan with greater profit the variety of forecasting techniques available and to be generated and extrapolate the next series of possible technological developments, and if the insights are adequate, project even longer range building blocks of technology. An openness and orderliness of mind is constantly in order as one lays bare the gap between art and science, an orderliness which strives for cohering reason from chaos; an openness to admission of error followed by the resolve to check forecast against subsequent events and to profit from the inevitable mistakes to improve the art and thereby fashion the basis for technological forecasting.

References

1 Donald A. Schon, 'Forecasting and Technological Forecasting', *Daedalus*, Summer 1967, p. 759.
2 Major Joseph P. Martino, 'The Methodology of Technological Forecasting', *The Futurist*, April 1968, p. 34 (Quoted).
3 Robert Prehoda, 'The Growing Role of Technological Forecasting', *The Futurist*, June 1967, pp. 1–3.
4 Erich C. Jantsch, *Technological Forecasting in Perspective*, Organization for Economic Cooperation and Development, Paris, October 1966, p. 4.

DAVID R. COATES

Technological Forecasting and the Planning of R and D

This paper is directed towards the problem of formulating the research and development programme in an industrial concern. The principles and methods of technological forecasting are introduced, and their usefulness in relation to the problem explored. The treatment is intended to be relevant whether the concern is large or small, and whether the research and development is conducted within its organization or by an external agency.

The Principles of Technological Forecasting

Technological forecasting is concerned with the forecasting of technological change. If by technological change one understands the development of the applied sciences and their industrial exploitation, then forecasting will primarily be concerned with the capabilities provided by the changing state of the art, and their influence on the materials and techniques employed in industrial production. However, the term can also be used much more broadly to include the economic and social changes which result from the development of technology and the methods of industrial production. Indeed, with the possible exception of research of a fundamental character, it is unrealistic to discuss any aspect of technological change without considering the social and economic environment in which it is expected to take place. It is the complexity of the interactions between changing technology and the complex and changing environment which presents technological forecasting with its most formidable difficulties. Analysis may help to break a question down into its component parts and allow a clearer base for judgment; it may also facilitate the use of quantitative as well as qualitative information. But because of the uncertainties involved, the interpretation and very often the basis for a forecast must remain a matter of judgment.

The term exploratory technological forecasting is used to note any attempt to predict the course of technological change. As we have suggested, the subject of such a forecast may be the course of development in a particular applied science, or to give a further example, the rate and extent of the diffusion of a particular new or improved technology in industrial practice during a given number of years. Exploratory forecasting may be based purely upon informed opinion, either that of an individual or of a panel, which may reach its conclusion by discussion, or in the case of the *delphi procedure*, through the medium of a secretariat. The advantages of Helmer's procedure is that views may be collected from dispersed individuals, if necessary under the cloak of anonymity. For those unfamiliar with the procedure, it should be explained that each panel member is interviewed by questionnaire as to his opinion of the details of a particular forecast. The opinions are aggregated and re-circulated. The process may be repeated until a consistent range of views is obtained. It should be noted that the method is particularly useful in dealing with the longer term, in particular with periods for which detailed analysis based on the projection of trends is unrealistic, because of the order of uncertainty involved in their projection.

The second main method of exploratory forecasting is based upon the more explicit approach of the projection of past trends. In such an exercise an attempt is made to identify the variables which best characterize the subject of the forecast, and time series data is collected which describes their past development. Statistical methods are then used to fit trend curves to the time series data, the shape of the curve being developed from the data, often with reference to a model which is supposed to represent the nature of the development in question. The details and application of this method will be further discussed below.

Where once a forecast has been made, it can itself influence the development of subsequent affairs. If the forecast is regarded as an indication, perhaps an authoritative indication, of what may happen in an otherwise uncertain future, the behaviour of both individuals and organizations may be modified according to their ambitions or previous expectations. If actions are taken to obtain the conditions forecast, the forecast is said to exercise a normative influence on affairs. Thus the term normative technological forecasting has been used to note the process of identifying the technological developments which will have to be made if specified social, economic, or industrial objectives are to be realized. The relation of this process to exploratory forecasting is that the likelihood of achieving those objectives may be considered by comparison of their technical requirements with the course of expected developments. As we shall explain in some detail later, the order of the deficiency between what is required and what is likely to be available on the basis of the present research and development programme provides an indication of the priority for additional technical work. In short, exploratory technological forecasting may be used to inform both the general formulation of objectives and the detailed process of planning the operations designed to achieve them.

Planning involves determining the objectives it will be desirable to achieve in specified periods, and deciding upon the operations which will have to be undertaken if the objectives are to be achieved. Many of the decisions will be interdependent, if not sequential, and will have to be evaluated as such. Moreover, whatever operations are intended will have to be viewed as being in dynamic interaction with a wide environment, the influence, development and response of which must be carefully anticipated. The term 'scenario' has sometimes been applied to such exercises.

Now forecasting, whether technological or otherwise, may be viewed as providing information for the decisions involved in the planning process. It follows that the relevance of a forecast is likely to depend upon the extent to which the correct questions have been asked in relation to the decision which is to be taken. It also follows that the value of a forecast, and therefore the order of the resources to be made available to forecasting activities, may be assessed following the principle of the value of additional information. A relevant forecast should put one in the position to plan activities with which less uncertainty and therefore risk is to be associated. The value of a forecast is computed in terms of the additional net returns which may be expected, or the additional net cost which may be avoided as a result of its information being available to planners. The other side of the coin is that there is little point in making forecasts unless a decision is to be taken which can be informed in such a way as to be likely to generate additional income, and unless it is clear that the implications of the forecast will be heeded.

Again, the more frequently a plan is reviewed and modified in the light of forecasts, the more closely are the activities of planning and forecasting integrated. One further point of principle should be added: as planning entails taking decisions which are intended to obtain results at some point in the future, the criteria for choice between the alternative actions becomes critical because the criteria relevant to present circumstances may not be relevant to those obtaining in the future. Where the criterion is relevant to technical choice, it should be recognized that it will depend upon the strategy and may be seen as a competitive position of the concern in relation to its environment during the period of the exploitation of the technology being developed.

The Projection of Trends and the Functional View of Technology

The function performed by a product or process, indeed by any technology, may for analytical purposes be considered independently of the means by which it is achieved. It may in principle be described by a set of parameters chosen so that a measure of its performance can be described by their quantitative evaluation. Parameters so defined are called 'performance characteristics'. Let us take an example. The properties of a steel may be expressed in terms of density, strength, resistance to corrosion, and so on. These are characteristics of its performance and may be used to describe the steel or to specify a requirement which could be met by its use. The characteristics may be quantified and cited as a full specification for the material. However, it should be recognized that a material of completely different chemical composition, for example a plastic, could have the same performance characteristics and therefore meet the same design requirements.

Now, supposing that we wished to forecast how high strength materials may develop in the next decade, we might decide to write the appropriate trend curves. The procedure in each case involves several stages:

(1) The choice of the performance characteristics representing the properties of materials most relevant to the question we wished to answer.

(2) The quantitative description of presently available materials in terms of the chosen parameters.

(3) The collection of time series data from reliable sources, bearing in mind that data should be collected for a period at least as long as that which is to be forecast and that the definitions employed in earlier data may not correspond to those used in the definition of the performance characteristics.

(4) The choice of a model or method with which to generate the trend from the time series data.

(5) The projection of the trend, taking into account constraints which may alter the form of its development but which were not explicitly or adequately incorporated in the model used to generate the trend. The trend should be drawn with a clear statement of the levels of confidence or uncertainty which are understood to apply. One way of assessing these is the examination of the sensitivity of the forecast to reasonable changes in its basic assumptions.

One of the more important points to be borne in mind in trend forecasting both in the choice of data and the interpretation of trends is the need to distinguish whether the data refer to exploited technology or to the limits of technical achievement yet to be incorporated in a device or process for which there is a commercial market. That is, it must be distinguished whether the trends or the data reflect the development of needs which have been met at acceptable costs, or merely the limits of available technology. Performance characteristics may be written as functions of cost as well as of technical capability and for this reason exploratory forecasting and functional analysis may be useful in market as well as in technical planning, indeed, they may provide a basis for relating market needs to the objectives of research and

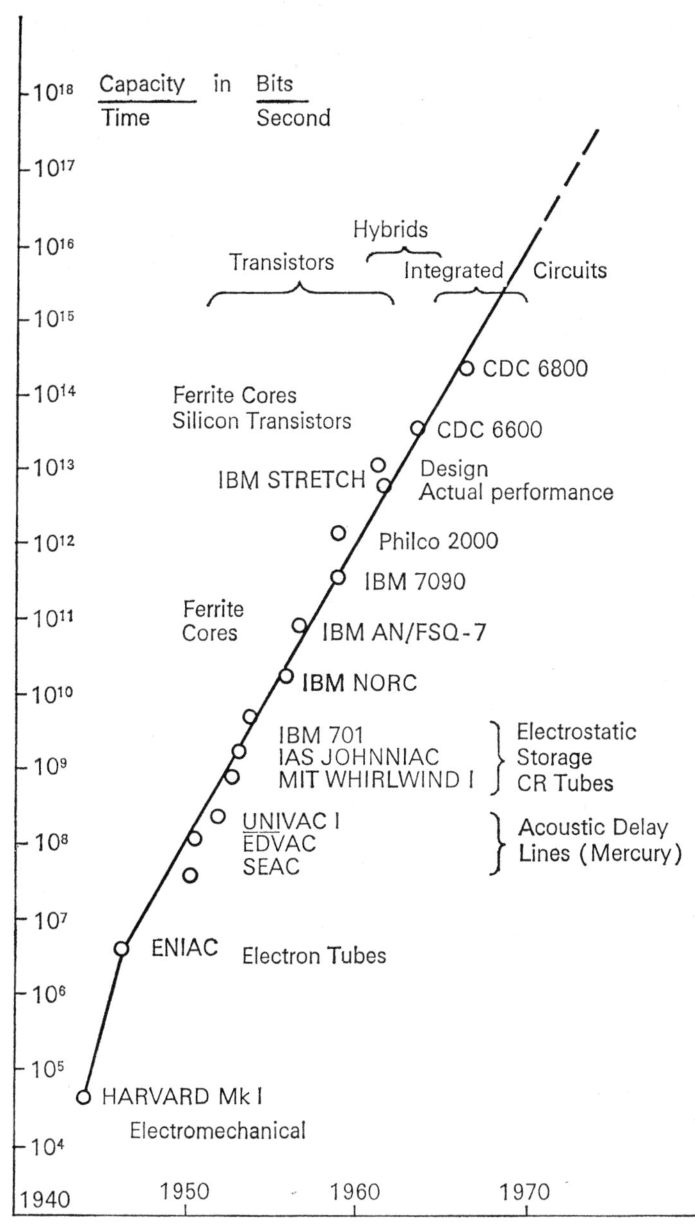

Source: Ayres

Figure 1. Computer trends.

development programmes. One way of conducting such an exercise is the method of *relevance analysis*, which will be described below.

The importance of taking a number of trends and of considering demand as well as technical factors in planning decisions may be illustrated with reference to the curve in Figure 1, in which a trend representing the capacity and speed of electronic computers has been plotted. Although such a curve may be useful for general planning purposes, suggesting the scale of larger machines for a given rate of data handling, it should be pointed out that too much attention to trends describing the most advanced capabilities may lead to a mistaken emphasis in development programmes, especially with regard to the market that the manufacturer might most profitably serve. This should be carefully examined as well.

Two models of the curve of technological development have been widely used in the projection of time series data. The first regards development as an exponential process, and displays forecasts as straight lines on semi-logarithmic graph paper. The second model in common usage is written by analogy to processes of biological development, for example the growth of an individual animal or the introduction of a new species into a given ecological environment, which may be represented by the familiar sigmoid S-shaped curve. The analogy is accepted because processes of change under conditions of opportunity and constraint which have been established by studies of growth, decay and competition in systems of natural organization apply in principle to human organization and in consequence to technological change. We have pointed out that either in the sense of technological development or the effects of the exploitation of technology, the rate and direction of technological change is influenced by the nature of the social and economic environment in which it takes place.

The advantage of the biological model is that it requires an explicit consideration of the mechanism generating the trend. However, it should be appreciated that the exponential is a special case of the sigmoid curve, representing development in the period before the rate of change begins to decrease under the operation of boundary constraints. In Figure 2 the orbital velocity of an aircraft is regarded, perhaps arbitrarily, as a boundary constraint, and although the trend towards greater conversion in Figure 3 can only tend towards completion, each of the separate trends under the overall 'envelope curve' has developed to a limit, governed by the mechanical and physical principles of the machines employed. In each case further development followed, presumably because there was a demand for increased efficiency of conversion and the recognition of the opportunity to employ new principles on the part of an engineer. Although this is quite a plausible account of technological change, we are concerned to ask whether the

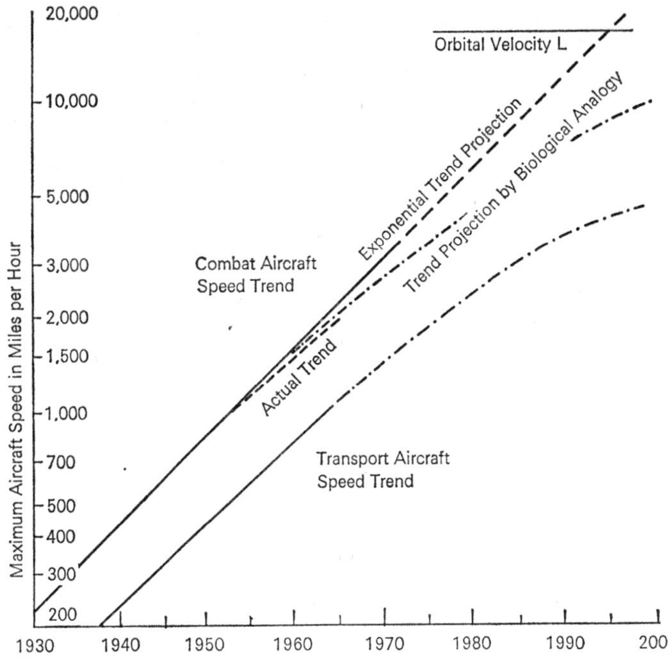

Figure 2. Speed trends of US Combat and Transport aircraft.

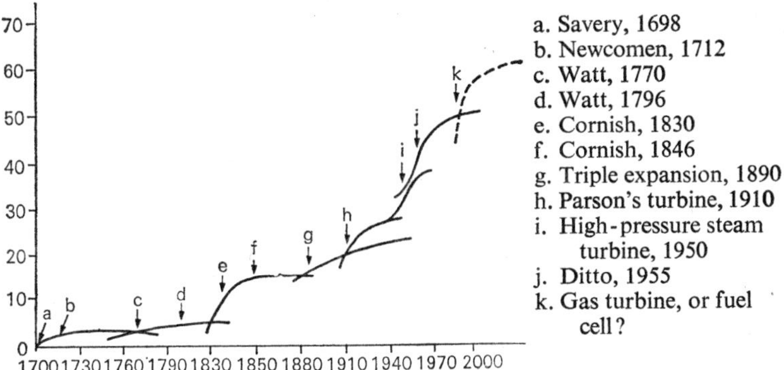

Figure 3. Envelope curves of percentage efficiency of External Combustion Energy Conversion Systems.

display of sigmoid curves is at all useful in the planning of technological change and therefore in the formulation of research and development objectives.

The problem with which we are thus faced is the identification of systems that will come to replace those with which we are now involved, so that an appropriate effort can be directed to their development. The first task in such an exercise is to prepare an exploratory technological forecast, paying especial attention to the way in which the curve may be expected to approach its limit. The second is to examine the market and market trends to identify how the preference for a more advanced capability is likely to develop. It may be that the further development of the existing technology will satisfy demand in the face of any conceivable competitive activity. If this is not so, and depending on the strategy of the concern for this particular area, it will be necessary to examine possible replacement technologies likely to have the necessary performance characteristics. The decision to go ahead with any required development work should then be based upon the appraisal of the usual kind. The situation may be illustrated:

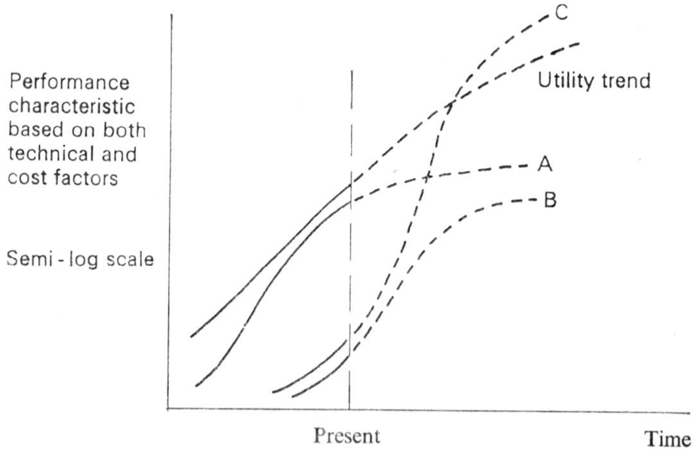

The trends show that system 'A' has begun to reach the limit of improvement, and that demand for an improved capability may be confidently anticipated. Replacement system 'B' is likely to fail whereas replacement system 'C' appears likely to succeed. The performance characteristic in this case is a function involving cost as well as technical parameters. Compounds of parameters are sometimes called 'figures of merit'.

A practical example of an exercise of this kind is described by Jantsch. In 1950 the measurement of the thermo-electric properties of newly discovered semi-conductor materials suggested that the threshold required for the economic application of thermo-electric refrigeration might soon be crossed. Westinghouse decided to initiate a fairly large development programme. General Motors, on the other hand, setting up a group to consider how the trends might develop, forecast a natural limit for semi-conductor materials which was still below the economic threshold. Their decision not to initiate a development programme proved to be correct.

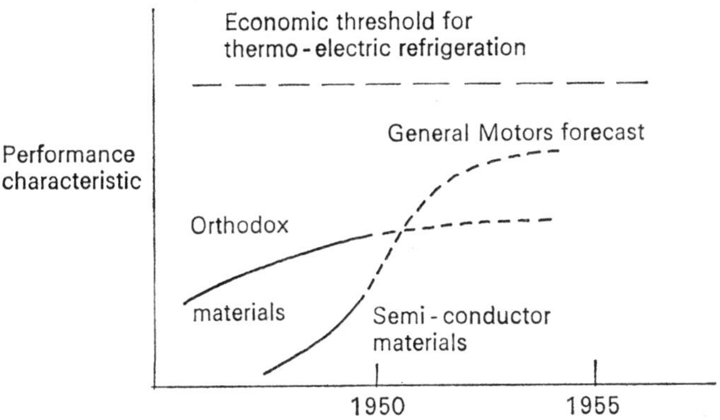

There have been a great number of examples in which the functions performed by products and processes based in one technology have been competitively replaced by those from another, often with the competitive advantage of a significant increase in the value of important performance characteristics. The kerosene lamp was replaced by the electric lamp bulb because of the considerable increase in the illumination obtained, and the conventional valve amplifier has been displaced as a result of developments in solid state physics, especially for uses in which the performance to be obtained from equipment of given size or weight is concerned. Indeed, a recent study by the A. D. Little organization has suggested that innovation, especially in the more traditional industries, is very often effected by the introduction of technologies from other industries. Thus, any review of present and intended operations, an essential part of a planning exercise, should examine each component, process, and product, asking what functions they perform and what ways, particularly cost competitive ways, there might be of performing the same functions. Where such an exercise considers the shorter term it may be described by the term *value engineering*; the method of approach for the longer term, especially in the face of changing technical requirements in the market, has been described above.

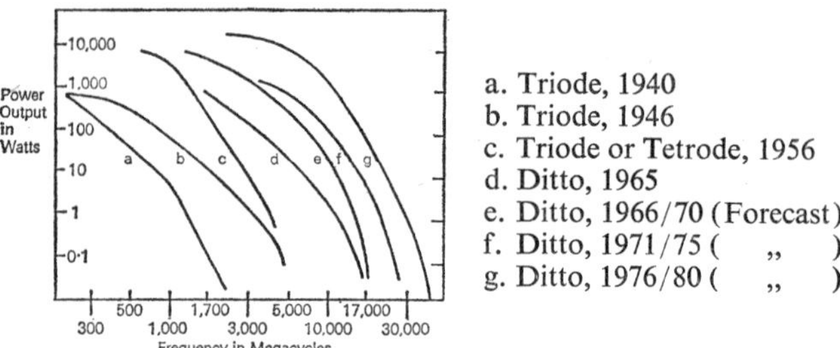

Figure 4. Progress in the capacities of micro-wave tubes.

Developments in one technology may create opportunities for the development of others. In Figure 2 the relation between the speed trends for United States combat and military transport aircraft is shown. The correlation of the two curves is high, and implies, as evidently happens, the transfer of technology from one activity to the other. In many cases, however, progress in the development of one performance parameter would depend critically upon others in ways which cannot be appreciated in a set of time dependent displays. In Figure 4, the interdependent characteristics of micro-wave electronic tubes are shown in a forecast in which time is a modulus rather than an independent variable. In Figure 5, the trend for the total aircraft miles that United States domestic airlines can expect to operate has been derived from passenger mile and aircraft capacity trends. This 'parameter dependent curve' further illustrates the importance of analysis and forecasting in planning. In consequence of the trends it is clear that authorities responsible for airports and for the systems of transportation related to them will have to prepare for the efficient handling of considerably larger groups of passengers if costly delays are to be avoided.

Normative Technological Forecasting and Relevance Analysis

Normative technological forecasting has been defined as the process of identifying the technological developments which will have to be made if specified social, economic, or industrial objectives are to be realized. It has also been explained that the likelihood of achieving the technical objectives may be considered by a comparison of the requirements with the course of expected developments as indicated by exploratory technological forecasting. Apart from such a discussion of the realism of various objectives, the comparison may also be used to deduce the order of the resources that may be necessary for their achievement. One very useful format for normative technological forecasting is that of relevance analysis, which has successfully been used

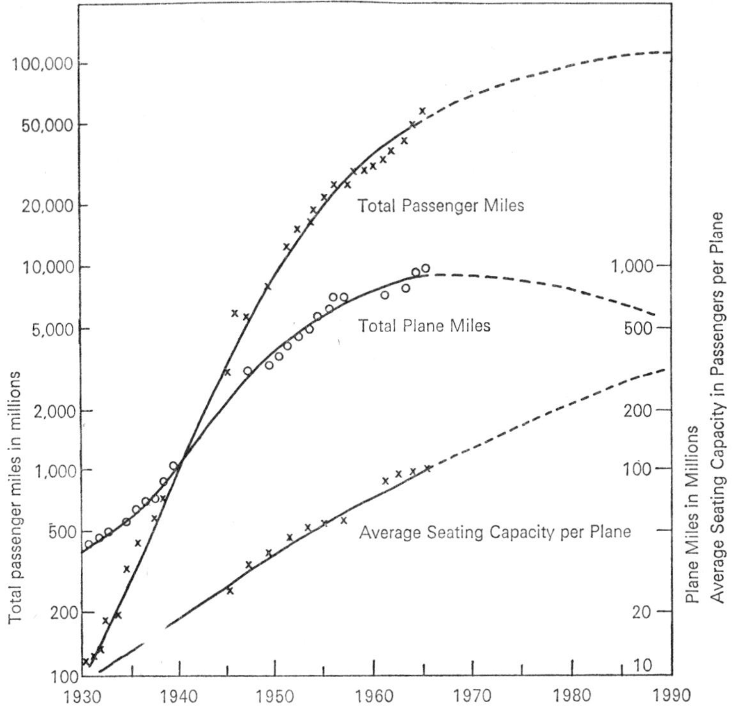

Figure 5. US Domestic Airlines.
(Plane miles = Passenger miles/seating capacity × load factor)

in the planning of complex research and development programmes in support of the achievement of wider objectives.

The analysis proceeds by requiring a clear definition of the broader objectives the organization is concerned to achieve in a given period of time. The next task is to set out each of the operations to be conducted in support of their achievement, specifying in as much detail as possible the technological systems known or thought likely to be required for the success of the individual operations. Each system that cannot be provided for by the use of currently available technology is defined in terms of performance characteristics and assessed as realistic with reference to the appropriate exploratory forecasts. The deficiency between what is required and what is currently available is known as a *technological deficiency*. The use of performance characteristics allows each deficiency to be expressed in quantitative terms.

The second phase in the analysis consists in the evaluation of the priority of meeting each of the recognized deficiencies, and secondly, of deciding whether to meet those recognized to be of high priority with one's own research effort or by contract work to outside bodies. This decision will depend upon a comparison of the required pattern of work with that already in progress, together with a consideration of the available skills and facilities, work load and cost. Again, it may be that some aspects of the relevant technology are already available but are protected by patents, and in such cases the question of licensing as opposed to circumventing the patent position will have to be considered. The relative priority of meeting each deficiency is assessed by compounding weighted judgments as to the relevance of each item in the analysis to that next above it in the appropriate 'branch' of the relevance 'tree'. Such an analysis should usually be complemented by an economic analysis of each of the operations envisaged, together with a judgment as to the likelihood that it will be possible to conduct it in the manner intended. The 'tree' is represented by the following illustration. In a complex planning operation it may be necessary to resolve the operations levels into several further levels of analysis.

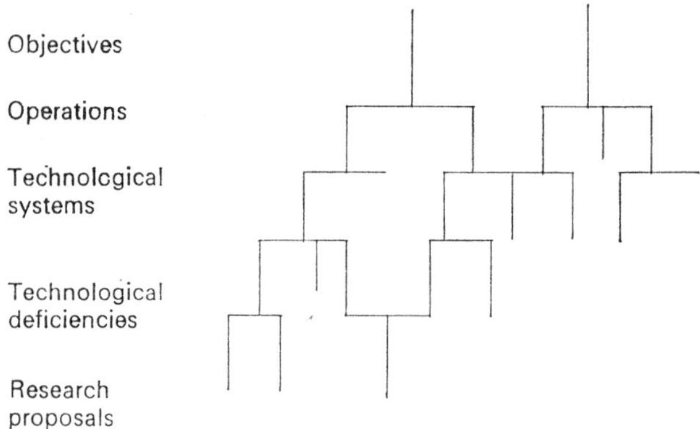

The third phase of the analysis consists in the generation of specific research and development proposals directed to meeting deficiencies of high priority not already encompassed by the existing programme. The whole research and development programme may now be scheduled in relation to the priorities revealed by the analysis, the difficulties envisaged, and the resources required at various times by each individual project.

The systematic presentation of the entire research and development programme required by relevance analysis also allows the opportunity to evaluate to what extent different projects or proposals are directed to similar or related objectives, a point illustrated by the linkage in the diagram. Thus, a project considered in its own right to be of relatively low priority may be selected because of its likely contribution to the success of other projects and operations, not necessarily conducted in the same part of the organization. The further point that relevance analysis may allow groups working in ignorance of one another to be identified and put into communication may be of importance in view of the critical threshold of human and other resources which may be required before even a promising programme of work can begin to be fruitful.

It should also be mentioned that the term *morphological analysis* has been used to denote that process of generating as many different ways as possible of meeting a given requirement, after which each alternative is considered on the basis of its technical and commercial feasibility and merit. It should be recognized, moreover, that the decision to replace one technology to any extent by another has often proved a very effective stimulus for its further development. It is always important to forecast the potential development of each of the technologies involved in such a decision.

It has already been urged that forecasting exercises should be considered only if a more productive allocation of resources is likely to follow as a result. Some five years ago the *Honeywell Corporation* developed a relevance exercise named PATTERN (Planning Assistance Through The Evaluation of Relevance Numbers) which examined the requirements of the United States military and aerospace market over the following decade as a basis for the planning of corporate operations. One of Honeywell's fields of interest was that of inertial guidance systems, and the existing research programme was directed towards the development of systems of greater sensitivity and accuracy. The analysis of likely strategic needs and priorities showed that a number of weapons systems requiring relatively simple but very reliable inertial guidance systems were likely to be constructed. The balance of the research effort was redirected, with considerable commercial success.

A further aspect of relevance analysis concerns the advantage given in specifying the objectives towards which research personnel may direct their efforts. *Project Hindsight* has examined the circumstances in which were made the six hundred and seventy developments said to have been basic to sixteen recent weapons systems. Ninety-five per cent of those identified as being responsible for the developments said they had been aware that a particular technical deficiency existed in equipment which had already been developed or which was in the course of development. It may be added that when a research objective is stated in functional terms, personnel are in no way restricted in their view as to the approach they should adopt to solving the problem that has been presented to them.

References

By far the most comprehensive account of Technological Forecasting both in theory and in practice is contained in the report prepared for the OECD by Erich Jantsch and published under the title *Technological Forecasting in Perspective.* The reader is referred to the very comprehensive annotated bibliography contained in the Jantsch report; the references given below acknowledge the sources that were especially useful in the preparation of this document.

E. S. Cheaney, 'Technical Forecasting as a Basis for Planning'. ASME paper 66-MD-67, presented at the Design Engineering Conference (May 1966) of the American Society of Mechanical Engineers.

M. E. Esch, 'Planning Assistance through Technical Evaluation of Relevance Numbers'. *Proceedings of the Seventeenth National Aerospace Electronics Conference*, pp. 346–351 (Institute of Electrical and Electronics Engineers, New York; 1965).

O. Helmer, *Social Technology* (Basic Books, New York; 1966).

R. C. Lenz, Jr., *Technological Forecasting*; Second Edition. Clearing House for Federal Scientific and Technical Literature: No. AD-408,085 (June 1962).

Arthur D. Little, Inc., 'Patterns and Problems of Technical Innovation in American Industry'. Report No. PB 181573 to the National Science Foundation (1963).

National Commission on Technology, Automation and Economic Progress; 'Role of the Federal Government in Technological Forecasting; prepared by an Inter-Agency Group'; (1966).

'Survey of the State of the Art: Social, Political and Economic Models and Simulations', prepared by Abt. Associates, Inc.

F. S. Pardee, 'State of the Art Projection and Long Range Planning of Applied Research' (RAND P.3181; 1965) reprinted in (Ed. Yovits, *et al.*) *Research Program Effectiveness* (1966).

J. B. Quinn, 'Technological Forecasting'. *Harvard Business Review*, **45** (1967) 2.

I. H. Siegel, 'Technological Change and Long Run Forecasting'; *The Journal of Business* (University of Chicago Press), **26** (1953), 141–56.

W. L. Swager, 'Industrial Applications of Technological Forecasting'. The Fourth Summer Symposium of the Engineering Economy Division, American Society for Engineering Education (June 1965).

A useful set of papers was presented to the First Annual Technology and Management Conference: 'Technological Forecasting in Industry', at Lake Placid (May 1967).

R. U. Ayres, 'Envelope Curve Forecasting'.

M. J. Centron and T. I. Monahan, 'An Evaluation and Appraisal of various Approaches to Technological Forecasting'.

J. P. Martino, 'The Use of Technological Forecasts for Planning Research'.

R. S. Isensen, 'Technological Forecasting Lessons from Project Hindsight'.

R. C. Lenz, 'Forecasts of Exploding Technologies by Trend Extrapolation'.

R. H. COLLCUTT

Planning Economic Development

I propose to discuss in this paper a series of ideas arising from the work that the Arthur D. Little organization has carried out in the general field of economic planning. These ideas do not in themselves constitute a proven method for planning an economic development programme but lead rather to proposals for research and development to this end. My colleague J. C. Hetrick has been the principal progenitor of these ideas. To understand how they have evolved it is necessary to know something of our capabilities. Arthur D. Little are contractors in research both in the normal R&D sense and in the area of the exploitation of the resulting technologies by industry and by governments, including the economic, decision, and organizational problems which arise thereby. Thus some of my colleagues spend most of their time in our very extensive laboratories in Cambridge, Mass., and others are experts in the management and behavioural sciences and are colloquially described as 'Management Consultants'.

In the last fifteen years an increasing and significant proportion of our work has been concerned with developing, for client companies, long-range strategies to take advantage of new technologies, some of which have been developed in our own laboratories. Also, we have assisted many regional and national governments to plan their economic development and then to work with them in implementing the plan; the governments concerned have been both of so-called 'western developed countries' and of the new and emerging countries of S. America, Africa and Asia.

Input-Output Tables

In the United States in particular one of the most powerful tools of economic planning is the formulation of the input-output tables with which many of us are now familiar. Basically, this is a matrix or tabular representation of the flow of goods and services among the various sectors that make up an economic system, taking into account indirect as well as direct relationships among these sectors. Its value for planning purposes lies in the ability to trace these relationships and to measure the effects of anticipated or proposed changes in individual sectors. The key assumption is that the flow of goods and services among various industries in the economy follows a regular pattern in which the relative rates of flow are determined by the production technologies employed in the economy.

The preparation of input-output tables of the US economy have been sponsored since 1939 by the United States Government and the most detailed and latest of them was produced in 1964 based on the 1958 census and broken down into 81 industrial sectors; a similar table in the UK published in 1961 divides 1954 census figures into 46 industrial sectors.

For the purposes of forecasting into the future, published input-output tables have one great drawback in that the industrial coefficients which describe the relative dependence of one sector on another are assumed to remain invariant over time. When one takes account of the fact that these coefficients are based on information observed, at best, six or seven years earlier then it is not surprising that forecasts based on them may not have great reliability.

To overcome this objection, to at least some extent, my company sponsored, jointly with the journal *Scientific American*, a study to determine how changing technology and production methods are likely to alter industry's future requirements of such basic materials as, steel, plastics, rubber, and selected non-ferrous metals, including aluminium and copper. Data was disaggregated for 50 industries for the US input-output table into 200 subsectors and projections were made of future basic material input. These forecasts were based on technical and market information compiled by about 100 ADL industry specialists. Major portions of the results of these studies were published in 1967 by *Scientific American* in a special report entitled 'Competition of Materials'.

One example of the corporate application of such tables is the study which we made for North American Aviation which identified long-range diversification opportunities. Co-operation with the Harvard Economic Research Project led to the construction of an input-output model with changing coefficients which could be used to forecast growth opportunities for approximately ninety industries. By using productivity rate projections for individual industry sectors and applying them to output forecasts of individual industries, the model also generated forecasts of future labour requirements. These forecasts were then compared with labour force supply projections derived independently. The model automatically balanced supply and demand at selected unemployment rates to obtain forecasts of overall economic activity, e.g. GNP, personal consumption expenditures and investment. The Company now uses the model as an on-going analysis tool for long-range planning.

Input-output has also been found useful in assisting in the solution of some national and regional economic problems. For example, the US Corps of Engineers engaged us to prepare forecasts of industry output and employment up to year 2000 for the ten state Ohio River Basin region and nineteen sub-areas within the region. These forecasts and other detailed projections are being used by the Corps of Engineers as guideposts in estimating the area's long-range multipurpose potential requirement for water and related land resources.

Economic Development

As each of the erstwhile European colonies have won their independence, usually the first thing they have done is to formulate some form of economic development plan. India was one of the first, and Professor Mahalanobis of the Calcutta Institute of Statistics advised the Nehru Government on the development of their series of five-year plans. He demonstrated in a series of papers the country's need to develop certain basic industries, steel, cement works, fertilizer plants based on indigenous raw materials to substitute for costly imported capital intensive goods; he also indicated that in the meantime the cottage industries in the villages of India should be expanded to produce the required agricultural and consumer goods and at the same time produce jobs for the masses of unemployed in India.

Looking back over the last twenty years, it is easy to see that the development of India's economy has not kept pace with her birthrate or her needs.

My own company in these years has been associated, too, with the development plans in many different countries from Operation Bootstrap in Puerto Rico in the 1940's to Algeria at the present time. Although consultants can guide their clients to a certain extent, they cannot stay in business if they oppose their dearest wish, particularly if they are unable to demonstrate conclusively the rightness of their opposition. Somebody has said that every new country must have its own airline and its own steel industry before it feels it can hold its head high in the community of nations; even if it goes bankrupt thereby.

The desire by the developing country to use the most up-to-date manifestations of technology is at least understandable, although from a more advanced viewpoint one does not find difficulty in doubting its feasibility. What we are only just beginning to realize, however, is that it may not be sensible for any country, so-called advanced or not, to attempt to apply technology irrespective of its resources to do so. In the UK the acceptance that we should not attempt to mount our own attack on the stars has been very reluctant, and there is still a vociferous minority who claim that thereby we shall fall behind in a vital technology. The counter argument that we do not possess enough resources to do all we would like is unassailable but does not in itself justify the

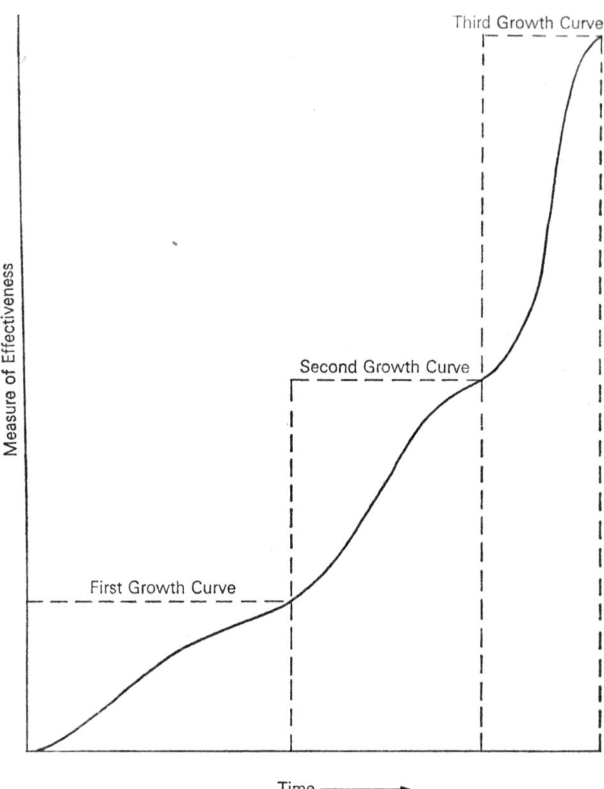

Figure 1. Historical development of the satisfaction of a need.

chosen allocation. It is to this problem of allocation I should now like to turn and suggest what I believe is a new approach.

In the succeeding discussion I propose to use the term *technology* in a sense analogous to the word *economy* so that it will be regarded as comprising an overall state of development of various applied arts, which takes recognition of their interactions and interdependencies. I shall use the term *technological sector*, or simply *sector*, to indicate a component of the technology, in much the same way as the term industry is used to indicate a component of the economy.

The term technological sector, as used below, may in fact apply to the portion or package of technology supporting an industry, but more usually it should be regarded as being the portion of technology which satisfies a want. This distinction may be an important one since it permits of several different sectors, which may normally be thought of as independent technologies, being perceived as different stages in the evolution of a single technological sector.

For example, in the study of the history of technologies, it has been observed that the development of a technological sector to satisfy a particular need or want may be represented as shown in Figure 1. In this Figure the vertical axis represents a measure of effectiveness in meeting a need, and the horizontal scale indicates the passage of time. It can be seen that the history of a technological growth is represented as a step or discontinuous function of a very particular type. Generally speaking, it has the following characteristics:

(i) The steps of each phase increase in size as measured on the scale of effectiveness.

(ii) The steps in general occur at decreasing intervals on the time scale.

(iii) Generally, a step can be represented as a logistic, or growth curve.

Examples of qualitative definitions of such phases in technological growth are not difficult to find. Consider the military application of the development of projectile weapon systems. Successive development of the first phase would be based upon the improvement of the ability to propel a missile by the strength of the human arm. Early on in this development would be the family of primitive projectile weapons, spears, bow and arrow, the throwing stick, perhaps the boomerang. The ultimate development of this particular phase might be thought of as the more advanced weapons of this type, including such things as the cross-bow. The next step in this technology would be the family of weapons based on the utilization of the discovery of gunpowder, varying from the crudest hand weapons to improvements on these by developments in field cannon and on up to very large weapons such as naval guns. The next step would be concerned with the delivery of the projectile by means of aircraft. This in itself would constitute a large range in effectiveness and a telescoping of the time scale. The next step would be the development of missiles, and then probably the use of space technology in military weapons support.

It will be observed that the orientation of the sector is concerned with the need to be fulfilled, rather than with the method by which it is fulfilled. The importance of this point is brought out in Figure 2.

In Figure 2, a technological sector is represented in which two stages are assumed to be existing simultaneously. One might think of this, for example, as being the sector associated with the production of energy. The lower of the two logistic curves on the diagram might be thought as the technology of fossil fuels, coal and oil, and the second curve of the sector the exploitation of atomic power. Thus suppose we consider a particular country and that the present situation of the state

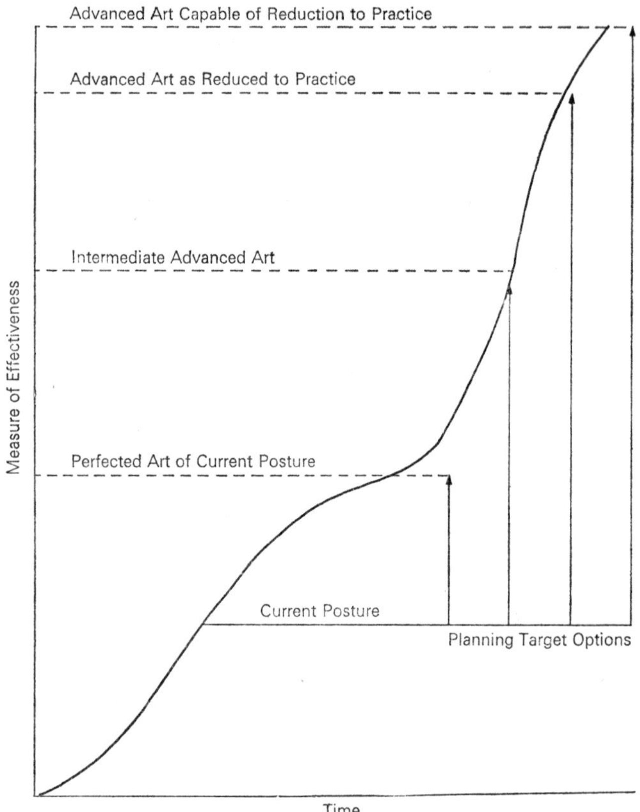

Figure 2. Use of History to define growth targets.

of their art is represented by the line marked *current posture* on the lower logistic curve. This might be the state of coal mining in that country today. Some point on the upper logistic curve would represent the most advanced current state of the art: for example, the most sophisticated existing plant using nuclear fission for the production of industrial energy. One could define a number of possible planning targets for the development of the economy. One obvious possibility is for the existing installations to be modified to utilize the most advanced technology represented by the limit of the logistic growth of that portion of the sector. In the case of the example this would require a thorough updating and modernizing of the operations of coal mines. However, the planner in looking further ahead may calculate that even by moving to the furthest practical extreme of this portion of the sector, the wants of the nation would still only be partially satisfied. He could then decide to treat the existing installations as a wasting asset and to plan to go immediately to the most advanced current art. Thus, if a new installation is to be created, he might decide to make use of existing knowledge which has not yet been reduced to practice and go to a posture which is a more advanced current art. Upon a review of the history of the way in which the art has developed, however, it may be possible to establish the existence of an intermediate point which would be intrinsically advantageous as a development preliminary to full exploitation of known or possible applied art.

A decision as to whether to choose an intermediate posture might well be based upon the availability of some particular scarce resource. Although the horizontal scale in Figures 1 and 2 has been labelled *time*, it may in fact be necessary to use, in practice, a more complicated function of time. Presumably, if one were in possession of full knowledge of the historical development of the art, then the scale could be related to the resources that were applied in its development. The effort in terms of research manpower, the investment of capital, the contribution from peripheral arts, all these factors might dictate the adoption of the intermediate posture. I propose now to outline a possible model of technology in terms of the above processes.

The Technology Model

The first step in the development of the model requires a consideration of what sectors of technology can be recognized and how many of these there need to be in a technology for a particular economy. It seems sensible to attempt to make these technology sectors as few in number as may be necessary for a realistic coverage of the technology being considered. Once this stage has been reached, one would then need to identify:

(1) The present posture of the technological sectors in the economy being studied.

(2) The most advanced posture presently available and reduced to practice.

(3) Conceivable targets for the planner to set as successive stages of development of the technological sector.

Now within a technology at a particular time the individual sectors must be in balance in terms of creating and satisfying needs. By this is meant that no technological sector can exist unless the input technological sectors exist as well; to be in balance, a technological sector at a particular stage of the art can exist only if the input technological sectors also exist in appropriate stages of their art. The model must be developed in the recognition of the above, from which it also follows that no technological sector should exist in a particular economy

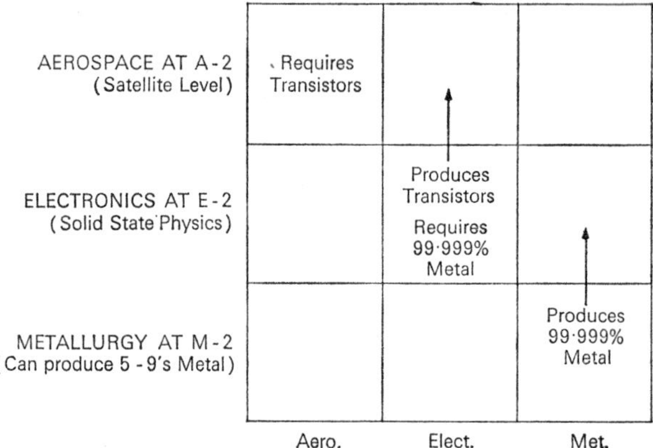

Figure 3. The individual technological sectors reduced to practice must at any given time be in balance in terms of creating and satisfying needs.

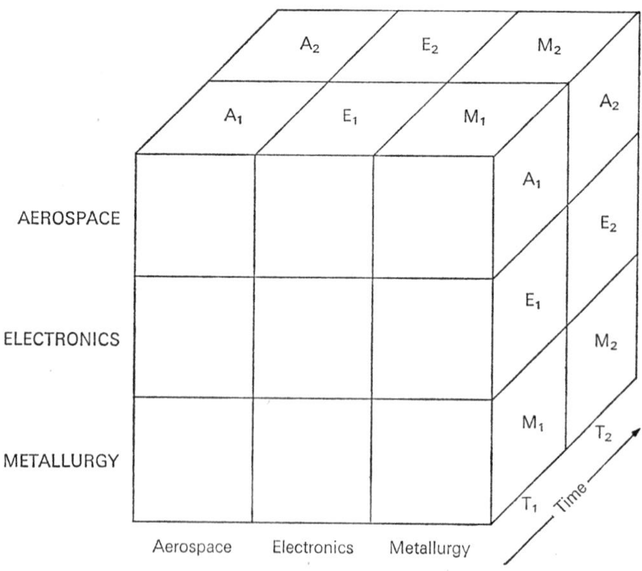

Figure 4. For these 3 sectors, two balanced technologies exist:

	T_1	T_2
Aerospace	Pre-satellite	Satellite
Electronics	Thermionic valves	Transistors
Metallurgy	99·99% metals	99·999% metals

unless its output either directly satisfies a need, or is required as an input to another coexistent technological sector.

As a further explanation of this argument consider a technology composed only of three sectors as exemplified in Figure 3. The sectors are aerospace, electronics, and metallurgy. For simplicity it is assumed that each exists in only two states. Aerospace will be considered as being at pre-satellite level and at satellite level. The electronics sector will be considered as being dependent on thermionic valves, or on solid state physics. Metallurgy will be considered to have the two states where it is capable of producing 'four nines' (99·99 per cent pure) metals or the state at which it can produce 'five nines' (99·999 per cent pure) metals. The diagram then illustrates a balanced technology in which aerospace at the satellite level requires the existence of transistors; transistors in turn require the existence of five nines metallurgy. For planning purposes, this three sector technology can then be represented on the three-dimensional diagram of Figure 4. In this diagram the horizontal and vertical axes represent input and output technological sectors and the third axis is a time scale, at present unspecified and possibly non-linear.

In this extremely simplified example then, two balanced technologies exist for this three sector system: (*a*) Technology 1 is pre-satellite aerospace, valve electronics, and four nines metallurgy; (*b*) Technology 2 is satellite aerospace, solid state electronics, and five nines metallurgy.

Now the definition of Technology 1 above covers a series of states from partial to full development and to take account of what is required to proceed within Technology 1, a more detailed description is needed. For example let it be assumed that: (*a*) The present is within Technology 1 at some state short of the ultimate development; (*b*) a fourth technology sector (computers) can be identified and that for the full development of pre-satellite aerospace this sector must be capable of producing computers based on transistors.

In this event at least three consistent technologies are possible as illustrated in Figure 5. In this diagram Technology 1 would be the previously identified Technology 1 which includes a computer and instrumentation technological sector which is in the pre-solid state development. Technology 3 in Figure 5 corresponds to the previously defined Technology 2 and includes a computer and instrumentation technology sector which involves solid state physics. In addition, however, there is an intermediate state, a new Technology 2, in which there is an advanced pre-satellite aerospace which requires a computer technology called Computer 2, which in turn requires an electronic technology Electronic 2, and this in turn requires an advanced metallurgy designated Metallurgy 2.

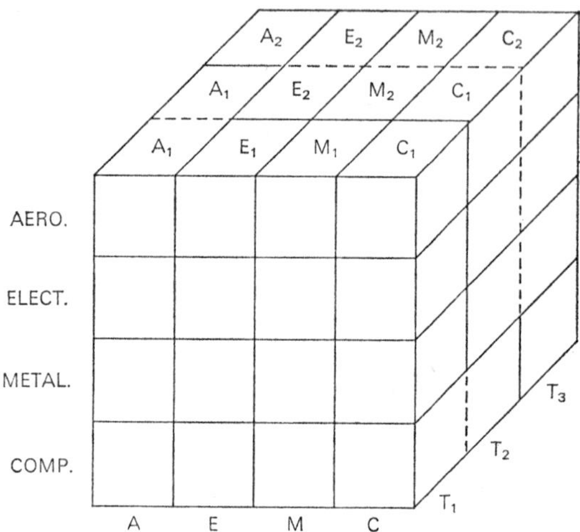

Figure 5. To go from T_1 to T_3, passing at T_2 first growth stage is: M-1 to M-2, then E-1 to E-2, then C-1 to C-2; second growth stage is: A-1 to A-2.

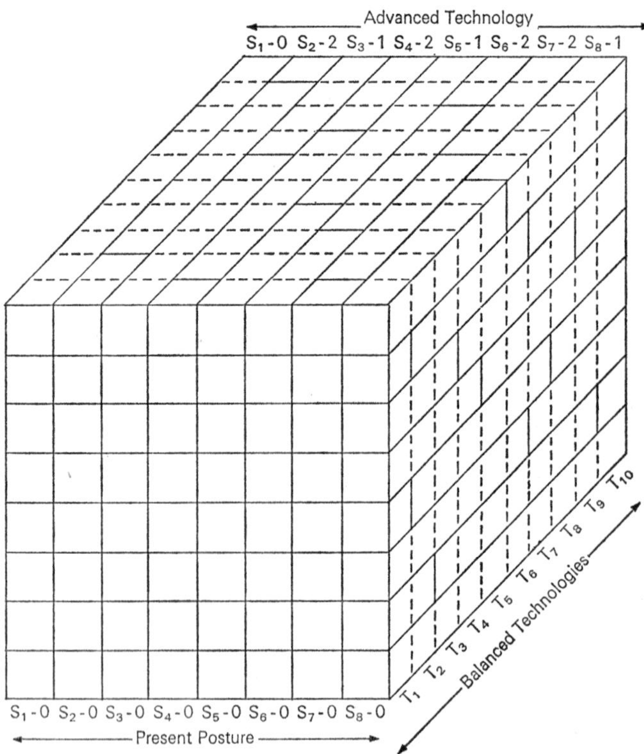

Figure 6. Eight sectors, in one to three stages, constituting ten balanced technologies.

If it is then assumed that the economy is at present in Technology 1, that Technology 3 represents the most advanced current state of the art, and that the planners have decided that for good reasons evolution should be through Technology 2, then an order of development might be in two stages of growth. Stage 1 would call for a plan in which the order would be: from M1 to M2, then E1 to E2, then C1 to C2. The economy would then be in Technology 2. As a second stage of growth the plan would be to go from A1 to A2 and hence to Technology 3.

Now it should be realized that it is intended in this model that: (*a*) The definition of the stages of the technological sectors is qualitative, based on expert opinion and after the fact observation; (*b*) A technology is defined by the logical necessity for the coexistence of individual states of technological sectors, with no quantitative measurement of flow between the sectors.

It is believed that one might start to build this model in the following way:

(1) By taking an existing input-output model of an economy and deducing from it a necessary set of interrelated technological sectors. (It is worth noting that the input-output model need not be that of the country or region to be studied. It might be that of the most advanced overall economy, or conceivably it could be a synthetic input-output model assuming the simultaneous existence in a single technology of the most advanced state of the art of each sector currently practised in any technology.)

(2) Having constructed a list of necessary technological sectors, say for Britain, then it would be necessary to identify for each: (*a*) Britain's present technology; (*b*) The most advanced existing or presently achievable technology; (*c*) Necessary and/or desirable intermediate technologies.

(3) Construct the three dimensional array of consistent technologies with an unspecified time scale.

Thus Figure 6 could represent the conceivable results of such a series of steps. In this diagram the technology is represented as eight sectors, with the present technology as State 0 for each sector.

The state of a technological sector is indicated for Sector 1 as S1-0, S1-1, S1-2, etc. according to whether Britain is at present, at one or two, steps away from, the most advanced state for that technological sector, in the opinion of the experts who have defined the states of the individual sectors. The diagram is based on the assumption that there is a necessary coexistence of the early development of the advanced state of one technological sector with the advanced development of the early state of another technology. Therefore although only three states, corresponding to two advances, are needed for any one sector, it is nevertheless possible in combination that nine balanced intermediate technologies may be defined, between the present posture and the most advanced technology.

It is important to emphasize that the design of the model so far does not imply the assumption that each of these intermediate technologies must in fact come into existence.

The Resource Model

The model so far defined is designed so that at each cross-section perpendicular to the time axis defines a consistent and balanced technology, from which an associated economy can be identified and for which an input-output matrix can be derived. Then for each pair of successive technology-economy complexes it would be necessary to specify:

(1) the identity and magnitude of the (scarce) resources needed to change from the first to the second state indicated;

(2) the sequence of allocation of the scarce resource;

(3) the rate at which the scarce resource can be accumulated by the first complex in order to bring about the existence of the second complex.

It should be noted that the term *scarce resource* as it is used here may be interpreted in many different ways depending on the economy. Capital is only one of the conceivable scarce resources, school teachers, management scientists, professional managers, etc., may be others. It is conceivable at least that education and management science might each be defined as a technological sector of importance. Even were this unnecessary it is virtually certain that they would both be scarce resources. Further, it should be appreciated that in the economy associated with the technology there may be constraints which need to be taken into account in its description and which arise externally either to the technology or to the economy and constitute limitations on development. Thus Government regulations, trade union practices, national agreements such as GATT, etc., may all be considered potential restraints of this type. Where such restraints arise, then for planning purposes at least, one should describe the economy as operating both with and without the external restraints in order that their effects may be determined by difference.

The manipulation of this second stage of the model might be diagrammatically described as in Figure 7. Figure 7 considers only one scarce resource, but in practice when enumerating any one pair of technology-economy complexes several such scarce resources may need to be included. It is possible that a single scarce resource is first limiting for all sectors being studied and then only the single model might be required. It is much more probable however that the limiting resource is different in different technological sectors.

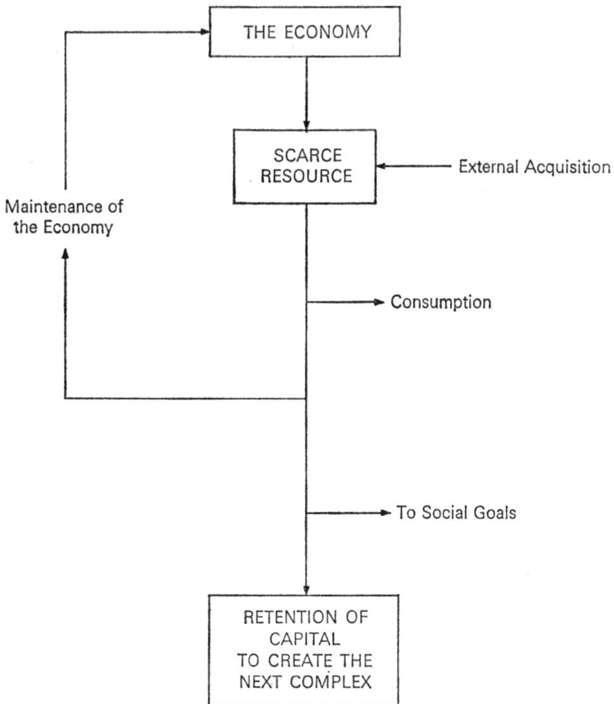

Figure 7.

The diagram illustrates that in the model, the economy is considered as a generator of the scarce resource. Now, the scarce resource which thus becomes available must then be allocated. The first and necessary allocation of the resource is the amount consumed by the economy and by definition removed from it. This loss from the economy distinguished from the second necessary allocation which is what is required to maintain the economy either as it is; or to expand, within the technology, to meet the needs of an increasing population; or to allow certain sectors to be treated as wasted assets when the next stage of the development of the complex calls for total replacement by facilities existing on the next of the appropriate logistic curves. The third allocation is to fulfil those social wants, which however desirable they may be, are not absolutely essential to the maintenance and further development of the technology-economy complex. Only after these three categories of allocation have been met should one consider the accumulation of the resource as 'capital' to be devoted to the achievement of the move into the next state.

Also indicated in this diagram is the acquisition of a scarce resource from external sources. This implies borrowing or purchasing the scarce resource from outside the economy. The term 'borrowing' could be applied, since purchase probably implies the trading of another potential scarce resource which although not then the limiting resource might become so for the next step.

This model will be familiar to those who are concerned with company planning as it is a derivative of the cash flow diagram for a company. In the latter case it has been found possible to perform mathematical manipulation which enable forecasts to be made of the rate at which scarce resources can be accumulated, and in some cases the rate at which it should be accumulated to meet some present criterion.

Conclusion

Once these successive stages of the model building have been achieved it should then be possible to use it to examine conceivable policies in so far as they affect:

(1) The technological sectors which ought to be developed.
(2) How scarce resources ought to be allocated.
(3) The extent to which scarce resources should be sought externally.
(4) The time scale required for overall development.

The above argument and description has been based on the assumption that one should proceed stepwise from Technology 1 to Technology 2 to Technology 3, etc., and examine the associated economy in each case. An obvious next step, however, would be to examine the consequences of moving in multiple steps. It is possible that although it may take twice as long to go from Technology 1 to Technology 4 as from Technology 1 to Technology 2 it is nevertheless less than the time to go from Technology 1 to Technology 2, to Technology 3 to Technology 4. Essentially one would need to examine all scarce resources whether they are capital, manpower, managerial talents, schoolmasters, etc., in terms which are analogous to the cash flow analysis of capital by normal discounting techniques.

The development of the ideas I have outlined above constitute a research programme and will need the combined efforts of people skilled in the history of technology, economists familiar with the concepts and manipulation of input-output models and management scientists skilled in the construction and manipulations of mathematical models. The crucial test of the usefulness of the model will be in the availability of the economic data which are required to support the application of the model. It is not at all clear that such data would be required in fine detail. It seems likely that many of the data are in existence either in terms of input-output data already gathered for more advanced economies, or in trade and industry association files.

I believe that this approach is feasible and could constitute a very valuable tool in the hands of government, etc., planning agencies, whether they are considering their own overall economies or those of less developed countries to whom they are proposing to give aid. Indeed, conceivably, the United Nations Agencies, and other International bodies might, by its use, improve very markedly the efficiency with which aid from the richer nation is allocated to specific projects to help the poorer ones.

Z. LUTOSLANSKI

The Role of R and D Units in long-range Planning of Technological Development in Poland

In 1945, Poland, after several years of occupation, was a country desperately exhausted. Industry was ruined, machinery destroyed or taken out of the country, 6 million people – including some 50 per cent of the total number of engineers – killed. This was the situation in which Polish industry started to function at the end of the war.

The first several years were a period of reconstruction, sometimes, no doubt, extemporaneous, for the point was to satisfy as quickly as possible the most pressing needs of society in the area of housing, transportation, power, steel, etc. At the same time, organizational foundations were laid for a new Socialist economy. Industry, transportation, the power system, were nationalized, and a uniform management was established. The State Commission for Economic Planning was established, and it began to prepare national plans.

The structure of industry, as a result of a lack of experience, underwent many changes. The present structure is based on Associations, which can be paralleled with concerns responsible for production and for the development of the given branch. They are subordinated to industrial ministries. Associations are composed of individual enterprises.

Production increased rapidly. It is already several times higher than before the war, and continues to grow at a rate of approximately 7 per cent per annum. This rapid growth substantially changed the employment structure in the country, i.e. the number of employed in the industries has greatly grown. Today, after twenty-odd years, the experience gathered permits us to direct the development of industry in a planned, thoroughly considered way. R&D units, which are the subject of this paper, play an essential role in this development.

The Formation of R & D Units

In the first period of reconstruction, factories worked to a large degree on the foreman system. Design offices were retracing pre-war designs, or were preparing new ones, mainly on the basis of models existing in the country or brought in from abroad. To provide for the best utilization of the very few specialists, central designing offices, central laboratories and institutes were established. In this way, central and branch R&D establishments were formed.

As the years passed, specific designs became the task of factory design offices, which were closer to manufacturing. Central establishments were at the same time directed towards more long-range problems, and questions of unification, typization, and so on. In 1951 the Polish Academy of Sciences was established. It undertook basic research. In 1966 it had 281 members (including 125 in technical sciences) conducting research in 76 institutes, departments and laboratories.

It was recognized that skilled manpower is the key factor in the development of modern science and technology. Consequently, from the very beginning a tremendous importance was attached to the development of universities.

The following table illustrates results achieved in this area.

	1938	1946	1967
No. of academic schools	32	54	76
Including technical ones	3	9	18
No. of professors	1,200	570	3,800
No. of students	49,500	86,500	272,500
No. of graduates	6,100	4,100	26,500
Including engineers	700	900	7,200

The number of graduates, although rapidly increasing, is not sufficient and does not satisfy the needs. Young engineers and researchers are faced with new tasks, which makes it necessary to bring universities closer to industrial problems and to transform them into schools of independent thought; these are the directions to which new curricula are being geared.

The growing importance of research to the national economy, the increase of its scope, and the need to co-ordinate efforts and the allocation of resources made it necessary to create a co-ordinating organ on a high government level. In 1963 The Committee for Science and Technology was established to serve as such an organ. It is presided over by one of the Deputy Prime Ministers. To provide for the co-ordination of basic research as well, the Scientific Secretary of the Polish Academy of Sciences became one of the deputy chairmen of the Committee. The Committee includes, *inter alia*, ministers of Economic Ministries, the Deputy Chairman of the Planning Commission, representatives of science and industry, and of professional and social organizations. The Committee is aided by the Council for Science and Technology and by a number of commissions for individual problems, serving as advisory bodies.

The statutory tasks of the Committee include: the preparation of overall national principles and policies in the area of science and technology; the related preparation of plans for the development of technology; plans for the development of the technical and physical facilities for research; making proposals concerning the necessary financial resources, etc.; organizational problems of R&D; co-ordination of scientific research activities of the Polish Academy of Sciences, of institutions of higher education, and of economic ministries; determining the policy for the training and development of scientific and technical personnel; drafting the decrees and regulations in the area of development of science and technology; determining tasks and co-ordinating in the area of basic problems of science and technology of an interministry or international character.

It is difficult to make comparisons concerning the size of R&D institutions and the expenditure on R&D in different countries. We have tried many times to analyze these magnitudes to compare trends. Unfortunately, as criteria for including various types of units in the R&D category are quite different, only approximate comparisons can be made.

According to OECD data, R&D activities include projects, the basic objective of which is the introduction of new improvements in products or processes. If, on the other hand, a project deals with a product or process which is basically known, and its object is to find a market, to initiate production, or to stabilize production processes, it should not be considered an R&D activity.

In our conditions, R&D projects in the above sense constitute only a part of the tasks of units, which according to our rules are statistically included in the R&D category. These include:

Government institutions:	Academy units, institutions of higher education
Central industrial institutions:	Industrial institutes, central designing offices, central laboratories, central engineering offices, experimental plants, pilot plants

Statistics for these units include the total number of employed, while a number of their employees carry out tasks connected with the servicing of plants and of the units themselves, which cannot be classified as R&D. On the other hand, a number of development projects are carried out in factory designing offices.

With this reservation in mind, the figures for R&D personnel in Poland in 1965 are presented below:

	research staff (thousands)	*technical and engineering staff (thousands)*
Polish Academy of Sciences	2·3	—
Higher Education Establishments	22·3	—
Industrial Institutes and Laboratories	4·9	5·0
Designing Offices, etc.	—	18·7

From the above one may conclude there is a comparatively large part of units carrying out research. To accelerate the implementation of research results, which often require development and testing, a number of experimental plants, employing some ten thousand people, have been established within the institutes. In an effort to bring research establishments closer to industry, a system of long-term contracts and various forms of agreements between them and industrial enterprises and units has been introduced. Recently, mixed industrial-university institutes are being formed, as well as research teams for the solution of urgent complex R&D problems. The teams – which, depending on the gravity of the problem, can be established by the chairman of the Committee, the Secretary of the Academy of Sciences, the minister concerned, or, on their authorization, by the director of the Association concerned – can include representatives of various R&D units, designers, project engineers, etc. We hope that in the next five-year period we shall be able to enjoy significant benefits from these steps.

Planning the Development of Technology

The methodology in a socialist state is the subject of a separate presentation, so I shall not discuss it here. I would like to limit myself to problems directly connected with R&D work only, namely to plans for the development of science and technology, which constitute essential elements of the national economic plans.

The whole planning system is based on long-term, five-year, and two-year plans. They are all interrelated and – as consecutive ones are being developed – adapted to changing circumstances. The five-year plans are basic for the development of technology, for the time-period necessary for the implementation of research, design and development projects is several years. Within the framework of these plans, until recently, detailed annual plans were prepared. They are now replaced by two-year plans, prepared each year. The plan for the first year of the two-year period covered is a detailed one; for the second one it takes the form of basic principles adopted.

The object of preparing plans for the development of technology is to outline tasks for R&D units, on the basis of a detailed investigation of world-wide developments in science and technology, which will provide for the correct lines of development of national economy – to provide means necessary for the performance of these tasks; and to determine partial time schedules for their efficient productive implementation.

Each of the plans mentioned passes through the following stages: basic directives: draft factory . . . Association . . . and ministry economic plans; approval; acceptance by factory employees.

The Committee for Science and Technology, in co-operation with the Academy of Sciences, with the Planning Commission, and with the ministries concerned (including the Ministry of Finance) determine draft directives for the preparation of plans, on the basis of the national economic policy, of a broad knowledge of the development of technology abroad, of domestic and foreign trade needs, of the capacities of R&D units, and of productive facilities. These draft directives are commented on by the main commissions mentioned above. Draft directives for projects included in the plan for scientific research are prepared by the Academy of Sciences in co-operation with the Committee for Science and Technology and in agreement with the ministries concerned. On the basis of directives approved by the Council of Ministers, the Committee for Science and Technology and the Polish Academy of Sciences in agreement with the Planning Commission emit supplementary directives, which are an elaboration of those of the Council of Ministers, and appoint leading units, responsible for the performance of established tasks. These directives are sent to ministries, and through them to Associations, leading units and enterprises.

Leading units, together with enterprises responsible for the actual performance, prepare programmes for the solution of the problem in the form of so called *problem cards*. These then serve as a basis for the preparation of draft plans. Draft plans are commented on by different levels of the administration. More important problems are included in Association and ministry plans. From these, the Committee selects most important problems, mostly of an interministry character, and includes them in the draft National Economic Plan.

The summary state-wide draft plan for the development of science and technology is prepared by the Committee for Science and Technology in agreement with the Planning Commission, and these two bodies submit it for approval to the Council of Ministers.

Approved plans are sent to ministries, Associations, and enterprises.

In these, management submit them to the employees for discussion and approval. In such discussions, suggestions are often made both concerning additional tasks which should be undertaken, and corrections to be made in tasks already included in plans. Such suggestions are next considered by higher authorities, which, in agreement with the enterprises, finally determine the obligatory tasks.

The breakdown of the plan according to the branches concerned has been recently replaced by an area problem-oriented one. Thirty-six main research areas have been established, and summary plans on the national level are prepared in such a breakdown.

Plans of more important R&D projects, including basic and applied research, development, designing, prototypes, as far as the implementation of results, are co-ordinated by the Committee for Science and Technology. Plans of more important basic research projects, including these in mathematics, natural, and social sciences, are co-ordinated by the Polish Academy of Sciences.

In view of the enormous changes which are taking place throughout the world in science and technology, planning for five-year periods has proved to be inadequate, as many problems need a longer period for their solution. For this reason, forecasts for longer periods, and at present specifically up to 1985, are being prepared. We shall return to this matter a little later.

Financing R & D

The system for financing R&D is suited to Poland's socialist economy. When we talk of the 'system for financing', we mean the principles for collecting and spending financial resources on research projects, on experimental and designing work, on development projects for new products or new processes.

Activities of R&D units can be financed from four sources: (1) the Budget; (2) special funds, named 'the technical progress fund' and 'the fund for new productions'; (3) the rotating capital of enterprises; (4) bank credits.

(1) The financing of specific research organizations through the Budget takes place in the form of direct allocations from the State Treasury. This type of financing makes it possible to influence the research policy of these organizations, to finance, in the form of grants, projects of special importance to the national economy, high cost, lengthy, or highly risky projects.

(2) Financing from special funds has been introduced a few years ago. Two such funds have been established: The fund for technical and economic progress, and the fund for new productions. Both these funds are formed from a levy on the value of industrial production; the size of this levy is determined each year for every

branch. The new production fund applies only to the chemical, engineering, and electroengineering industries.

The first of these funds is centrally allocated in ministries, and by ministries to individual Associations. The second, also centrally established, is at the disposal of Associations. If products, made by means of these funds, have commercial value and are sold, the income is returned to the factory concerned. The fund for technical and economic progress can be used for financing individual stages of research and development projects; the fund for new production can be used to cover additional costs which arise when the production of new products is being started.

The introduction in a plant of new technology as a rule requires additional effort on the part of the staff and additional expenditure. It often collides with the performance of current tasks, adversely affecting financial results, and therefore the interests of the employees. This is the essence of the so-called technical progress conflict.

The new funds are, therefore, intended to neutralize these conflicts by separating current production costs from R&D costs, connected with the future, by covering often serious expenditures in a way which does not influence the current effects of the enterprise; and by assuming the risk connected with the introduction of new technology. Such risk may be connected with inexact estimates of the expenditure necessary, with the possibility of not achieving the required results, and finally, with erroneous forecasts of the time and conditions necessary to introduce the new technology.

Projects in the area of organizational progress may also be financed from these funds – i.e. projects concerned with the preparation and implementation of improved organization and improved management methods.

(3) Rotating funds are used to finance projects, directly connected with the enterprise and the performance of its current production tasks. These expenditures, if the projects are lengthy, may be treated as overhead costs spread out over a period of two to three years.

(4) Finally, the financing of R&D projects through bank credits in Poland has only a supplementary character. Such credits may only serve in anticipation of the allocation of funds from appropriate sources. There is an interest-rate on these credits. They are repaid from subsequent income.

When determining the form of the system of financing R&D units in a Socialist economy, two extreme possibilities exist: (i) it can be a budget unit – receiving all the financial resources necessary for covering its planned expenditure from the treasury, and paying into the treasury all of its incomes as well as the non-utilized part of the allocated resources. In Poland, this form is used for financing R&D establishments of the Polish Academy of Sciences, of higher education, and of non-economy type ministries; (ii) it can be a business-type unit, financing all of its activities from income acquired through the sales of the results of its work.

This organization, i.e. expenditure fully dependent on income, has not yet been introduced in the pure form. An intermediary type, however, has been introduced, namely the so-called *budget-sponsored unit*. That part of its planned expenditure, which is not covered by contracts for sales, is financed by grants from the Treasury. If additional income is achieved, such a unit may increase its expenditure, without, however, exceeding the planned wage and salary fund and fixed assets investment.

Three years ago the rule was introduced in Poland that R&D units are obliged to sign contracts for carrying out specific R&D projects. These contracts determine the object (goal) of the project, technical-economic parameters, target dates, costs, and mutual rights and duties. The system provides for the specific features of R&D, such as the approximate character of its parameters, the risk involved, etc., allowing at the same time for deviations, within certain limits, from the predetermined costs, for receiving payment even in case of negative findings, etc.

R&D expenditure in Poland in 1960 amounted to 1 per cent of the national income. By 1967 this increased to 1·3 per cent. This figure applies only to centrally allocated resources.

Within the fund for technical and economic progress a certain amount is set aside for bonuses. These are awarded to employees in industry, in pre-determined sums, for performing specific tasks leading to the introduction of new technology. They are, to some extent, a reward for additional efforts.

R & D Units in View of the Development of the Engineering Industry

I would like to illustrate the development of R&D units with an example of the engineering industry. In a Socialist economy this industry has a special significance, and the efficiency and quality of its products is a decisive factor in the development of almost all the other branches of the national economy. Increasing tasks and existing difficulties in obtaining foreign currency for imported machines and equipment which are necessary in view of the insufficient capacity of the machine-tool industry to cover full demand, make it necessary to search for optimum solutions, both in respect to the programme for satisfying domestic and export requirements for modern equipment, and to the timing for the performance of these tasks, through accelerating cycles for introducing new products. These problems are being solved by R&D units.

Research units were developed; experimental plants, testing stations, prototype plants etc. were organized; these, free from current production problems, could concentrate on new designs. Cycles of introducing new products were accelerated through shortening of the basic stages of developing new designs. The new procedure limits the discussion and approval of design blueprints to basic designing data and the acceptance of testing results of prototypes. In parallel, the problem of assuring a modern character of products was worked on. This is of real importance in view of the fact that competition does not exist in the country, and in a number of branches demand exceeds supply.

A system was introduced to prevent the production of outdated machines. Originally, committees of experts, including professors, researchers from institutes, users, representatives of foreign trade organizations and producers, determined the level of all mass-made and series-made products in the country, assigning each of them to one of the following three categories; world-wide standard; average design; outdated. This was based on a comparative analysis of the design and parameters of the product in comparison with several foreign products, considered to be outstanding achievements in the given area. On this basis programmes were prepared for the modernization of average designs, and for replacing the outdated with modern ones. This action has brought positive results. Therefore, an evaluation procedure of new designs for mass and series production was introduced on a permanent basis, and on its basis so-called certificates for production are being issued. These certificates are issued, on request of the producer, by selected R&D units, which are called *branch leading* ones. The certificates are valid for the number of years, during which it can be expected that the given product will not become obsolete.

The importance of a modern design of industrial product can be illustrated by an example of the development in Poland of an important branch of the engineering industry.

As the development of the power industry is of great importance, it was decided to start the production of high power steam turbines. In 1953 the Soviet Union provided us with blueprints for the production of 25 MW turbines. The prototype of such a turbine was completed in 1957. This was a great achievement, as such machines were previously never made in Poland. But before industrial production of the turbines was started, the power industry stated that it would not accept them in the future, as they were already uneconomic. In view of this position blueprints for a 50 MW turbine were received from Leningrad and the turbine was subjected to factory tests in 1959. But again, before industrial production started, the power people warned they would only buy those they had already ordered, as, in comparison with world achievements, they were uneconomic. The factory concerned turned this time to British producers and bought a licence for a 125 MW turbine. This turbine was completed in 1961, but then the power industry required still bigger ones and for the Turoszow Power Station bought 7 200 MW turbines in the Soviet Union.

The industry again had to adapt itself and last year delivered the first 200 MW turbine. But technical progress makes ever-increasing demands; it was calculated each new 200 MW turbine installed signifies lost opportunity costs of many million zlotys; we therefore see the need to start producing in the country 500-600 MW turbines, realizing that abroad still bigger ones are being built.

Five times in eleven years, subsequent achievements had to be discarded, as new, more efficient and economical machines were needed. Technical progress is quicker than the execution of new designs in metal. Many other such examples could be quoted.

As was mentioned elsewhere, R&D units are quickly developing. In spite of this they still cannot catch up with industry's needs. In 1966 in the engineering and electrical engineering industries the following number of engineers and technicians were employed in R&D units:

	(*thousands*)
In industrial research institutes	4·8
In central laboratories and designing offices	5·3
In factory designing offices	12·50

It is difficult to determine what fraction of the number employed in these units work on current production problems, and therefore not on R&D ones. The fraction differs widely from branch to branch, which makes it impossible to make comparisons with other countries.

The tendency at present is to decrease the percentage of institutes and central designing offices in the total number of R&D units. The existing high percentage is the result of the period of their rapid development, when, to provide for a better utilization of the scarce staff and small amount of research equipment, central units were formed as strong as possible. Such units, having a strong staff, were also more effective in training new personnel.

The quantitative development of R&D units is hampered by limited possibilities for increasing the number of qualified personnel and for providing the necessary apparatus, equipment and research facilities. International co-operation on a broad scale, which will be mentioned later, can be of great help in this respect.

The rapid growth of the engineering industry and the necessity to adapt its structure and programmes to constant changes due to new technical and scientific developments present serious problems and tasks in the area of managing R&D and the industry as a whole. Some of them are: the variety of organizational forms of R&D, and their systematic improvement; a broad range of experiments, partially based on tested and adapted to our needs solutions of other developed countries and in the first place; continuous, intensive training and development on all levels.

International Co-operation

Not being a very large country, we neither can, nor wish to, make a full range of products. Still more so, we cannot independently carry out a broad range of research and development projects. This general principle is widely recognized.

The Soviet Union greatly helped us in the first years of reconstruction in the form of raw materials, machines and equipment, and expert services. This help accelerated reconstruction during the period, when our own capacity was still very small. Also, large orders from the Soviet Union at that time facilitated the rapid development of a number of branches. As our economy became stronger, the forms and extent of this co-operation were considerably increased.

Developing trade and specialization, i.e. the division of tasks, both in production and in research, are the basis for co-operation within the Council for Mutual Economic Assistance (COMECON). Significant progress was made in scientific and technical co-operation. International Committees for economic, scientific and technical co-operation facilitated a wide exchange of plans, experience, and results of research, as well as process and product designs.

In 1966 alone, Poland received from other countries – members of the COMECON – more than a thousand sets of technical and scientific documents, giving its own in exchange. During that year there were some 2,500 experts from Socialist countries in Poland, and some 4,000 Polish experts were abroad. These figures do not include visits to international fairs, meetings, etc.

Member countries exchanged lists of completed research projects, to avoid duplication. In 1966 for the first time the Soviet Union and Poland held consultations on five-year plans for the development of technology. As a result it was considered useful in several hundred cases to solve specific research and design problems in a common effort. Moreover, both parties could delete some hundreds of projects, as their results are available from neighbouring countries.

Some forty R&D and designing units started direct co-operation with corresponding units abroad. Similar consultations with Czechoslovakia led to an exchange of technical documents and designs, and to determine a number of subjects for a common effort. Some 15 per cent of new designs and processes in the engineering and chemical industries in Poland in 1966 were acquired through co-operation with COMECON countries. This is a considerable result.

Specialization agreements, which provide for contracts on mutual purchases of specific types of machines and equipment, permitting decisions not to make them at home, have a particular importance for the development of industries. They make it possible to concentrate research efforts, and besides, to increase production runs. This is not easy – many difficulties must still be faced, but it is being developed in view of its tremendous influence on the development of industry through the possibility of reducing the number of different items produced.

In view of the fact that a number of products were developed in Western countries sooner than in Socialist ones, it was decided to buy, on a planned basis, licences for designs and know-how in Western companies. A number of such contracts were signed within the last few years, with mutually advantageous results. Many such contracts were signed also with British firms, such as with AEI for 125 MW turbines, with Davidson for ventilators, with Leyland for diesel engines, with Walmsley's for paper-making machines, with Platt for textile machines, with ICI for terylene and polyethylene, to mention a few. Licences were bought also from firms from other countries, such as Sulzer, Burmeister Wain, Fiat for diesel engines, Fiat for motor-cars, Demag for compressors, etc.

When we buy a licence, we do not suspend our own research and designing work on the subjects. Designs change – they are modernized – and our designing offices, working on these changes in close co-operation with the licensing firm often contribute an important part to the technical development, at the same time improving their own designs. We have numerous examples of such positive results of licences. An additional trend in the development of co-operation on the basis of licences takes the form of co-production and joint penetration of foreign markets.

On the basis of agreements on co-operation both with Socialist countries, and with the Western ones, Polish industry makes use of foreign experience, training its staff, inviting experts, adapting production processes and techniques for production control. The range of this experience does not, however, cover all our needs. The serious tasks with which our industry is faced require the training of a large number of managerial personnel, require the formation of model enterprises which would be a training ground for managers. In this area, also, we made use of foreign experience, i.e. thanks to the ILO in Geneva, and of expert services in the field of management.

In 1960 the Polish Government signed an agreement with the UN

Special Fund and the ILO concerning the Polish Management Development Centre. Under the terms of this agreement, the Centre received equipment (including an ICT 1300 computer), expert services – in majority British – and a number of fellowships. The contribution of the UN Special Fund for these purposes was $900 thousand.

Making use of management consultant services is another way of profiting from foreign experience. A year ago such a contract was signed with a consultancy firm of Urwick, Orr and Partners, Ltd, for a project covering complex organizational changes in a large engineering enterprise. The project is under way and we expect that the adaptation of foreign management principles and procedures to our conditions will provide us with an amount of new experience, which we shall be able to elaborate and develop.

Work on the Future Development of Technology and the Needs of R & D

Initial assumptions, made by the Planning Commission, concerning forecasts on the population, its needs, on the size of the export, on the national product, on productivity, employment, investment, on the relative development of individual branches, on the development of higher education, expenditure on R&D, etc., were the basis for determining long-range forecasts of the development of science and technology in Poland up to the year 1985. On this basis ministries and Industrial Associations, with domestic and foreign trade organizations, made an analysis of the development of individual branches, determining the directions for developing technology, production, necessary investments, etc., and thus the need for research projects and for new designs of machines and equipment.

The engineering industry associations thereafter prepared forecasts concerning the development of science and technology in their branches. These forecasts include domestic needs, export possibilities, needs in the area of research and designing, of developing R&D units, the equipment necessary, etc., forecasts concerning domestic production and import, and the needs concerning co-operation with foreign countries in the area of technical documentation and licences. Such material, often in alternative forms, was submitted for discussion on several levels: Scientific and Technical Councils of Associations, Main Commissions of the Committee for Science and Technology, and finally the Executive Board of the Committee for Science and Technology. In these discussions a wide range of specialists took part, including representatives of science (both from universities and from the Academy of Sciences) of Industrial research units, and of users.

The level of technology in many areas of industry in our country is still below that of developed countries. As a result, R&D projects in the engineering industry in the first place are concerned with the adaptation of solutions already existing elsewhere, and only in sporadic cases deal with basic inventions and fully original solutions. This puts the stress on development and implementation projects rather than on basic research ones. The evaluations of forecasts, therefore, made by the bodies mentioned, are based primarily on comparisons between the proposals put forward by the branches concerned and the results achieved in the given area elsewhere.

Even the initial summing up of tasks of R&D units in different branches confirmed the expected difficulties in meeting the needs of the national economy by the domestic engineering industry, the capacity of which is still inadequate. For this reason it was necessary to establish priorities in forecasts for individual branches and to determine a plan for allocating resources so as to meet in an optimum way the most pressing needs of the economy, ensuring a possibly largest export pool. In the analyses made, the necessity to increase imports of those products which are not made, or are made in insufficient quantities, is taken into consideration.

Determining priorities for branches at a period of rapid development in industry, of increasing economic needs, is difficult, for every user is convinced his needs are the most pressing, and the opportunity for importing are limited. Work on methods of doing this has been started, but it is not easy and needs time. In parallel, there are discussions on specialization of production within the COMECON countries, which also seriously influences priorities for different branches.

Among more important factors which are taken into consideration the following might be mentioned: the future capabilities of the branch – the rate of replacing product designs; the utilization of domestic raw material resources; material availability – size of necessary imports; specialization within the COMECON framework; needs for investment and manpower, the size of domestic markets and export opportunities; development tasks of R&D units and the necessary expenditures.

Forecasting the development of R&D units and determining the resources necessary for the facilities and equipment is closely linked with the determining of priorities of different branches. R&D is a decisive factor not only in respect to the modernity of design, durability, and quality of products and in respect to their cost, but also in respect to their economical utilization by their users. The growth of R&D units is not proportionate to the number of new products. Production will increase at a quicker rate than R&D units. The difference in these rates will vary with the branches concerned.

I would like to point out a few factors which in our opinion, influence the dependence of the volume of R&D facilities, from the number and the type of new machines and equipment necessary for the national economy:

obsolescence;

number of operations performed by any one machine and the degree of automation;

increasing batch sizes;

developing proprietory and standard parts manufacturing industries.

(1) The rapid development of science and technology leads to machines becoming obsolete before they are physically worn out. This period, which still recently exceeded ten years, nowadays in some branches has fallen down to three to five years, which to a considerable degree influences the speed of replacement of equipment. As one of the indices for calculating the size of R&D units we took the ratio of the sales value of new products (in the year following the run-in period) to the total sales volume of the branch. There will be differences in introducing unit production and mass production, even if differences in the work content of preparatory work in both cases are taken into account.

(2) The second factor, leading to an increase in R&D activities, is the introduction of specialized multiple-operation machines and equipment, connected with the mechanization and automation of production. New machines permit a serious increase in productivity, often replacing several ones used formerly.

In contrast to single operation machines used so far, these special machines are usually made for a single product. Depreciation periods should, therefore, be seriously shortened, which is connected with the length of the production life of the given product.

(3) The size of R&D is influenced in the opposite direction by the continuing increase of batch sizes of products and of their parts, due to specialization, typification, and widely applied unification, and standardization. This is a factor which makes it possible to apply more efficient batch-sizes production methods in unit products – this factor also changes the scope of designing, through the introduction of the 'building-block' systems.

(4) Finally, the development of industries (producing proprietory and standard parts) has a limiting influence on R&D. The development of these industries in our country is seriously retarded, as in the first year stress was put on investing in industries which made final goods. Specializing plants to produce elements makes it necessary to carry out designing work in the R&D units of these plants, which makes it possible to limit this work in the final production.

On the basis of the present state of research on an international scale, it is not possible to foresee all the changes which will take place in science and technology within the next ten to fifteen years. The time period between the conception of a novel idea and its implementation in industry has become so much shorter that we must recognize that materials and processes, which we do not yet know, will be in use ten to fifteen years from now. In forecasting, it is necessary to keep some reserve R&D capacity to facilitate undertaking of such new projects.

As in the meantime undoubtedly further R&D and production ties and agreements on an international scale will take effect, the whole organization of R&D must be sufficiently flexible to be able to adapt itself to quickly changing conditions. This presents enormous tasks to management both in industry and in R&D units. Management must also pay constant attention to the training and development of its staff, to keep it able to grasp and implement new scientific and technical developments.

Conclusion

The breath-taking rate of development of science and technology throughout the world, with seriously increasing costs of scientific and technical research on the one hand, and the need for a rapid increase in the standard of living of our population on the other, face the Polish national economy with immense tasks. The Socialist economy gives us tremendous possibilities for a complex, planned solution of these problems – but we are aware of the fact that we are not a large enough country to afford the luxury of independent solutions of all industrial problems connected with development. International co-operation today is a necessity – there must be a division of tasks, both in research and in production: common solutions of increasingly complex and complicated problems must be reached. Specialized production, co-operation in research projects, exchange of information and of experience – all these are factors affecting economic development.

Within the Socialist camp work in this area is done on a large scale. Poland has also established contacts with many Western countries, including Great Britain, based on mutual good will and mutual benefits. Successfully developing contacts between scientists and industrial specialists of both our countries undoubtedly contribute to a better knowledge of mutual needs and achievements, which in turn facilitate the development of trade. Our last meeting in Warsaw six months ago with the Joint Parliamentary Secretary in the Ministry of Technology, Dr Jeremy Bray, and with a group of British scientists, who took part in a Symposium, organized by the Committee for Science and Technology, and the Exhibition of British Scientific Achievements, shown in Warsaw, are a distinct symbol of our closer contacts.

References

M. Lesz, 'Cooperation in the Field of New Technology as a Factor in the Development of Socialist Countries'. *Nowe Drogi*, **3** (1968).
National Management Development Centre – Poland (ILO, Geneva; 1965).
Working Papers of The Committee for Science and Technology:
M. Marlewicz, 'The System of Financing Research and Development Work in Poland'.
Z. Ostrowski, 'Characteristic Features of Scientific and Research Organizations in Poland'.
S. Gebalski, and E. Zakrzewski, 'Programming, Planning and Co-ordinating Research and Development in Poland'.

TABLE 1 Reference systems for describing the R & D position ▶

main topic	*reference system or concept*
(A) Organization	1. Bureaucratic *vs.* free, organic
	2. Project organization (e.g. 'Viggen')
	3. Sectorizing – 'Profit centres'
	4. 'Theory Y – Theory X' (importance of the human factor)
	5. 'The company=a guided system'
(B) R & D process	6. Preparation – incubation – insight – verification
	7. Basic research – applied research – development
	8. 'Systems engineering'
	9. Offensive – defensive research
	10. Forecasting the technology of the future
(C) Product	11. Value analysis (analysis of function costs)
	12. Thinking in terms of function (to shape, to milk, to drill, etc.)
	13. Property profiles
	14. Machine – process – medium – environment
	15. Commercial life
	16. Market – technology

JAN R. SCHNITTGER

R and D in the Swedish Engineering Industry

An Analysis of the Problems

The Public discussion on 'innovation' has now reached the point where new contributors have to face the question whether they are not actually adding to the confusion at present characterizing this group of problems.

In discussing the Swedish engineering industry, the conditions affecting individual companies vary to such an extent that hypotheses of a general character have in any case only a limited applicability. Even a medium-sized Swedish enterprise, i.e. a small company relative to international competition, very often has to adopt a 'both-and' system for the organization and environment of its technical research and development.

Choosing systems of reference. In recent attempts at proceeding beyond mere descriptions of current development positions, use has been made of various systems of reference or concepts.

Every concept in Table 1 has its current Swedish applications. The choice of concept depends on what is considered critical with respect to success or failure. Importance has to be attached to the level from which observations are made in the company or society.

Obviously, we are at liberty to choose our system of reference. In the present paper an attempt will be made at analyzing the current position of the Swedish engineering industry in a constructive way.

The concepts of information, guidance and resources seem to possess not only sufficient universality but also qualities enabling them to be used for apposite descriptions of individual cases.

Information

Two types of enterprise showing different information profiles. The sources, flow and processing of information offer a good grasp of the character of an enterprise and are of decisive importance also with respect to R&D activities. This may be elucidated by the Swedish engineering industry's biggest joint undertaking so far, the *Viggen* jet-fighter project (Figure 1). This provides an excellent example of systems engineering. *Marketing* and *Sales*, otherwise the dominant

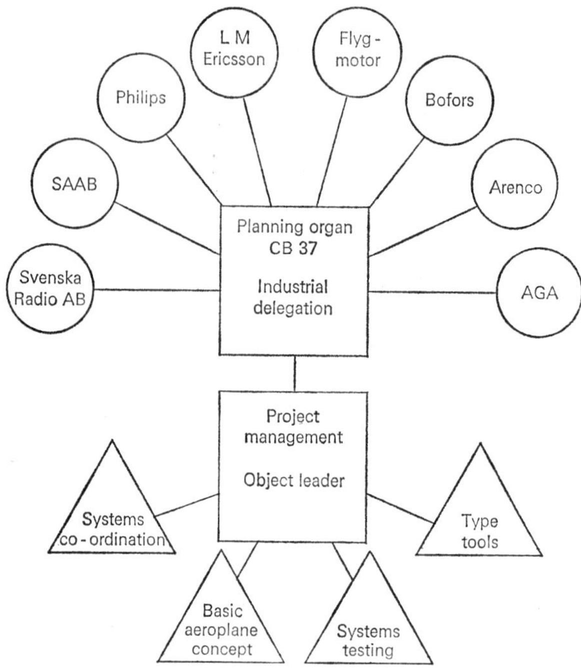

Figure 1. Organizational co-operation within R and D in a 'systems-orientated' enterprise.

sources of information for the development work in many engineering enterprises, are missing entirely in this case. There is only one customer (however many-headed): the Swedish Government. Naturally, certain changes in the objectives occurred, and will still occur, during the prolonged period of planning (1952–70) but the majority of these may be considered results of logical processes, which may be traced, documented and counteracted by corresponding measures. Thus ensue decisions and solutions; universal aeroplanes. STOL performances, single-seat and single-motor concepts, delta-shaped nose and main wings, central computers, etc.

Another obvious consequence of the conditions is that information flow and guidance are integrated parts of the project-object management that is a characteristic of the *Viggen* project.

Apart from a few generalizations, many of the recommendations put forward in the current 'innovation' debate cannot really be applied to the *Viggen* case; however, it is obvious that both technically and in an administrative sense the project does incorporate quite a few 'innovations' and 'spin-off' opportunities.

In many other engineering enterprises the situation is quite different. These companies, with their turnover more or less located abroad, are selling 'engineering' in one form or other, e.g. as applied to bio-chemical analysis, surgery, compressed air, electric power generation and distribution. So, for example, Alfa-Laval is manufacturing equipment for foods and foodstuffs processing, for the chemical processing industries, for agriculture, with special emphasis on equipment for centrifugal separation, heat transfer, and related auxiliary equipment. In all industries of this general type the situation as concerns 'information' differs from the situation typical of a heavily *systems-orientated* enterprise.

In this case it presents a critical problem to obtain sufficient market information or, more precisely, information about all possible applications within the sphere of interest of an individual company.

Sources of information are of many kinds, such as local sales companies, centrally located sales organizations, staff organizations dedicated to marketing planning, technical documentation, etc. Staff organizations may be useful for analyzing official statistics and organizing the flow of information fed in by various professional information collectors. In Alfa-Laval's case such organizations watch the sequence of events associated with the production of foodstuffs in different countries, the expansion of the chemical industry, and the gradual changes taking place in agriculture. Other self-evident sources of information in aid of R&D work include participation in congresses, visits to fairs and exhibitions, and last but not least the overwhelming flora of periodicals.

Still much remains to be gained by systematizing pertinent sources of information. In marketing research of a project character, the sources are generally traced with great accuracy. The objective being well defined in these cases, the selection of informative material may be made at, or close to, the source.

It is equally important, however, to keep a continuous watch on a large size stock of informative material. Here, a sifting procedure has to be interposed in order that the individual consumer be rescued from supersaturation. This brings us to the internal flow of information.

The internal flow of information and how to treat it. In our company we have taken the first step towards a technique that may become known as *data-bank information supervision.* We have now reached a stage characterized by supervision, within the various company departments, of our printed documentation. We have divided this into three classes, viz., basic research, applied technology, and miscellaneous.

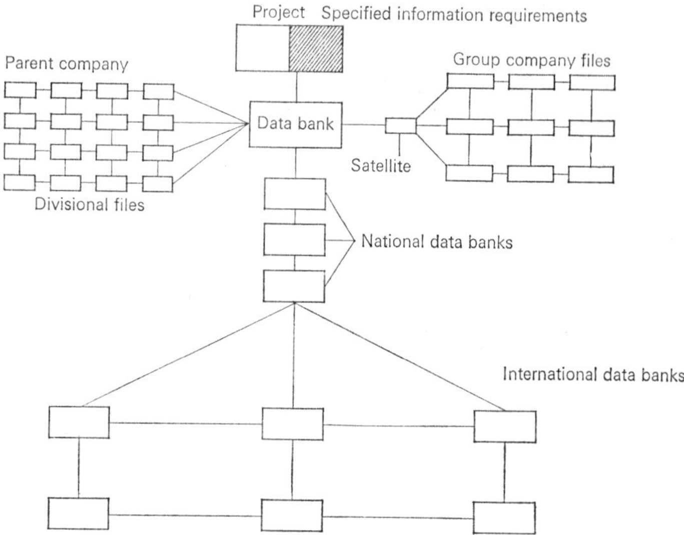

Figure 2. Diagram indicating the company's future system of information retrieval by means of modern data-processing techniques.

Figure 2 gives an idea of the data-retrieval flow sheet of the 1970s. It will be necessary to devote a few years to preparatory work prior to the introduction of the ADP procedures suggested.

The new classification technique in the information sphere, i.e. the introduction of classification keywords, facilitates among other things a selective service of information (SSI). This technique is at present being evaluated in co-operation with the library service of the Technical University of Stockholm. A number of *search profiles* for the company have been elaborated. The present stage coincides with the upper portion of the flow sheet. We are also studying methods of systematizing the various decentralized archives of the parent company by applying a similar keyword classification principle.

The central records unit of the parent company of the Group now contains roughly ten per cent only of the internally generated information. Organizational improvements to the various information files within the company should enable us to retrieve much of this decentralized information, at present practically non-existent to prospective users outside the various departments. Applying the new information guidance system, an increase in organized data decentralization now seems to be within reach. To achieve this end, each department has to build up its activity profile by grouping in a classification system the necessary number of keywords divided into categories. The filing binders are arranged according to category, each document entering the files being accounted for, stating reference data. All such information is punched on cards or tape at a central unit and is then filed in the data bank.

Here, the internal material is combined with the flow of information coming from national and international data banks. The retrieval of information in the 1970s as based on this combination of internal and external flows of informative material would thus be carried out along the following lines:

A. Determination of the information requirements for the current project. Establishment of a search profile.

B. Feeding the search profile to the data bank. Have projects of a similar nature been performed earlier? What documentation is available within the project sphere?

C. Transfer of the search profile by the company's own data satellite (now in operation for some time) for searching in a central external data bank.

D. Retransmission of the question(s) to national or international data banks.

A realistic programme for the next five years could no doubt be summed up like this: 'Information with a more personal approach, adjusted to individual information profiles and tuned to time, for example to fit into current development projects. A considerable cut in the circulation of periodicals within the company as the information they bring is often delayed and oversized.'

For the guiding of R&D activities, information processing is becoming an important prerequisite. The development dynamics of the market-centred type of enterprise as described above are now gradually escaping from the bonds of the comparatively short-range type of activity pattern with its dominating market linkage. One reason for this is that research and development take time.

Earlier, most events encountered on the market could be met by appropriate measures of a relatively short-range character. The demand for innovation is increasing, however, and as a result we shall have to appropriate more staff and invest more money toward these distant future objectives than we have ever done before in these sections of the engineering industry. It should be noted here that the long-range plans of the future are intended to offer guidance and bases for the planning for each period of time involved in the company's future activities, i.e. along the entire time axis in question.

To attain the objectives of the future we shall now have to start each project at an earlier date. Even quite a normal product development process as based on conventional techniques can rarely be accomplished in less than three years from the date of decision to the date of introducing the standard product on the market. To carry out a moderate innovation, as founded for example on the results of certain scientific or technical research, another two or four years will have to be added in most cases. This will thus require a total of five to seven years for the development of sophisticated products as compared to three years previously. The matter is further complicated by the political, economic, and social changes showing an obvious trend in the opposite direction as far as rate is concerned.

From these facts we have to conclude that the average span of our planning horizon will have to be widened. Our planning will have to be based on processed information, i.e. a forecast. Such forecasts may be designed along slightly different lines of thought, depending on the prospective dominance of the company's share in the future market, etc. The stronger the dominance, the greater the influence of the company's own activities on the future situation and the more 'normative' the forecast. Figure 3 shows a forecast situation. The sequence is roughly as follows, starting with 1968:

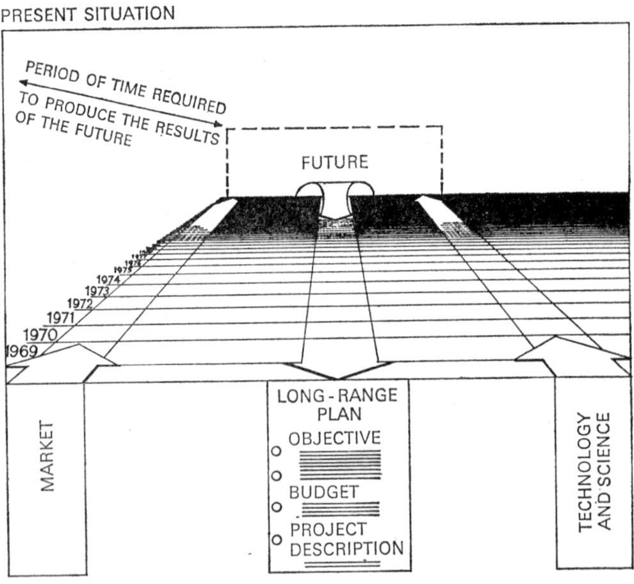

Figure 3. The line of development of the market and of technology and science extended toward the future. At a sufficiently distant point of time it will be necessary to provide alternatives founded on these two basic factors. The long-range plan thus obtained has to be extended back to the present time to offer the practical use expected from it.

General marketing conditions in industrial processing engineering in 1975 →. Properties of processed products (e.g. a certain type of processed foodstuffs) that may presumably be of current interest in 1975 →. Outlines of alternative processing equipment that, in 1975, may possibly correspond to the properties mentioned →. Progress in organic chemistry, microbiology, etc., that are apt to influence the processing techniques of 1975 (in reality, most of this progress has to be known already as an outcome of research activities) →. Progress in the manufacture of apparatus and related branches of engineering →. A revision of the ideas about possible forms of processed foods for consumption →. Revised forms of processing equipment →. Let us put a stop to the sequence here.

Using such pilot studies as a basis, we may arrive in the future at certain estimates concerning the *direction* of our own R&D resources, the existence of certain *gaps in our knowledge*, and the size of the total *need of resources.*

By amalgamating such forecasts during the next few years we may eventually arrive at a new overall concept of the company's objectives. We are not of the opinion that it would generally be feasible to make up forecasts for all areas of current interest simultaneously but that our activities should centre round one area at a time, maintaining a cyclic rolling planning.

The company's product programme and its possibilities of technical expansion may often be studied to advantage from an 'innovation space', a three-dimensional diagram (Figure 4). Horizontal integration, e.g. the separation function as applied to milk, yeast, starch, vegetable oils, etc., is generally predominant in the beginning of a technical development. Vertical integration of the type known from the *Viggen* project has its counterpart at Alfa-Laval in the medium, milk; proceeding all the way from feeding the cow up to the various milk products ready for consumption. Integration in its initial stage within a new area is represented by the 'chemical block' in Figure 4.

It will be a job of considerable immediate interest in the near future to apply various methods of information processing to facilitate the adaptation of our products to the market conditions.

Using relationship matrices for the system, machine – medium – process – environment we have managed to treat manually bulk information of the order of magnitude of 10,000 individual relationships. Table 2 gives an example of a data-processed subsystem in such a four-dimensional matrix.

In this connexion all information processing aims at facilitating the planning activities or, putting it another way, at reducing the degree of uncertainty as concerns the consequences ensuing from each individual activity. This is a basis for the guidance of the R&D work.

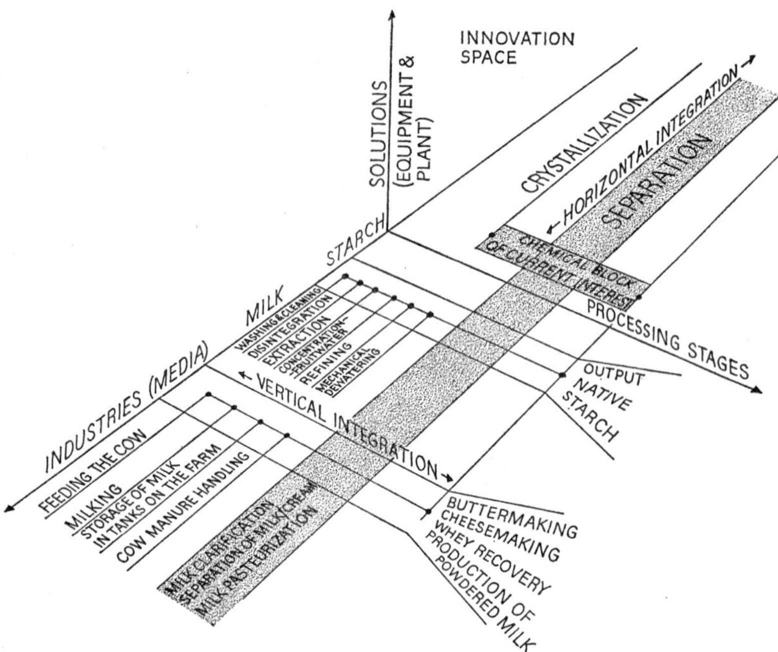

Figure 4. The innovation space offers a feasible way of demonstrating the company's activities. Industries (or media) generally coincide with various groups of customers whereas the processing stages, on the other hand, do rather direct attention to the company's technical activities. Every coupling between industries and processing stages may give rise to alternative solutions.

TABLE 2 indicating relations between the solid-liquid medium and the machine subsystems

	pretreatment	*feed inlet*	*feed outlet*	*sedimentation*	*sludge transint*	*effluent control*	*sludge outlet*	*effluent outlet*	*sludge transext*	*seal system*	*rinse system*
Composition	1	0	0	3	2	1	3	2	1	0	0
Density differential	0	0	1	3	0	1	0	0	0	0	0
Density of input material	0	0	0	0	0	0	0	0	0	0	0
Particle size distribution	0	0	1	3	0	2	0	1	0	0	0
Flocculation	1	0	0	1	2	0	0	0	2	0	0
Sensitivity to mech. handling	2	2	3	1	1	2	0	0	0	0	0
Foaming	0	1	2	0	0	0	1	2	0	1	0
Surface tension	0	0	0	1	1	0	0	0	0	0	0
Coefficent of friction	0	0	0	0	3	0	1	0	0	0	0
Chemical affinity	0	0	0	0	2	0	0	1	1	0	0
Flame point	0	0	1	0	0	0	0	0	0	3	0
Chemical aggressiveness	0	0	0	0	0	0	0	0	0	0	0
Erosiveness	0	0	0	0	2	0	2	0	0	0	0
Emulsive characteristics	0	2	3	3	1	2	0	2	0	0	0

Explanations: 0=independent; 1=some interrelation; 2=distinct relationship; 3=dominant relationship.

Medium/subsystem interrelationship, originating from a current data programme. It shows the dependence of various functions of the equipment on the properties of the conveyed medium.

Guidance

A natural law of organization. Much deep thinking has been devoted to the problem of what is the optimum system of organization as applied to R&D activities. How are the valuable innovators to be found and utilized, how it is possible to grasp promising ideas before they evaporate?

Even to these company activities the 'natural law' of organization applies, saying 'There is a direct relationship between results and efforts'. This may be represented here by (1) information, (2) guidance and (3) resources. In each of these factors there is an interaction of quality and quantity. If anything is missing this will impair the overall result although the other variables may be good. Having recourse to a slight simplification in the interest of easy thought transmission, the economic result may be expressed by the formula $E = I \times G \times R$.

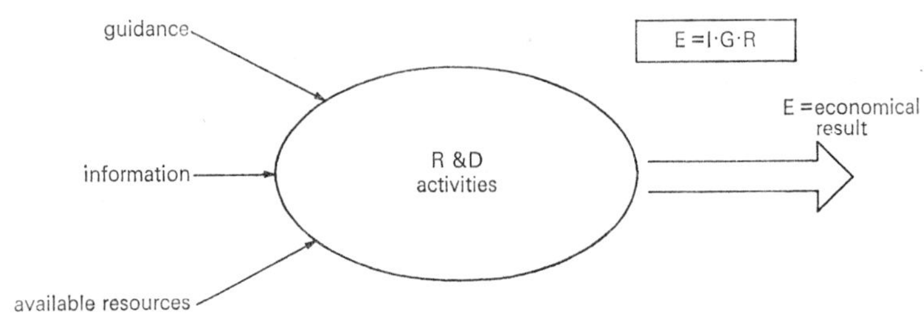

Figure 5. Results of the R and D activities.

This way of expressing the economic outcome as a kind of product of information by guidance by resources reminds me of a Swedish proverb stating that decisive importance must be attached to the weakest link of a chain.

The conclusions are direct and straightforward: to attain original products, methods or services on a high innovation level the company will not only have to employ men of original qualities but will also have to develop a system of information and guidance to put their creations into practice.

If it is considered adequate to elevate the technical level of the company's products so much as to open out entirely new spheres of interest it will be necessary to employ additional highly qualified engineers with an intrinsic capability of treating the company's current and future products from their particular angles, and these people will have to be supplied not only with correct information on markets and technical developments but also with the appropriate frame of guidance.

From these examples and the simplified formula, $E = I \times G \times R$ it may, however, be concluded that a R&D philosophy that exaggerates the problems of guidance to the detriment of the problems of resources is just as inappropriate as a policy leaving a team of innovators to themselves without information and guidance.

Furthermore, it is quite clear that every company management has to make up its mind as to what combination of information, guidance and resources should be considered the optimum solution for that particular company. It has become popular at the present time to make comparisons of the Swedish and the American situation. As far as the matter in question is concerned, our chances need not be inferior although they may be somewhat different. A Swedish innovation does not turn out to be a success as long as it remains within the home market whereas American innovations prosper once they have gained national acceptance. Conditions like these will obviously exert an influence on the balancing of the variables in our equation.

Experience seems to verify the validity of this argumentation both as concerns innovations of a more technical nature and with respect to ordinary consumer goods, i.e. where the public acceptance of novelties plays a role. Obviously, our home market for capital goods (intended mostly for 'manufacturers') is too small whereas our consumer market is not only too small but also more conservative than its American counterpart.

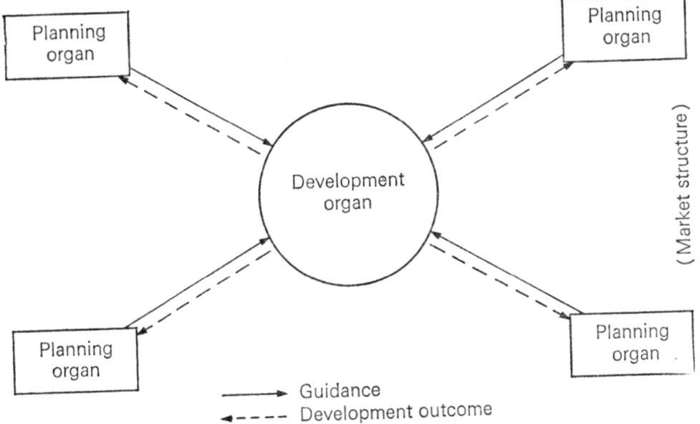

Figure 6. A common way of arranging the guidance of the R and D activities of a 'market centred' company. The planning organs pick their impulses for the development work from various market environments.

Guidance design in R & D. The following two sample cases seem to be quite common in the Swedish engineering industry (Figure 6). A 'market centred' company, selling 'engineering' in one form or other, tends to establish a number of planning organs surrounding a common development unit. The latter unit is mainly responsible for a development of the company's market towards horizontal integration. The various planning organs are mainly sales and market orientated, and *hence the linkage between them is often rather weak.* The development unit involved will consequently experience (*a*) priority problems and (*b*) difficulties in establishing a long-range plan. This will make it difficult to reach a satisfactory innovation level in accordance with our previous discussion on internal information processing. On the other hand the planning organs with their ties to the market will often initiate a series of minor innovations that are generally founded on current techniques, in most cases using the market and the factories of the customers as laboratories.

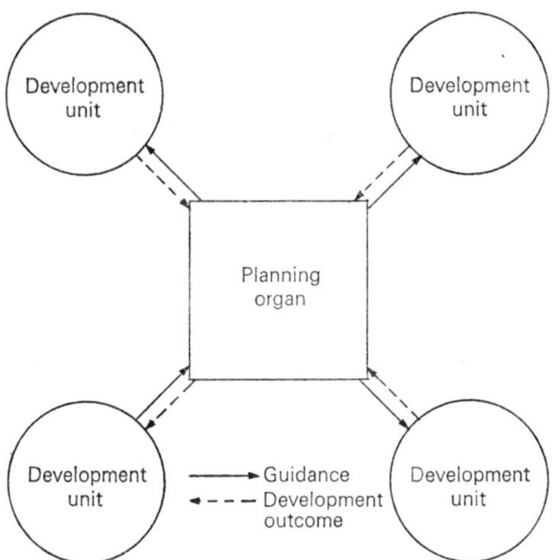

Figure 7. A common way of arranging the guidance of the R and D activities of a 'systems orientated' company. It does not show in what way the planning organ has collected its basic information. This material is brought together from various sources, including state agencies and companies.

The other model of R&D guidance is a complete inversion of the one just described. Let us call it 'systems orientated'. This model comprises a *single* planning organ in a central position surrounded by a number of development units. An organization of this type operates in favour of a deliberate vertical integration. By adopting this system it will be comparatively much easier to arrive at a long-range plan, thus producing the massive innovation that is now becoming popular. The system shows close resemblance to that described by Servan-Schreiber in his book, *Le défi américain*. A recently founded Swedish innovation company, *Projektion*, is said to be organized along the same lines. There are reasons to believe that this company as well as other similar structures for government and private co-operation will have ample opportunities of utilizing the same information and guidance in the common interest. This should place them in a position enabling them to co-ordinate a number of development units and stages exactly as described here.

Naturally, the cases are less clear-cut in reality. The future guidance of the R&D activities, however, will in all probability develop into a mixed pattern featuring:

A. A superior structure that even in the case of a traditionally market-centred enterprise bears a definite resemblance to the systems-orientated model.

B. A local infrastructure that offers optimum possibilities for *innovation* within the frames of the superior structure. The guidance and flow of information associated with an infrastructure of this type resemble those of the market centred model.

It will then be possible to arrange 'islets of spontaneity' in the pattern, corresponding to the liberal organic variety of guidance that may give rise to unconventional solutions (Figure 8).

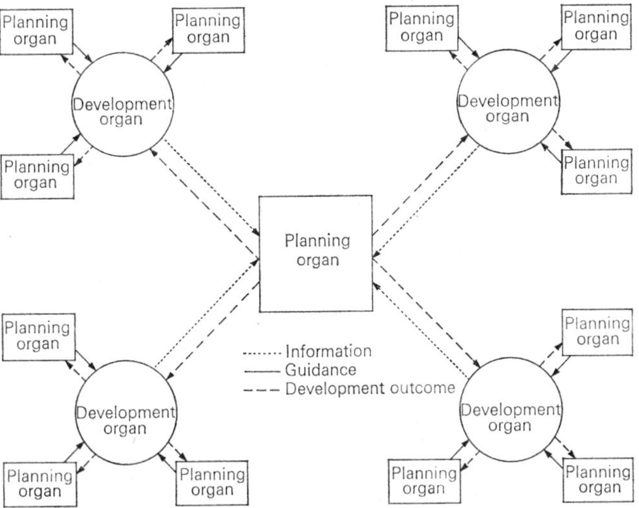

Figure 8. The R and D of the future will incorporate the best properties of the preceding guidance models: a 'systems orientated' basic structure, offering, on a slightly local level, flexibility, concentration toward the market, and the space necessary for thoroughbred innovators.

Resources

The human factor. Resources in a wide sense include personnel, premises, fixed assets, instruments, and experimental worskhops. They all have a qualitative and a quantitative aspect. In so far as the entire Swedish engineering industry is concerned, limits should not be drawn too tight when summing up since the resources of colleges, universities, and consultants are also of considerable import.

It goes without saying that the premises and equipment of various kinds have to be adequate. In fact, such topics are scarcely our main concern.

The human factor is the most important R&D asset. According to information recently obtained from France, the human factor may consume two-thirds of the R&D budget. Mismanagement of this vitally important asset with respect to utilization and maintenance may turn out particularly deleterious as damage affecting this sector takes a longer time to be remedied.

More than 40 per cent of all industrial enterprises in Sweden belong to the engineering industry. Owing to the high value of its finished products, the engineering industry employs more people per invoiced krona than the basic industries do. There is hence a strong connexion between the engineering industry and the community as far as the human resources are concerned.

There are reasons to believe that we are now running certain risks of mismanaging, on a growing scale, the human contribution in current industrial connexions. The situation has, in fact, been aggravated lately owing to international competition.

In our market-orientated Swedish engineering enterprises R&D has yielded an overall result which, according to the previous argumentation, has been dependent on the quality and quantity of information, guidance and resources involved.

Everybody realizes the importance of increasing efficiency, of elevating the technical level, of putting more sophisticated products on the market. But we seem to be lagging behind in the utilization of the human factor.

In the companies you find very few, if any, engineers who are in a position to devote their time to free and active meditation, encircling problems of technology and products and applying professional knowledge of the highest grade. In Sweden, few prominent engineers are allowed to remain as such after the age of thirty-five. They are made into administrators and from then on their lag in technical matters is growing steadily. Much too little is done to counteract this lag as far as possible.

Using the technical universities as an instrument, society is increasing the output of qualified engineers. This development is founded mainly on a previous forecast based on a joint state-industry-commerce basis. It seems quite natural that a growing number of people, and especially young people, are now anxious to know whether the Swedish industry of today is capable of offering intelligent work for all these young engineers. The immediate situation is, however, that a number of adjustment processes are running in parallel at present and that their phase coincidence is not too good.

On one hand the people of the engineering industry are well aware of the demand for better education and technical training. Many jobs now carried out with a moderate technical background will require an engineering training in the near future. The ultimate reason for this is the notable rise in the educational and training level in other countries, especially in the United States. Many other jobs that have never been considered as 'technical' so far will be classified as suitable objectives of engineering students in the future. On the other hand there is a considerable need for improving the information and guidance that is necessary on an average to fully utilize the new engineers, making them contribute in an efficient way to an increased competitive ability of our products. As concerns our human resources there are at present two 'gaps' to be filled:

(1) The engineers active in industry at present have not been given sufficient quantitative and qualitative opportunities of maintaining and renewing their professional skills, and hence they are not sure how to utilize their younger colleagues in the most effective way.

(2) The systems of industrial information and guidance are now, on an average, in need of a restoration unless the overall result is to remain much the same despite increasing the resources.

(3) We have so far not had an opportunity of studying in all its various aspects the overall balance with regard to the R&D activities that ensues from these facts. It is thus a matter of doubt if our young engineers have really been trained to meet the actual requirements of the industry. The fact is probably that neither the technical colleges nor the industries conform to optimum conditions. As for industry it will be necessary to adopt a higher rate of revaluation, enabling a gradual elevation of the technical level by utilizing qualified engineers in greater numbers. For obvious reasons a technical achievement of this kind should find its due justification in the economic performance of the companies. Of course, this development will only be gradual, since the underlying phenomena are of a long range nature. The technical colleges and universities are in need of a better contact with industry in order to prevent the possible formation of a utilization gap between the educational institutions and industry. This may be illustrated by the fact that this very day, with a growing need for a revision of the information and guidance systems for R&D, there is a noticeable lack of engineers qualified for this particular type of work.

Internal and external resources. From a national point of view we have to economize our human resources. It should indeed be possible to distribute the work in a more sensible way over the internal and external resources. As you know, there has already been a revaluation as concerns, for example, service activities of various kinds. These are now being arranged externally on a growing scale.

In the company represented by the present writer we have been working to a certain extent according to a pattern which, when slightly generalized and somewhat more elaborated, would take the following shape as far as the engineering industry of the next five-year period is concerned:

(1) Optimum utilization of materials and production engineering requires more production research. In this respect Sweden may be lagging behind in certain fields. In all probability the development work necessary here should be carried out to advantage by the engineering industry itself. The question of distributing such assignments on individual companies and trade research institutions requires further investigation, yet the principle remains that these assignments are mainly to be considered duties of the industry itself, and probably duties of individual companies to a greater extent than before.

(2) Constructional engineering in its further development will have to find partly new paths to follow. It will be necessary to link in with the above-mentioned R&D work for the combination of materials and production so that our constructional techniques may fully utilize the new opportunities offered. It will also be necessary to reckon with construction and production as a more and more integrated process. The term 'automated construction' has been coined for this case but that is just a way of establishing the fact that it has been possible to co-ordinate the activities, for example by more extensive utilization of the computer, causing much of today's drawings, processing and tool design to assume a different character or disappear completely. In my opinion, co-operation between the engineering industry and the technical universities should be able to yield much more than it does at present.

(3) The products of the engineering industry are increasingly intended to meet specialized demands. In certain cases these may be expressed in a comparatively exact and logical form, e.g. as concerns the supply of energy. In many other cases, however – and my own company, Alfa-Laval belongs in this group – the deep background of the products is to be found well outside the physico-mechanical sphere. This background is founded on environmental biology, microbiology, biochemistry, medicine, surgery, the agricultural sciences, town planning, sociology, and so forth. Certain methods of work as applied in other connexions have been described as cutting across, or forming links between, two or more sciences; this way of approach is being used in solving scientific problems generally of a basic research character. This is where we have combina-

tions of pure science and applied technology with the same objective, i.e. solving problems that could not be solved entirely by any party alone. The engineering industry supplies one form or other of 'mechanical geometry' to promote a solution of the problems. Here, in my opinion, lies the greatest idle potential to be utilized by the Swedish engineering industry. Especially within these areas there should be a more vivid interchange than today of thought and experience between industry on one hand and technical colleges and universities on the other.

Conclusions

This outline of questions concerning the organization and environment of the Swedish engineering industry is incomplete in many ways. Thus, for example, the writer has made no attempts at recommending infallible methods of making innovators feel at home. To a Swedish mind these and other related conditions are scarcely controversial as such; they may rather be attributed to the general structure of the Swedish industry's R&D activities at present. Other objects worthy of attention are capital accumulation and profitability. Although they have been touched upon only very slightly the writer is well aware of their importance.

The following facts have been established within the frame of the present investigation:

(1) A number of reference systems are available for describing the organizational and environmental conditions of the R&D activities. Which system is adopted much depends on what is considered critical with respect to success or failure.

(2) The R&D work and its conditions cannot be treated without involving the other functions of a company and its overall conditions. Information, guidance and resources are specific to the individual case.

(3) The economic overall result of R&D depends on several factors. Using a conceptual simplification, it is dependent on information, guidance and resources, i.e. $E=I\times G\times R$.

(4) The problems associated with information are growing. For a number of concurrent reasons we are now compelled to devote more work than before to information processing, including long-range forecasting, in order to achieve the optimum economic result.

(5) Changes are to be expected in the structure of the guidance of our R&D activities. There will probably be a superposition of several types of guidance systems in our enterprises.

(6) Human resources form the most important asset of R&D. Various 'gaps' of a transient nature can be noted in this connexion. Because of the competitive position today there is a growing

aggravation of these conditions, calling for thinking along new lines in many spheres associated with the human factor both in the engineering industry and in society.

(7) The role played by the community as concerns R&D work will gain more and more importance. It will be necessary for the government to co-operate by extending our information network and, as in the case of the engineering industry, by securing access to the international data banks that may be expected to start operations in the near future.

We shall need government co-operation to obtain such significant control signals as to enable us not only to elevate the technical level but also to make it useful in practice. Achievements of the systems-orientated type will be unavoidable unless we are willing to lag behind our competitors. However, the system results for domestic use also have to be of a character that makes them useful in international connexions as far as possible.

The greater part of our education, professional training and basic research must be considered one of the government's tasks. By its achievements in these fields the state rounds off its role as environment creator in favour of industry's own development activities. This may be described as an injection of human production resources and something of the counterpoint enabling us to utilize the interaction of basic research and technical development across and above individual branches of science.

Preparations are now being made to determine the appropriate overall part in the R&D work to be played by the community. If the state does co-operate by providing the above outlined support with respect to information, guidance and resources there will no doubt be a positive outcome. In this interaction the development and marketing of industrial products should, however, remain the primary task of the engineering industry.

Means of Further Study

Företaget och innovationerna (*The Company and Innovation*), a book published by IVA, Stockholm, in 1967 presents a most valuable survey of the literature, describing a number of reference systems. Six different field studies provide an interesting though of course limited background.

In their book, *The Management of Innovation* (Tavistock Publications, London: 1961) with its background of British experiences, T. Burns and G. M. Stalker give a description of the new, innovation-positive form of co-operation known by them as 'organic' as contrasted with the conventional bureaucratic type. D. McGregor in his book *The Human Side of Enterprise* (McGraw Hill, New York; 1960 puts forward points on co-operation and social relations, launching his well-known 'Theory Y – Theory X', showing a slight resemblance to the ideas expressed by Burns and Stalker. The book by Rensis Likert, *New Patterns of Management* (McGraw Hill, New York; 1961) presents a good account of the problems of teamwork. The author even manages to measure the result of certain forms of co-operation.

The enterprise as a guided system is the object of an exhaustive quantitative description by J. W. Forrester in *Industrial Dynamics* (J. Wiley & Sons, New York; 1961). The book, which is rather exacting, has a technical bearing and offers a valuable background for a deeper understanding of the dynamics of guidance.

A concise and valuable summary of many of the prerequisites of successful technical research may be obtained from a paper by R. Cheradame, 'Les conditions du succès de la recherche technique' (*Chimie Industrie – Génie Chimique*, Vol. 96, No. 6, Dec. 1966). The outline is based on practical experiences gained at the French research institutions CERCHAR and ANRT.

Basic research, applied research, and development nowadays form a conventional theme. However, J. E. Goldman in his article, 'Basic research in industry' (*Int. Science & Technology*, No. 36, Dec. 1964) presents a most interesting account of these matters from Ford Motor Company, an enterprise running all three activities in parallel.

Systems Engineering may be considered a kind of work philosophy. A good introduction to the topic is given by H. A. Affel in 'System engineering' (*Int. Science & Technology*, No. 35, Nov. 1964). The outstanding book by A. D. Hall, *A Methodology of Systems Engineering* (D. van Nostrand Inc., New York; 1962) still remains unsurpassed and should be studied especially by those who are not on the outlook for specialized technical methods as such.

The concept, 'commercial life' has become commonplace. The first full account of the concept should probably be attributed to Stanford Research Institute ('Proceedings of the Long Range Planning Service', Client Conference, Feb. 7–9, 1962, a work covering more than 300 pages). The book clearly shows, among other things, that in the period 1900–60 the commercial life was gradually becoming shorter.

The linkage between market and technology has, naturally, been documented by various writers. So, E. J. Kelly in *Marketing, Strategy and Functions* (Prentice-Hall, Englewood-Cliffs, N. J.; 1965) has pointed to the drift of primary problems and orientation in the company. The first stage, manufacturing-financing was followed by a second stage, manufacturing-sales, which in turn was replaced by a third stage of marketing-customer. During recent years, systems integration and technology-marketing are coming to the fore.

In his article, 'Produktutvecklingens förnyelse' ('Renewal of the product development') (*Tekn. T.*, No. 46, 1966), O. Sundén exemplifies various methods of mastering R&D. The paper also gives examples of so-called feature profiles. J. Schnittger in his article, 'Teknisk innovation i koncernföretaget' ('Technical innovation in the group company') (*Tekn. T.*, No. 33, 1966) demonstrates how the reference system, machine – process – medium – environment may be utilized.

The importance of technical forecasting as an aid to companies will increase. The most thorough survey of this topic is to be found in a book by Erich Jantsch, *Technological Forecasting in Perspective* (OECD, Paris; 1967). The same topic has been treated by Professor J. Quinn in a series of articles in Harvard Business Review in the 1960's.

The book by Servan-Schreiber, *Le défi américain* (Editions Denoel, Paris; 1967), although it was conceived as a contribution to a debate, brings examples of many of the phenomena mentioned in the present paper. It is written in an entertaining style.

A comprehensive description of the 'Viggen' project can be found in the January 1968 issue of *Industria.* The article, written by Nils Kjellström, mainly deals with the administrative aspects of the project.

Swedish Government bill no. 68, 1968, 'concerning an increase in the Government support for the advancement of technical research and industrial development work'. 'Appendices to the Swedish parliamentary records', Series 1, No. 68, 1968, offers descriptions of the attitude of the Swedish state towards the role of the community in R&D and of the reactions shown by the staff organizations to proposals for a 'technical development board' and a 'state-owned development company'.

I. F. CLARKE

A Brief History of Technological Forecasting

The most useful beginning I can make to this paper is to emphasize the very recent origins of the kind of technological forecasting that interests this audience. The attempt to foresee – and to act upon – anticipated changes and developments in the next ten, twenty, or fifty years is a post-war phenomenon which has only begun to attract attention in Europe during the past ten years. Technological forecasting has appeared because it is badly needed: we live in a close-knit world society that is changing rapidly; we live at a time when technological innovations can have profound, far-reaching and at times almost catastrophic effects upon human society. One has only to think of the proliferation of nuclear weapons and the most recent developments in chemical and bacteriological warfare, or the rapid increase in world population, or the growth of great cities, or the great advantages to be gained by early investment in industrial products that can be manufactured to satisfy an anticipated demand at some date in the future.

It is no accident that the wealthiest country on this planet, the United States, is also the home of technological forecasting and has been the first to promote specialized institutions for this work in the Rand Corporation, the Hudson Institute, and the Long Range Planning Service at Stanford. Today in America there are some 600 large and middle-sized firms that do their own technological forecasting. According to Erich Jantsch, who prepared the OECD survey on technological forecasting, American companies spend at least ten million dollars per year in the business of forecasting future trends and developments, whereas all the European companies together spend little more than one million dollars. An indication of the scale of American activity in this field is the Xerox Corporation which has set itself a target of two thousand million dollars for 1975; and in order to obtain half this future turnover the corporation will rely on new ideas suggested by technological forecasting.

This search for the future patterns of development – the attempt to divine the shape of things to come – is a condition of modern society; and in the last analysis it derives from and depends upon an historical habit of mind – an unique Western habit of regarding the future as a distinct and discernible area of time. A television programme such as *Tomorrow's World*, the *think tanks* of the Hudson Institute, the work of Dr Robert Jungk's foundation in Vienna and of Bertrand de Jouvenal's Paris centre for the study of the future – these are all manifestations of that deliberate enquiry into the shape of tomorrow that is so decided a characteristic of modern civilization. These derive from a process of enquiry that has been going on – and gaining in accuracy – for no more than two hundred years. Most of the major developments in this field are very recent. Seminars of our type are an innovation of the nineteen-sixties – certainly in Europe. The stage before this was marked by a flood of books about the future that came out in the nineteen-fifties. Some of these were: Sir Charles Darwin, *The Next Million Years* (1952), Sir George Thomson, *The Foreseeable Future* (1955), the Russian forecast translated as *Life in the Twenty-first Century*, and the comparable American forecasts of *The Shape of Tomorrow*. Before these books there were only occasional attempts to describe the probable line of future developments. The most notable was the work done by the United States Natural Resources Committee which was established by President Hoover in 1932. The committee presented its findings in 1937 as a report on *Technological Trends and National Policy*. This was the first-ever major attempt to give an account of the anticipated inventions that would affect living and working conditions in the United States between 1940 and 1960. In the view of the committee the great importance of their work was the attempt to forecast future developments, even in an approximate manner. As the committee observed, this 'will help to prepare man for their arrival, and help him, while it is still easy and before the new interests created by the new inventions have crystallized, to avoid unnecessary social disorganization and draw the maximum benefit from his own achievements'.

This kind of thinking is familiar enough today. In the nineteen-thirties it was remarkable for what it set out to do. Up to that time the few predictions that had appeared were the work not of a group of experts but of individuals who gave their own often very amateur views of what they thought the world would be like in the future. The progress we have made in our capacity to measure the course of future developments can be measured by the difference between – for example – the close reasoning and the many sophisticated techniques that mark the articles in the special number of the *Science Journal* on 'Forecasting the Future' and the almost total failure of the first serious attempt at a prediction of the future to appear in the English language. This prediction was published under the title of *The Reign of George VI*, 1900–1925; the author was an anonymous Tory writer, and the date of publication was 1763. This first vision of the future returned a report of 'No Change': there would not be any significant changes in population; there would be no great cities, no steam power, no electricity, no ocean liners – in fact, there would be no scientific advance of any kind. The picture of the future seen from the angle of 1763 was no more than an ideal image of the eighteenth century. The world would go on as it had always done, and the only changes would be political. For example, the battles of the future would continue to be fought in the style of Marlborough and Frederick the Great by troops armed with pikes and muskets. At sea, naval engagements are fought out by frigates and old-style ships of the line. Kings are still the commanders-in-chief of their armies; and the best king of all – of course – is King George VI who leads his troops into battle, acts as his own general, and defeats both the Russians and the French. In consequence, the British troops occupy France, and the United Kingdom becomes the dominant power in a Europe that lives happily thereafter within a new *Pax Britannica*. Our guests from America will be interested to know that according to this forecast of 1763 the American colonies would still be part of the British Empire in the twentieth century. In that happy world of time-to-come, as the author remarked, the American colonists had never made the least attempt to shake off the authority of Great Britain'.

The almost total failure of predicton in the *Reign of George VI* was a natural consequence of its time; for it had appeared during the last stages of the pre-technological period, and unknown to the readers of 1763 the process of technological change and innovation had already begun. In the same year of 1763 a young instrument mechanic in the University of Glasgow had begun work on a defective model of the Newcomen steam engine. James Watt had obtained his post in Glasgow University on the recommendation of John Anderson, Professor of Natural Philosophy, who left all his possessions to found another university in Glasgow that would devote itself to the teaching of science. The instructions in his will were put into effect in 1796 with the foundation of Anderson's College – an institution which has grown steadily ever since and is now this University of Strathclyde. In their different ways both James Watt and John Anderson knew that the pursuit and application of science would affect the condition of human life on this planet. James Watt knew that, if he could improve the thermal efficiency of the Newcomen steam engine, he would tap a source of power greater than anything known before; and John Anderson knew that a systematic education in science would greatly benefit a nation.

Social and scientific considerations of this kind helped to generate the general expectation of change that has marked our world ever since. Europe learnt very quickly that technology – or invention as they called it then – meant innovation and that innovation gave the chance to change the state of the world. And here it is possible to date the beginnings of this new-found sense of expectation. By 1781, for example, in consequence of Watt's discovery of the separate condenser, the whole of Britain was reported to be 'steam-mill mad'; and by 1783, when news of the first balloon ascents spread through Europe, men began to realize that Western civilization was entering on a period of unprecedented change. At the beginning of 1783 there was nothing, and by the December of that year the idea of manned flight was everywhere taken for granted. The hot-air balloons of the Montgolfier brothers and the hydrogen balloon of Jacques Charles had given all Europe the first spectacular demonstration of the power of applied science. One of the observers of the famous ascent of 21st November was Benjamin Franklin, special representative in Paris of the new American republic, who sent regular reports filled with scientific information about the balloons to the President of the Royal Society in London. One of these reports contains a primitive example of technological conjecture; for Franklin saw an immediate military application for the new balloons. He wrote of the possibility of 'ten thousand men descending from the clouds (who might) in many places do an infinite deal of mischief before a force could be brought together to repel them'.

The balloons and the steam engines of the seventeen-eighties represent the point of origin for that habit of mind that seeks to divine the shape of things to come. From the time of Watt and the Montgolfier brothers there has been a succession of accounts and forecasts about the future state of mankind; and these have ranged from hard-headed, objective analyses – for instance, *Anticipations* by H. G. Wells – to that unique collection of satires and ideal states of the future that range from Wellsian visions of a vastly better world to the protests of Huxley's *Brave New World* and the ominous warnings of Orwell's *1984*. These reveal the twisted relationship of love-anxiety-hatred that exists between Western man and the consequences of his own inventiveness.

From the seventeen-eighties, therefore, the practice of extrapolation and prediction has been a fact of life in technological society. From the first it was assumed that the inventions of today would decide the pattern of life tomorrow. As soon as the first balloon ascents had been made, engravers throughout Europe began to produce their own visions of future developments: vast balloons capable of lifting thousands of passengers, balloons towed by eagles, and even balloon trips to the moon. Similarly, the example of the early steam engines inspired some engravers to imagine a London full of steam-driven private carriages, even steam flying machines. These crude essays in prediction were, of course, made to entertain, but they are important because

Plate 1. ‘Balloons towed by eagles . . .’

Plate 2. ‘A London full of steam-driven private carriages . . .’

I say Fellow, give my Buggy a charge of Coke, your Charcoal is so D_d dear.

THE PROGRESS OF STEAM.

UN QUARTIER EMBROUILLÉ.

Plate 3. 'Entertainments, but not idle fantasies . . .'

they demonstrate the new-found readiness to accept any possibility or innovation that had the support of scientific ideas. One of the most telling indications of the new habit of mind was the flood of extraordinary reports about the inhabitants of the moon that swept through Europe and America in 1836. This fascinating episode – the first of the science-based myths of our time – began in 1834 when the astronomer, Sir John Herschel, went out to the Cape in order to check the distribution of stars in the southern hemisphere. This investigation was of great interest to all who could read and in consequence Herschel's work was extensively reported. One enterprising journalist, an Englishman who had emigrated to the United States, saw a chance for himself in this interest, and he sold the *New York Sun* a series of articles which were based – so he claimed – on the original reports of Herschel's investigations that had appeared in the *Philosophical Journal* of Edinburgh. The articles were cleverly written fantasy, and they contained enough scientific detail to convince the ignorant. They described how Herschel had turned his telescope on the moon and had been amazed to see lunar cities and winged creatures flying about in them. Such was the general readiness to accept any innovation or discovery announced in the name of science that this Lunar Hoax took in many readers in Europe and America. It was immensely popular for a brief period: it was reprinted in many newspapers in Europe; it was translated into most European languages; it sold by the tens of thousands as a pamphlet; and it provided subjects for innumerable engravings of life on the moon.

Thirty years after the episode of the Lunar Hoax the movement towards the future made another advance when Jules Verne started on a long and very profitable career as a writer. This was an important stage, because for the first time in the history of fiction it was possible for a writer to make a fortune by using science as the material for his stories; and for the first time in human history the entirely imaginary exploits of scientists and engineers were read – not in France or Europe only, but all over the world. For this reason Verne is important, since more than any other writer in the last century he helped to encourage the general expectation of future change. Verne dealt in new and potent images, new enterprises, and new men. His major figures are – again for the first time in fiction – heroic technologists who conquer the last barriers: Captain Nemo penetrates the depths of ocean in his submarine; Robur conquers the air in his flying machine; and Professor Liedenbrock penetrates to the centre of the earth. These stories were entertainments, but they were not idle fantasies. The ideas behind them are the very stuff of extrapolation. As Verne wrote, 'Robur is the science of the future. Perhaps the science of tomorrow. Certainly the science that will come.'

From Verne it is a natural progression to H. G. Wells who was one of the first men to attempt a logical investigation of future developments in Western technological society. Up to this time, that is up to the beginning of the present century, most attempts at prediction had been presented in the form of fiction or as idealistic plans for a better world. This was because, in part, material advance had generally been seen as a steady succession of inventions – from the steam engine to electricity to the aeroplane; and it was not until the last two decades of the nineteenth century that men began to take a more global view of what they called 'progress'. Wells himself followed at first in the older tradition of examining future possibilities in the form of fiction. His *War of the Worlds*, for instance, contained some remarkable predictions of what might happen if technology gave the military everything they wanted in the way of fire power, protection, and mobility. Another story of his, *The World set Free*, gave an amazing prediction of atomic warfare; and that was written in 1913 at a time when few had heard of Lord Rutherford. In fact, in that story Wells gave the term 'atomic bomb' to the English language.

What is more relevant to our purpose, however, is a book published in 1902 in which Wells attempted the first major forecast of future scientific and social developments ever made in English, This was *Anticipations; or the reaction of mechanical and scientific progress upon human life and thought*. In the book Wells surveyed a number of possibilities in locomotion, the growth of cities, social organization, warfare, communications and so on. He forecast the end of horse-drawn transport and the coming of 'the motor truck for heavy traffic'. He expected that, since transportation would develop, there would be a corresponding increase in the size and complexity of great cities: he expected that large commuter groups would come into existence and that to serve them there would be a network of surburban centres with their own local services.

On the matter of warfare he is more interesting, since he was more far-sighted than the general staffs of the European armies. It is true that he missed the mark with his prediction that the submarine would be incapable of 'doing anything but suffocate its crew and founder at sea'. But he was very much on target when he predicted that modern war would bring mass state intervention in civilian life: 'the state will be organized as a whole to fight as a whole'. And again he was on the mark when he wrote that 'once the command of the air is obtained by one of the contending armies, the war must become a conflict between a seeing host and one that is blind'. The most spectacular forecast of all was the account of mechanized artillery and of 'a sort of land ironclad' that would be used to attack defensive positions. This idea of tank warfare was developed in a famous short story in the

Strand Magazine, in which Wells described how land ironclads won a devastating victory against an enemy drilled to fight the traditional kind of war expected by the European armies.

Nowadays we expect that the general staffs of armies will have a sound appreciation of the effect of new weapons on the conduct of war. Half a century ago it was only the rare civilians, like Wells, who foresaw the future pattern of warfare; and it is sad to recall that Wells was unfortunately proved to be right in many of his forecasts, whereas the general staffs of the European armies were quite wrong in their estimates. Here, then, in the early years of the twentieth century it is possible to examine some of the problems that affect the business of forecasting; for the civilians were right about the next war and the staff officers were wrong. Indeed the Commander-in-Chief of the British Expeditionary Force later admitted that things had turned out very differently: 'No previous experience, no conclusion I had been able to draw from the campaigns in which I had taken part, or from a close study of the new conditions in which the war of today is waged, had led me to anticipate a war of positions'.

The French generals were no better. Their estimate of future wars was the old-style expectation of swift moves, rapid concentrations, a major battle or two, and all over by Christmas. None of them anticipated the kind of siege war that came in 1915, and the measure of their failure can be seen, for example, in the fact that during the First World War the French army increased its heavy machine guns by a factor of five and that the total of light machine guns rose from zero at the beginning of the war to some 50,000 at the end. And yet there is a lesson for us in this, since the accurate predictions of future warfare was the work of men who were not military experts. Wells gave the perfectly logical answer to increased fire power in his account of 'land ironclads', and his contemporary, the banker and economist, Ivan Bloch, deduced from the fact of increased fire power and mobility that a future war between major European powers would be 'a great war of entrenchments'. In his book, translated into English in 1900 as *Modern Weapons and Modern Warfare*, he presented a statistical investigation of the capacity of new weapons and of the changes that had been taking place in warfare. His verdict was entirely accurate: 'The war, instead of being a hand-to-hand contest in which the combatants measure their physical and moral superiority, will become a kind of stalemate, in which neither army being able to get at the other, both armies will be maintained in opposition to each other, threatening each other, but never able to deliver a final and decisive attack'.

I close with this unique forecast of a future war, because Wells and Bloch take the theme back to where it started in the twentieth century, and because in their successful forecasting there are matters for the consideration of this symposium. Why was Bloch right and the general staffs all so seriously wrong? Can it be that the expert may often be the wrong man to attempt to discern the pattern of future developments? Wells, for instance, by education was a biologist, and by interest and study he had gained an understanding of the history and workings of society that helped him to discover part of the shape of things to come? But since genius of this kind is rare, would it not be possible to provide a substitute by means of a team of indivduals – all expert in special fields – who together could work out the complicated details of the forecast for tomorrow?

Reference

1 *Science Journal*, **3** (1967) 10.

Part 2

Techniques

GEORGE P. MANDANIS

The Future of the Delphi Technique

Historians tell us that the Romans foretold the future through inferences (apparently very powerful) drawn from flights of birds, thunderbolts, and other future-revealing omens. To this end, the Romans, quite determined, also engaged in the laborious enterprise of inspecting the vital organs of sacrificial animals. Apparently even this had some relevance to their planning needs.

The ancient Greeks, approaching the future with equal intensity, preferred to consult a deity. The utterances of those pioneering planners – no matter how vague – are said to have been highly influential; for example, in matters of morality and politics. Apparently they even inspired and directed the course of Greek colonial expansion.

Today, we seek to reduce uncertainty about the future by applying 'forecasting' techniques of increasing complexity and sophistication. These techniques normally assume operational essence when they are a part of a dynamic planning process. Today's claims about the quality of our forecasts are no more modest than those of our ancient predecessors. In fact, the more enthusiastic among contemporary forecasters attribute to them scientific elegance and rigour – a position which, understandably, has been often challenged principally by sceptics among their ranks. Nevertheless, such excessive claims have fallen far too often on responsive clients' ears, where, apparently, it matters most.

The fact that these aggressive professionals come under such diverse labels as planner, operations researcher, systems analyst, futurist, etc., explains why today's buyers of forecasts prefer to contract for the services of organizations, not of single individuals, in the management consulting field. (Presumably, the latter do not possess as high a degree of knowledge-integration). This client bias has been observed and understood well by our academic colleagues who, of late, posture themselves in the market place in the form of impressively labelled centres, and even 'institutes', of planning. That such proliferating university adjuncts frequently have a select membership of one, is to the enterprising academician's credit, who, exceeding his industrial adversary in the latter's own game, has managed to secure the best of both worlds.

Conventional Methods afflicted by the Data

Unfortunately, the rate of increase in the quality of forecasting has lagged behind corresponding increases in forecasting costs. If I were to venture on a single explanation for this disparity, I would say that forecasting methods are oriented, today, to the use of data alone, with a few exceptions. The problem derives from the basic, hard reality that the utility of data diminishes with the time-distance of the planning horizon. This is because reliable data pertain to the past, and perhaps to the present and the near-term future – not the long-range. Yet, it is the long-range which increasingly concerns organizations in rapidly evolving societies. Consequently, this proneness of data toward increasing unreliability – as we push out the planning horizon of interest – inevitably reflects manifestly on the quality of forecasts. It places firm upper bounds on the utility of such traditional, data-oriented methods of forecasting as multiple correlation analysis, fourier analysis, and econometric modelling.

The deficiencies of conventional forecasting methods, rooted in the quality of data on which they so vitally depend, have operational implications that are serious and pervasive. For example, in industrialized societies technical progress does not always produce social advancement; and the cause of this is, to a large extent, traceable to the numerous uncertainties that surround the origins, trends, and potential effects of technological change.

These uncertainties have been, far too often, difficult to reduce, absorb, or effectively plan against (if, indeed, attempts were made at all in these directions). As a result, the residual uncertainties, with which planners regretfully confront their clients, can affect severely the ability of the latter to plan and control technological change purposively, or to assess and anticipate reliably its social impact.

Deficiencies in measurements of technological change lead to public misconceptions; to invalid claims for compensation; and to creeping adverse effects as evidenced, for example, by the misfortunes of the urban complexes in the United States. Deficiencies in our ability to make credible forecasts, or to produce persuasive anticipations of technological change in the distant future, permit inherited and emerging technologies to swell dislocative effects, to dehumanize our environment and to multiply social costs. They limit the ability of society to marshal technological change toward beneficial ends. Deficiencies in evaluation of the factors that promote technological change, and of the social effects of such change, can be similarly detrimental. Indeed, our industrialized societies have been, and still are, too sparsely populated by men who are both motivated and intellectually equipped to understand the social interactions that ensue from technological change. These people are needed to take into account of such interactions when technology-development decisions are made.

Ironically, while society's control over technology is diminishing, its impact – in shaping social institutions, values and pursuits – is becoming ever more pervasive and serious. These limitations in understanding seem paradoxical when viewed in the light of society's well-tested ability to focus its resources toward the fulfilment of a wide variety of technology-based pursuits. Perhaps the paradox is explainable by the fact that the processes of technology-generation and application are of a lower order than the process of technology's interaction with society. Symptomatic of the existence of this process hierarchy is that commentary, by laymen and professionals alike, has been centred on the observable social consequences of technology rather than on the process that generates these consequences.

For instance, it is generally agreed that the most significant set of technological changes facing us has to do with future developments and applications of computers. However, I am not aware of any careful exploration to determine the validity of this premise. In this case, and as in almost any other, analytical treatments of technological change are to be found in its incorporation, as an unanalyzed whole into certain econometric models. In this treatment the process of technological change is an exogenous variable which has as its output the generation of, say, a 3 per cent annual increase in productivity. Here, the economist takes technological change as given and assumes it to be independently responsible for the generation of increased productivity. However, this black box – technological change – is seldom explored internally to understand better its dependencies on such environmental variables as values and organizational dynamics.

Worse, in the instance of capital investment analysis, we seldom ever venture including R&D projects in direct competition with so-called capital projects. In fact, formal analysis is seldom used effectively as an aid in the management of R&D investments. Yet, the product of R&D – namely, technology – is a higher form of capital than, say, a manufacturing plant. Accordingly, its selection merits comparatively more scrutiny than it receives.

Communications Barriers

By and large, in both industry and government, there still exists a polarization between the staff-planner (who tends to rely mainly on data and quantitative methods) and the manager-planner (who tends to rely mainly on 'intuition'). Consequently, the dialogue between the two is often very inefficient. Even though a common language has been slowly emerging, their perspectives, and the processes they employ for the explication, evaluation, and selection of alternatives, continue to differ fundamentally in most places. As a result, the barrier between the 'paper' world and the 'real' world remains standing – at least in an uncomfortably large number of public and private institutions.

But the barriers in planning work do not exist only between the staff professional and his supervisor or client. They exist, also, between the staff analysts themselves, who often experience acute agonies in attempts at persuading one another to accept their personal conclusions without being able to say why. Generally, the language of face-to-face conversation is too inefficient for this; and such conversation oftentimes degenerates into unproductive debate even with the best of intents. The means that would be suitable for inquiring effectively into someone else's hypotheses and models, to understand better the process that led him to his conclusions, are more often than not lacking.

Comparable language and perceptual barriers exist between substantive experts in different professional fields, and often among experts in the same field. They all persist partly for lack of suitable communication mechanisms. I believe that it is in relation to this pervasive communications problem – among professionals pitted together in supposedly interdisciplinary pools – that the full extent of potential usefulness of the Delphi technique can be properly assessed. In the event that some among you are not familiar with this technique, I will describe it briefly and then go on to conjecture about possible extensions to this technique in the course of the next decade.

The Original Delphi Experiment

In its restricted original form, the Delphi technique was intended to replace direct debate by a carefully designed programme of sequential interrogations. In it, sequentiality derived principally from the fact that the respondents do not always agree in the initial cycle and, since consensus among them was of central interest, the experimenters had to feed back, in statistical form, information on responses from one cycle to the next. They did this until either consensus and/or residual 'dissensus,' were achieved.

Those who have participated in a Delphi experiment will recall that, if their initial responses were extreme in relation to those of the other participants, they were asked to edify their colleagues as to why they were not in the mainstream, in the hope that they may persuade them to their view. However, it should be noted that while consensus is of central interest in Delphi, care is taken for it to be genuine and not to derive it artificially. Information exchange, through the means of questionnaires, is fully exploited to this end. Furthermore, the creators of the technique (Helmer and Dalkey) made sure that anonymity of responses was preserved throughout this exchange. Their intent was to eliminate the influence of coercion, unwillingness to abandon publicly expressed opinions, and the 'bandwagon' effect of majority opinion.

In sum, in its original form, the Delphi technique was a method employed for the systematic solicitation, self-review, and aggregation of experts' conjectures about matters that are uncertain. With respect to the future, the Delphi experimenters were not interested in producing a forecast in the traditional sense. Rather, their aim was to explore courses of action; and to explicate them to the extent that their feasibility can be at least grossly estimated, and their operational consequences at least generally understood.

In the first Delphi experiment, eighty-two individuals from all over the world were carefully selected to 'conjecture', together, about several aspects of the human environment fifty years hence. The foci of the questionnaire designed for this purpose were: scientific breakthroughs, population growth, automation, space progress, probability and prevention of war, and future weapon systems. Since this initial experiment, others have adopted and used the technique, for a variety of purposes, in the United States and elsewhere.

The originators of the Delphi technique did not intend to restrict its use to the exploration of the future. The improved understanding of past and present was also of interest. The misconception that the technique is to be used only on matters pertaining to the future may result, perhaps, from the fact that the report that first described the technique [1] has not been disseminated as widely as the report on its first serious application, in long-range forecasting [2].

To a large extent, Helmer's and Gordon's initial experiment was motivated by their critical awareness that as the horizon of planning concern is moved further and further into the future, uncertainties multiply, confidence in prediction is degraded and scientific theories and techniques of forecasting increasingly give way to intuitive judgment. In their view, since such intuitive forecasts *do* affect current planning decisions (or lack of same), anything that can be done to improve them will be of value.

Apparently, the *operational* importance Helmer and Gordon attached to their initial effort was not significant – as suggested by their selection of the word 'experiment' in reference to it. They viewed it merely as a beginning and they took great pains to evaluate it objectively. For example, they cited several areas of improvement that might, hopefully, derive from further research. The last one listed in their report is, in my view, of the greatest importance to the future usefulness of the Delphi technique. The authors recommended: 'development of techniques for the formulation of sequential questions that would probe more systematically into the underlying reasons for the respondents' opinions, in a deliberate effort to construct a theoretical foundation for the phenomena under inquiry'.

Promising Trends

Gordon and Helmer are already following their advice. For example, in recent research conducted with Harold Hayward at UCLA, Gordon has been concerned with the development of more rigorous methods than are currently available, to account for the causative connections between events [3]. In this effort they look back, in an attempt to explain how the Minuteman missile came about; and they look ahead, to explore transportation systems that might take care of the long-term needs of the US 'northeast corridor'. In both cases they took account of what they call 'enhancing' and 'inhibiting' events. In relating this more recent work to the initial experiment, Gordon and Hayward note that participants in a typical Delphi experiment might be asked to accept certain assumptions; for example, that world population will not exceed a certain value within the time span under consideration; or that all-out nuclear war will not occur. But they observe that what is generally missing in such an experiment is a consideration of the interacting effects of forecasted events. Indeed, without considering the interdependencies among forecasted events, a given list might well contain mutually exclusive events, or the chances of occurrence of certain events on the list might be enhanced in view of the occurrence or non-occurrence of others.

We might infer from this that the originators of the Delphi technique are already in the mood of putting future Delphi participants to the rigours of accounting for the reasoning that underlies opinions they initially express and subsequently modify. What I believe will be needed in this kind of experimental research is the development of techniques that would enhance materially the capability of Delphi participants to communicate with one another, in any manner they wish, whether with regard to opinions they hold, or to reasons underlying them. In particular, I have in mind a time in the future when men from dissimilar backgrounds, experience, and professional training will be able to communicate through a computer more effectively than in face-to-face conversation or through filling out stylized questionnaires and receiving back statistical abstractions on their prior responses. For some, the day when the computer becomes a communications channel in interdisciplinary research is only a few years away.

The notion that the computer will soon serve as a communication device among professionals engaged in creative team efforts was articulated first, to my knowledge, by Licklider and Taylor [4]. In their article, they visualize the computer as a flexible, dynamic medium that serves each participant as a store and processor of historical and synthesized data; of rigorously stated hypothesis as well as unarticulated hunches; and of tentative as well as well-tested models. In this futuristic research setting, each participant would be able to contribute to the computer's store and interrogate and experiment with the other's stored materials according to agreed upon rules as to research procedure and protection of the security and privacy of information.

Licklider and Taylor label this advent 'creative, interactive communication'. This form of multi-person, mutually reinforcing, communication would increase reliability in information exchange and would enable more explicit concern with detail (whether of process, or data), than is possible in the current Delphi experimental setting. Licklider and Taylor visualize, resulting from this, what they call 'co-operative modelling'. This type of intellectual activity may require, initially, the interactive involvement of the participants toward reconciliation of structural dissimilarities of their respective models. Alternatively, they may be fortunate enough to be able to start with an agreed upon structure. In this case, the co-operative task would be to cause convergence on the values of the model's parameters.

The General Direction of the Evolution of the Delphi Technique

If these visions are realized – and I believe that they will be early in the next decade – there will be profound changes in intellectual, exploratory activities involving communities of interest. Probably, long-range planning and technology forecasting will be the first to be vitally affected.

It is this possibility, of computer-based co-operative modelling and exploration, that suggests the next major step in the evolution of the Delphi technique. Now, with its limited technology, this technique can accommodate only opinion – albeit, hopefully, expert opinion – as its input. With sophisticated computer programming it will be able to utilize any form of information: from proven to exploratory models; from algorithmic to heuristic rules; from actual to synthetic data. Opinions will be traceable to their respective premises, and be amenable to detailed scrutiny. The output from such enriched Delphi experiments need not be only a consensus, or dissensus, on matters explored. Perhaps more importantly, it will be a learning experience which the participants could not acquire by any other means. For example, in business, it can take the form of a detailed understanding by corporate executives of the reasoning that underlies their respective staffs' recommendations; conversely, it can help the latter appreciate, more intimately, the biases and style of those they counsel.

I relate this prospective advancement in methodology to the Delphi technique (rather than to any other method of forecasting, planning, and environmental exploration) because this technique is inherently the most encompassing; also, because it is the lack of such a methodology that Helmer and Gordon recognized as a shortcoming that should be eventually removed. Even though currently only primitive in operation, the Delphi technique places no constraints with respect to methodology, e.g. on how the participants should go about forming and revising their opinions or underlying premises. Input-output tables, morphological analysis, decision-trees, modelling of any kind – and even concealed sophistry – are inherently admissible.

By acquiring the new communications technology that Licklider visualizes, the Delphi technique will come into its own. It will bring views that are derived objectively into direct and synergistic interaction with subjective beliefs. This new planning technology will put co-operative, disciplined, and detailed exploration of the future, through the use of 'open' stimulation, in the place of the relatively constraining and sterile questionnaires and feedbacks currently employed. The Delphi technique may thus provide a unifying structure, or an 'embedding vehicle', for planning work in which projections, conjectures, and anticipations derive only after careful scrutiny of premises and methods of analysis. Generalist experts would be given a genuine opportunity they now lack, for evolving the macro-structures of future environments; and specialist experts will be able, in regenerative interaction, to partake of truly interdisciplinary planning work.

It has been suggested that the Delphi technique should be applied in the future to the setting of goals on higher levels, e.g. social goals. To be sure, this would be desirable, and it should be done at different tiers of aggregation; but, hopefully, *not* without due regard to feasibility considerations. If they are ignored – and in Delphi's present form they probably would be – our reaching consensus (or knowing our differences) on goals would be almost an academic exercise. If feasibility considerations are included, the research effort would involve mainly the formulation and evaluation of strategies and the selection means for goal implementation. However, for this type of goal-setting we must wait for a long time – even with an early arrival of 'co-operative modelling'.

The Vital Need to Understand the Past

My preference with respect to the next major step in the exploratory use and development of the Delphi technique is to look back and understand the past better. This will be intrinsically useful, in that it will give us the opportunity to improve our understanding of history; and the transfer value of the experience gained would be invaluable to future-oriented research. I do not suggest that we look to the past exclusively. Rather, I view it as the most feasible and promising next step. Placing the emphasis on exploration of the past has particular relevance to those concerned with technological forecasting. This is because an improved understanding of technological change that has already occurred may prove to be an indispensable guide to projecting future changes.

For example, in looking to the past, we might ask: if the long-run effects of technology A had been taken into account would it have occurred at all; and, if so, would it have occurred in this form? Indeed, were these long-run effects considered when President Roosevelt was persuaded by Albert Einstein to invest two billion dollars for the development of the nuclear bomb? To be sure, this development served, although unexpectedly, the mediate goal of normalizing relationships among the larger post-war powers. But, in the light of the trend toward nuclear proliferation, was Roosevelt's decision beneficial over the long run? Did he not, inadvertently, discount the future to the point that the so-called victory in 1945 and post-war stability were traded for nuclear crises in the 1960's and 1970's? How do we answer such questions?

Let us look elsewhere in the technological history of the United States, and again with our attention on the related formal and informal decisions of the Federal Government:

(1) The decisions to subsidize the railroad industry through major land grants, to allow this industry substantial monopoly rights; and then to blink at its rather unorthodox financial practices. Undoubtedly, these decisions enhanced greatly the initial success and subsequent proliferation of the railroad industry.

(2) The decisions to extend a different kind of social subsidy to the coal and steel industries – a subsidy that was implicit in the basing point pricing systems – a practice which was continued until recently. But does this account for the principal forces that produced and sustained these industries?

(3) The decisions for a rather liberal granting of the right of eminent domain to private petroleum developers; also, the granting of very generous tax benefits. What model do we now possess that tells us of the extent to which these government decisions enhanced the viability of this industry?

(4) The government policy to extend an indirect subsidy to the automotive industry; primarily in the form of highway development grants; the subsidy of the aircraft industry, from its very inception, by virtue of the involvement of the US Armed Forces in aircraft development and procurement; and the direct subsidizing, until very recently, of commercial airlines. How consequential was government's role in these instances?

The list is large: it covers nuclear weapons, nuclear power plants, rockets, telecommunications, and computers – nearly all of the principal technology-based industries in the United States.

I isolated here only one domain of the variables of interest; those that pertain to the 'metasystem' of technological change. Of course, the total dimensionality of such inquiries into the past would be much larger, and the methodological problems to be encountered formidable. However, I submit that unless we invest some of our best analytic and creative talents toward an improved understanding of important matters of the past, the arts of forecasting and planning will continue to be only arts.

Summary

Planning has in the past drawn, primarily, on data and experience derived from the past, and on methods of analysis involving mainly trend correlation. The inevitable result has been at best, good extrapolations, and, an inevitable consequence of this, the 'perpetual present'. The utility of this form of planning is necessarily limited because, in many cases, it could lead to erroneous projections. More recently, professionals concerned with the advancement of the methods of planning have drawn heavily on computers – in the form of interactive aids to planners – in order to expand the scope of options considered; look at them in greater detail and evaluate them more precisely; and reduce the reaction time of responses to anticipated environmental events. Although a distinct improvement, this form of contingency planning is still terribly inadequate. A process of enumeration, no matter how inclusive one attempts to make it, simply cannot account for all that might happen. One's environment is, inherently, only partially subject to his direct control or influence.

Much more is needed. Basically, this entails a new kind of man-machine resource capable of augmenting historical data with synthetic data, extending experience gained from synthesized future environments of interest, and exploring on the basis of hunches as well as with the benefit of a rich panoply of rigorous analytic models. These technology-augmented, planning professionals would be able to understand, more reliably and with greater attention to detail, what the consequences of today's decisions will be and not be, and what their interactions will be and not be. They would have the means to avoid forecasting the future in stylized and abstract terms and make the products of planning more reliable and operational. They would be able to generate and explicate a much broader range of options that are potentially open to society, to estimate more precisely their relative feasibility, and to make more compelling the understanding of their potential 'benefits' and more clearly visible attendant risks.

It is through such an enriched and more rigorous understanding of the possibilities ahead of us that the advice of staff men, and the decisions of managers, can be expected to improve materially.

References

1 N. Dalkey and O. Helmer, 'An Experimental Application of the Delphi Method to the Use of Experts', *Management Science*, **9** (1963).

2 T. J. Gordon and Olaf Helmer, *Report on a Long-Range Forecasting Study* (The Rand Corporation, 1964).

3 T. J. Gordon and Harold Hayward, 'On Correlations Between Events' (Unpublished paper, 1968).

4 J. C. R. Licklider and Robert W. Taylor, 'The Computer as a Communication Device', *Science and Technology* (April, 1968).

OTO SULC

Forecasting the Interactions between Technical and Social Changes

The closer we approach the time when everything which is conceivable is feasible also, at least from a technical point of view, the more important become the normative elements in technological forecasting. In consequence, *axiology*, the science of the definition of values and of their change over time, should have an important influence upon those responsible for technological forecasting. In this paper we wish to describe a method which may be used to reveal the relationship between changes in social values and changes in technology. The hypothesis basic to the development of the method is that the optimal exploitation of human and natural resources depends on knowledge about the extent to which progress in technology is likely to be affected by changes in the future social environment, and vice versa. Such an understanding is basic to the choice whether and in which direction to adjust investment in technology to the existing social structure, or to attempt to modify the social environment better to accommodate changes in technology.

Present Approach to Social Technology

The pioneers of social technology are Helmer and Gordon, who have based their long-range forecasts of scientific, technological, and social changes on the use of Helmer's Delphi technique. As the important determinants of the society of the future, they chose six topics: scientific breakthroughs, population control, automation, space progress, war prevention, and weapons systems. In *Social Technology* [1], the opinions of six groups of experts were obtained and arranged in six independent lists of forecasted developments. Automation was the only topic where the interactions between the social environment and technology was described; in particular they discussed the relationship between legal and organizational methods and the unemployment entailed by automation.

Similarly, Kahn and Wiener have emphasized in a chapter of their recent book [2] headed 'Policy of Research and Social Change', the possibility that current technological and social forces may have extremely undesirable consequences. They were considering some of the ways in which technological policy decisions can have detrimental consequences even if the decisions were made for other and very good reasons. The need to take note of the now famous list of '100 technical innovations very likely to be made in the last third of the twentieth century' was emphasized by Gabor in his recent seminar *Technological Forecasting in a Social Frame* [3]. Gabor commented on various possible social repercussions of the technological innovations, and he listed a number of innovations, from different technological fields, which were intended to alleviate problems created by megalopolis and traffic congestion.

Methodology

Authors other than those already mentioned have contributed to the problem of classification and nomenclature in social technology. Our endeavour was to find a methodology suitable for the identification and the quantification of complex interrelationships and interactions understood to obtain between developments in social and technological fields. As a preliminary test of the approach we chose to analyze the interactions between trends in: (*a*) computer control of industrial and administrative processes; and (*b*) behaviour and structure of the organizational environment in which they may come to be operated.

In order to write initial lists of potential developments both in computer techniques and in organizational and social behaviour, the forecasting literature was scanned and a series of interviews was held with experts in the social and computer sciences. Secondly, the experts' views were evaluated using the Delphi technique, following the procedure described in Helmer and Gordon's Rand Corporation report [4]. Our own contribution to this technique is based on the relevant scheme given as Table 1 and three-dimensional matrix given as Table 2. With their aid, it is possible to depict quantitative relationships and interactions of forecasts in both fields over a fifteen-year period.

Thus the first task was to forecast potential developments in computer control, and to present the results as a Delphi exercise to a panel of eight computer scientists drawn from the Ministry of Technology, Research Institutes, and computer manufacturers. The Delphi method can obtain forecasts which reflect the consensus of a panel, for each member has the opportunity to consider the views of all his remote colleagues in a systematic manner. The panel of experts from industrial management, which was composed of forty-five members of the managerial and senior executive courses of the Manchester Business School, was asked to express its opinion on the likely effectiveness and generality of implementation of various organizational measures intended to help management in adapting to computerization. The measures were drawn from the literature and from earlier discussions

TABLE 1 Inter-relationships between changes in management adaptability and impacts of development in computer control

Measures improving the management adaptability to future trends in computer control	*Impacts of future trends in computer control engendering the resistance of management*				
	1. Demands for qualification and personal dispositions	*2. Redundancy of middle managers*	*3. Loss of responsibility and decision autonomy*	*4. Impersonality of procedures and communication*	*Total relevance*
1. Training of operational management staff in computer application, throughout all aspects of the firm's business likely to be affected by computer technology starting from junior graduate posts.	1	4	1	2	8
2. Acquiring operational management staff so trained in computer application from outside the company, particularly from Research Institutes.	2	0	0	0	2
3. Development and application of methods for selecting computer system managers and scientists with appropriate intelligence and personal characteristics.	4	0	2	2	8
4. Inter-company agreements on the transfer of displaced middle managers.	0	3	0	0	3
5. Inter-departmental transfer of displaced middle managers to newly created jobs within a company.	2	3	0	0	5
6. Inter-departmental training and experience for middle managers before introduction of computer.	3	0	1	2	6
7. Changing the social prestige image from membership of the decision hierarchy to that of a technically-expert elite.	3	1	2	0	6
8. Greater adaptability of computer programmes to conform to the varying qualifications of operators and programme users (for example, by more flexible sub-programmes, and more natural computer 'language').	1	0	1	1	3
9. Designing the technology of computer maintenance and service with the aim of employing a greater number of semi-skilled operatives rather than a few highly skilled ones.	3	0	0	3	6
10. Changing the social prestige image of managers in the environment as a whole, from decision and control functions to co-ordinating functions.	0	0	3	1	4
11. Facilitating and simplifying flow of information between: (a) highly specialized groups or departments (horizontal flow of information)	1	0	1	4	6
(b) between staff and line functions such as systems design, computer personnel and operational management (for example by the introduction of suitably qualified liaison officers).	2	0	0	3	5
Total relevance	22	11	11	18	

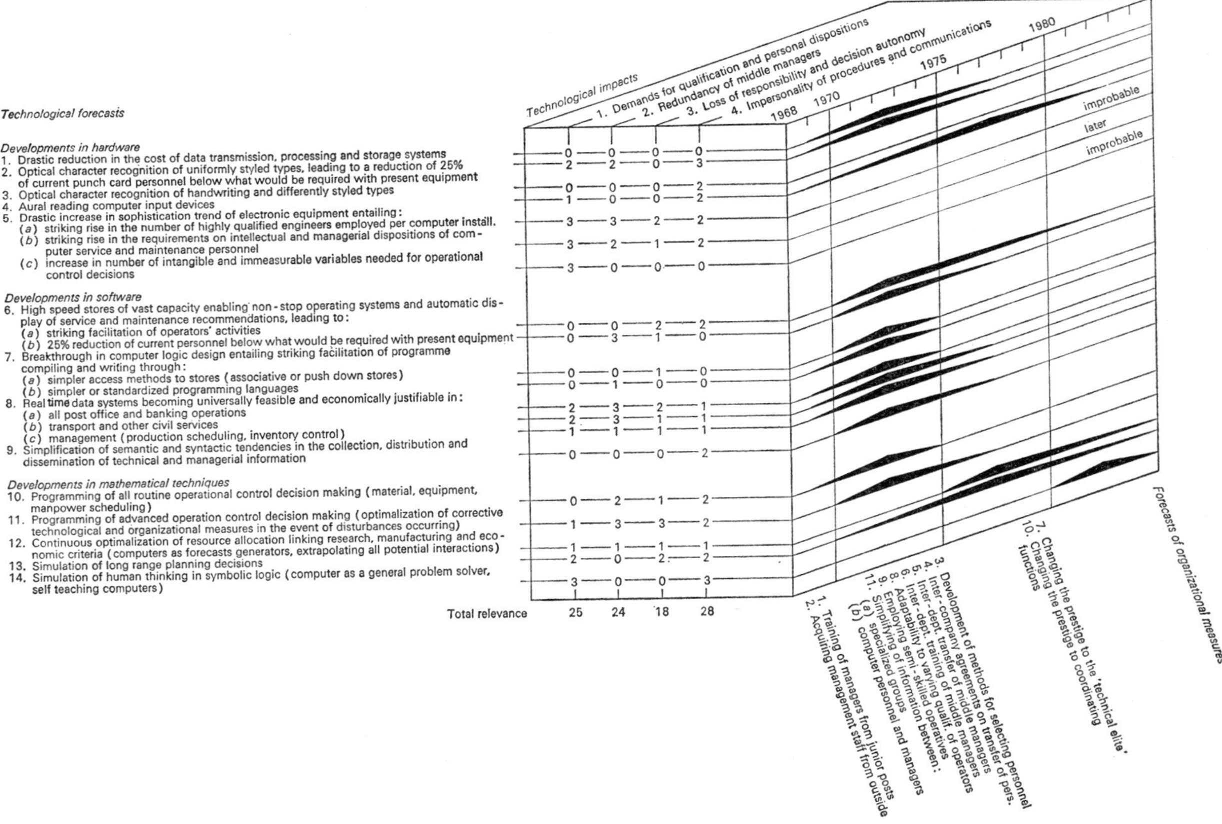

Technological forecasts	1. Demands for qualification and personal dispositions	2. Redundancy of middle managers	3. Loss of responsibility and decision autonomy	4. Impersonality of procedures and communications
Developments in hardware				
1. Drastic reduction in the cost of data transmission, processing and storage systems	0	0	0	0
2. Optical character recognition of uniformly styled types, leading to a reduction of 25% of current punch card personnel below what would be required with present equipment	2	2	0	3
3. Optical character recognition of handwriting and differently styled types	0	0	0	2
4. Aural reading computer input devices	1	0	0	2
5. Drastic increase in sophistication trend of electronic equipment entailing: (*a*) striking rise in the number of highly qualified engineers employed per computer install.	3	3	2	2
(*b*) striking rise in the requirements on intellectual and managerial dispositions of computer service and maintenance personnel	3	2	1	2
(*c*) increase in number of intangible and immeasurable variables needed for operational control decisions	3	0	0	0
Developments in software				
6. High speed stores of vast capacity enabling non-stop operating systems and automatic display of service and maintenance recommendations, leading to: (*a*) striking facilitation of operators' activities	0	0	2	2
(*b*) 25% reduction of current personnel below what would be required with present equipment	0	3	1	0
7. Breakthrough in computer logic design entailing striking facilitation of programme compiling and writing through: (*a*) simpler access methods to stores (associative or push down stores)	0	0	1	0
(*b*) simpler or standardized programming languages	0	1	0	0
8. Real time data systems becoming universally feasible and economically justifiable in: (*a*) all post office and banking operations	2	3	2	1
(*b*) transport and other civil services	2	3	1	1
(*c*) management (production scheduling, inventory control)	1	1	1	1
9. Simplification of semantic and syntactic tendencies in the collection, distribution and dissemination of technical and managerial information	0	0	0	2
Developments in mathematical techniques				
10. Programming of all routine operational control decision making (material, equipment, manpower scheduling)	0	2	1	2
11. Programming of advanced operation control decision making (optimalization of corrective technological and organizational measures in the event of disturbances occurring)	1	3	3	2
12. Continuous optimalization of resource allocation linking research, manufacturing and economic criteria (computers as forecasts generators, extrapolating all potential interactions)	1	1	1	1
13. Simulation of long range planning decisions	2	0	2	2
14. Simulation of human thinking in symbolic logic (computer as a general problem solver, self teaching computers)	3	0	0	3
Total relevance	25	24	18	28

TABLE 2 Three-dimensional matrix of interrelationships between computer control tendencies and management adaptability

with experts. In the introduction to the questionnaire put to the panel, the managers were informed in general terms about the potential developments in computer control, as forecast by the computer experts. The change in the content of management functions likely to impede the acceptance of the various innovations had already fallen within the panel's experience, at least to some extent, and did not need further amplification. The relevance numbers express the median opinion of all experts involved and therefore represent the 'average' interactions, which can be expected in British industrial or civil service conditions. The knowledge of the average effectiveness of interactions between variables is considered as a heuristic element of the method. The forecasts of a majority stimulate in this way the deeper thinking over potentialities in the concrete environment of a particular company.

The Results

In Table 1 managerial opinion is presented as to the relevance of counter measures intended to mitigate the negative effects of predictions in computer developments. The measures listed in rows represent diverse means for influencing the behaviour of employees who will be affected by the introduction of changes in computer technology. The relevance scheme presented as Table 1 is to be read as follows:

(1) *Relationships between organizational measures and the effect of future developments*

Reading down the Table, for example, shows that although middle management will be made redundant by the introduction of computer control techniques, training from junior levels, leading to flexibility and ensuring easier redeployment, is the most effective way of mitigating the effect. On the other hand, reading across the Table, training from junior posts is most relevant to mitigating redundancy rather than any other 'negative' effect. Again, the relevance indices in the Table show that measures 4 and 5 are of little importance to initial training in mitigating impact 2.

Table 1 is of a very general character. To use the method to understand a specific instance would clearly involve the inclusion of factors which describe the elements of the instance in very much greater detail. For example, the displacement of middle management in the chemical process industry would more clearly involve those responsible for routine process control rather than functions connected with the assignment and supervision of personnel. Acknowledgement of the latter kind will be displaced only to the extent that the numbers of personnel requiring supervision is diminished, as can be expected in technological industries.

(2) *Total relevance*

Total relevance indices express the ranking and overall importance of measures and impacts in both the columns and the rows. The results show that in preparing for the introduction of computer control (above all, potential organizational changes) considerable attention should be given to measures 1 and 3, which are highly related to the majority of technological requirements. Similarly, attention should be given to the resistance of managers engendered by the threat of redundancy or loss of responsibility. The total relevance indices of these impacts show that their negative effect was only to a lesser degree mitigated by counter measures which were available. The addition of relevance figures implies the equal weight of variables, which need not be the case in particular circumstances.

(3) *Substitutability of measures*

The effort needed for the identification and application of suitable measures can be estimated and weighted according to the values of relevance indices. Measures with equal individual or total relevance indices can be regarded as having the same effect or importance. This knowledge could be useful if a company's resources are limited and it is desirable to obtain a proper balance of effort. Again, these suggestions indicate only a general approach to the problem. In practice a company's specialists must identify the more detailed mechanism and anticipated interactions, defining a more precise and sensitive scale of indices to the particular variable recognized.

(4) *The relevance scheme may be viewed and emphasized in many other ways* [5]:

For example, in ranking the company's long-range objectives; for the recognition of weak spots in the present organization; as a basis for feedback from industrial management to computer producers, and so on.

The three-dimensional matrix displayed in Table 2 may be used to describe interrelationships between three variables, all of them subject to forecasting. Technological forecasts extending to the year 1985 have been derived from the questionnaire submitted to the experts on computer technology. For greater clarity, the matrix cube has been divided into particular forecasting periods. It expresses the following main relationships:

(1) *The coincidence in the year of implementation.* The ideal case is when the widespread diffusion of technological principle and the corresponding organizational measure occur at the same time. The data of the technological forecasts can be read from horizontal lines on the side of the cube. The peak of each bar represents the median opinion of experts, the whole interval contains middle 50 per cent of

forecasted data. The widespread application of organizational measures was assigned to five-year periods. Thus the absence of organizational measures in the period 1980–5 indicates that the computer innovations, coming into operation during this period, may be impeded by the unprepared organizational environment. For the full phrasing of the measures see Table 1.

(2) *The relationships* between technological developments and their impacts are expressed by the relevance scheme in the frontal side of the cube. The relevance numbers do not represent an average as in Table 1. They were estimated only with respect to conditions in chemical process technologies and were not drawn from the respondents' panel but represent the opinion of an individual. The remaining mechanism of the reading is similar to the Table 1.

(3) *The analytic approach.* The matrix can be disintegrated across each of the planes and the interrelationships between individual variables identified. After this isolation the Delphi method can again be employed, involving panels of experts in the company's problems of management, technology and organizational behaviour.

(4) *The synthetic approach* lies in simulating the dynamism, interactions and external interventions to all future tendencies involved. Again there are numerous explanations and ways of reading this model and it is at the discretion of the user how he will adapt the suggested methodology to his specific environment.

Conclusion

In judging the described approach to forecasting, based on intuitive and heuristic thinking, we should like to emphasize our intention to build a framework of references to the interactions between technological changes and changes in social environment which might occur. Which of them will occur in reality depends on the availability of capital for development or investments and in a broader sense on the strategy of each company.

The knowledge of the average interactions and probable date of technological diffusion has a considerable importance for the assessment of company's opportunities in future competition. The suggested model should serve as a starting point for drawing up forecasts and integrating them into long range plans at company or government decision levels. The overall purpose of the method is to draw attention of research, industrial, and civil service managers to the subject of social technology with regard to technological forecasting.

Notes

In addition to the topic of computer control and management adaptability, the method has been used to examine [6]: (1) Interrelationships between changes in workers' adaptability and changes in technology. (2) Interrelationships between technological and social developments influencing urban transport. (3) Interrelationships between changes in communication and changes in human attitudes and needs. (4) Interrelationships between developments in shift work and social environment.

References

1 O. Helmer, *Social Technology* (New York, London, Basic Books, 1966).
2 H. Kahn and A. J. Wiener, *The Year 2000* (New York, London, Macmillan, 1967).
3 D. Gabor, 'Technological Forecasting in a Social Frame', *Seminar of Science Foundation* (London, 14 and 28 February 1968).
4 T. J. Gordon *et al.*, *Report on a Long Range Forecasting Study* (Santa Monica, California, The Rand Corporation, 1964).
5 Besides numerous methodological references on relevance schemes in forecasting literature the related topic was described in: Mason Haire, 'Human Resources for Enterprise Management', *Technology Review*, (M.I.T., November, 1967).
6 O. Sulc, 'A Study in Social Technology', *Report of Manchester Business School* (July 1968).

C. A. GOODWIN

Evolutionary Forecasting for Designers

It could be said that anyone who has the job of making any kind of plan is a designer, in that he has designs on the future. We can even think of prediction as design in the case of pure curiosity, for in this case the would-be seer is designing a model of the future. In this paper I want to discuss prediction from the designer's viewpoint, and so I shall start with a brief description of designing.

If we are to say that designing is a process of modelling the future, we must distinguish between two different types of model. One type is the model of what the designer is trying to bring to fruition and is executed in great detail, sufficient for production. This modelling is concerned with that part of the future over which the designer has direct, even if conditional, control. The conditions that may modify this control are those imposed by the designer's client, who may decide not to follow the model set up by the designer, or who may require modifications. The degree to which the client gives this control of the future to his designer is dependent on the second type of model, which is the one the designer has of how the rest of the world is going to develop. This second model is a model of a situation over which the designer has no effective control, but which is essential as the context within which the design model must be judged.

We have thus two models of the future which are essential for effective design, a design model and a contextual model. The design model is a detailed model, which must be fully compatible with the production techniques available, and which is under the designer's control in so far as he retains the confidence of his client. Compatible here means compatible with the production facilities that are available, or can be brought into being within the production time-scale planned. We could, in fact, discuss three models, a design model, a production model, and a market model, but for the sake of this discussion I am going to assume that the production model is known with a high degree of certainty, in that the productive capacity available can be adjusted readily to any desired state.

The contextual model is highly selected from a vast range of largely irrelevant data. Most of our models of the future are simple and highly structured, but we know that the future will be fully as complex and uncertain as the present. This *simplicity of futures* is a major bias towards the status quo, in that any proposal for change presents a model which is infinitely less detailed, and hence less useful in resolving doubts, than is our knowledge, however inadequate, of the existing world. Any attempt to develop a more detailed contextual model thus has a major disadvantage in that there is great scope for confusion, disagreement and suspicion in deciding which aspects of the future world should be considered. At the same time this context has the advantage that it is likely to be more general than the design model, and offers more scope for cross checking with predictions made independently in other fields.

How is the designer to construct his models of the future? In the past the situation was much simpler, in that the contextual model changed so slowly that it could be regarded as fixed. The designer could keep abreast of changes in his field, and concentrate his own effort on changing a single part of it, the bit he himself designed. However, this contextual stability is now gone, presumably for ever, and so the designer, like the manager or the politician, must find some better way to model the future. Numerous techniques are open to him, all of which have their merits and weaknesses. I propose to describe yet another, in the hope that it may prove useful to designers who are not content with their own intuitive judgment, nor with expert opinion, nor with scenario writers, nor chicken entrails, nor any of the other devices described in the literature. This new technique may be described as an evolutionary process, based on the population of all previous artifacts, and on the interaction between these and the world within which they were manufactured, sold and used.

Evolutionary Forecasting

When predicting the future it is necessary to make judgments about how the present will change, and these judgments will be based on the experience of the person whose judgment is sought. Yet experience consists only of the knowledge that this person has gained from the past, and the question arises, if we are to utilize knowledge of the past to help make possible useful predictions, can we do this only through those sections of the past that have been woven into the memory of identifiable and available experts? I believe that this is not the case, and that it is possible to use our knowledge of things past to identify the kinds of design features that affect the success of future designs, i.e. we can enhance the (explicit) experience of men with the (implicit) experience that men have lavished on objects made and used in the past.

The procedure may be described thus:

(1) Identify the object which is to be designed.

(2) Collect specimens of similar objects in the past, or if this is not

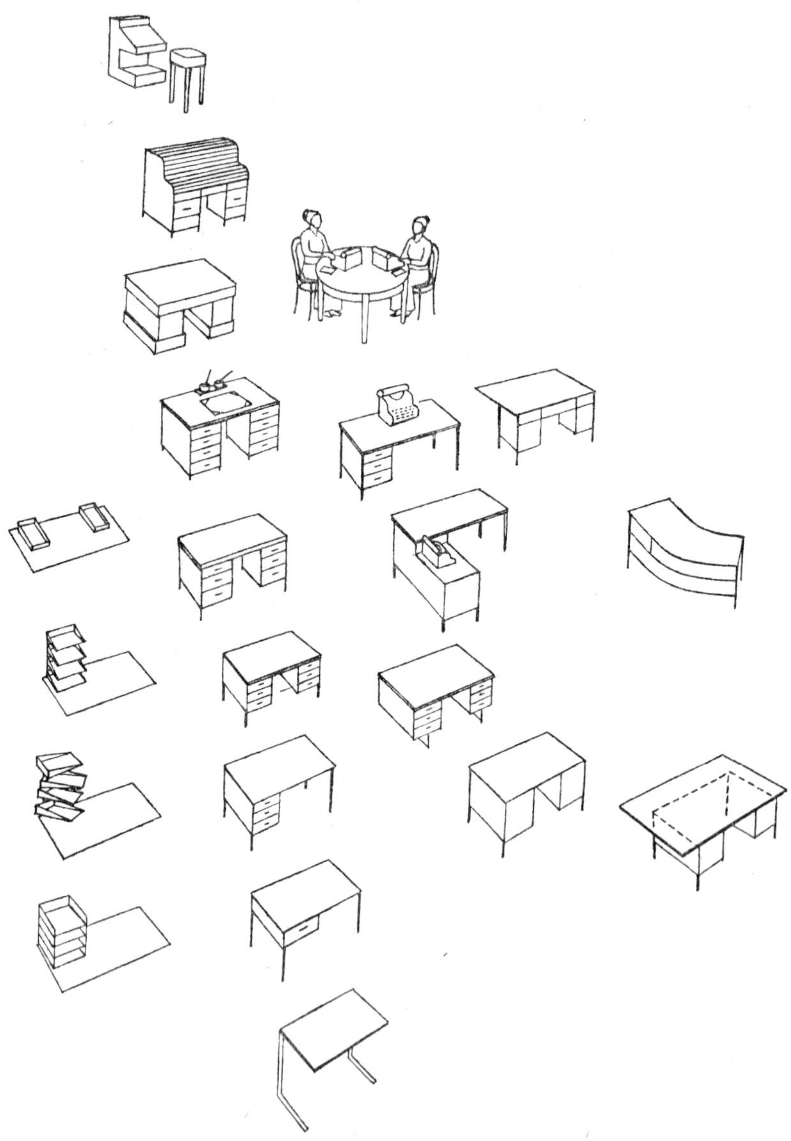

Figure 1.

feasible, at least drawings, descriptions, models, etc. Ideally this collection will cover the entire population of relevant artifacts; in practice it will only be a sample (see Figure 1).

(3) Collect also information on the performance of these specimens in the past.

(4) Note the interrelationship of the past population with its environment, and identify likely successful features for future designs.

Now it may be objected that having removed individual bias by examining the population of artifacts, I am now reintroducing this perilous commodity, human judgment, when I say 'identify likely successful features'. It may also be objected that human judgment is required in collecting the specimens. Before describing how we tried to get round these difficulties in practice, I would like to discuss these two objections.

The first and, in my opinion, the major difficulty is that of extracting clues to the future from knowledge of the population of existing specimens. I think we must admit that all forecasting techniques do involve human judgment, and in considering the merits of different methods of utilizing this we must remember what the purpose of technological forecasting is. Two simple explanations are: (1) to be right; (2) to inspire sufficient confidence to enable people to act.

The first of these is intriguing but useless, in that it will take far too long to validate the long-range techniques that are most useful. The second alternative, that of inspiring confidence, can be achieved by a plausible lie, and I am therefore led to believe that the real function of technological forecasting is to enable people to take in some of the mass of information that they appreciate is relevant but cannot directly comprehend – i.e. to provide a language against which, and through which, the existing range of options can be better understood. A particular technological forecast is thus a beginning and not an end – it may be an end in itself for the man who is asked to do it, but it must also be the beginning of the discussion, 'What is to be done in the light of this forecast?'

Viewed in this way, as an initiating statement in a field of uncertainty, evolutionary forecasting has the virtue that human judgment is applied at the end, where it can be appreciated for what it is, before it is encapsulated in a set of figures to be taken on trust, and which if rejected leaves the designer back at square one. The way in which evolutionary forecasting lends itself to exploitation by the designer may be better understood when I have discussed what happened in the case of desks.

The other objection, that human bias may be reintroduced in the selection of a sample of specimens, is less serious in practice than it is theoretically, for our primary concern is with the successful designs, which are unlikely to be overlooked. Rare market freaks may have a high information value, but cannot be recommended as a basis for future design.

An opportunity to apply evolutionary forecasting to the modelling activities of both designer and management was supplied by S. Hille & Co. Ltd, of Watford. A confidential report (Jones *et al.*, 1968) contained a section in which we try to envisage the desk of 1975–80, and various forecasting techniques, such as the Delphi method and scenario writing, were considered. Along with these we tried evolutionary forecasting.

The data was presented in graphic form with a few drawings to illustrate each evolutionary change. Since this is a historical description of what we did, I have left the drawings in their original form.

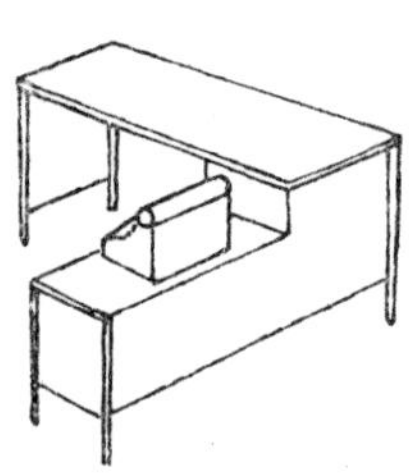

Note here the change in the desk top, from convex to concave. Another way of describing this is as an increase in the numbers of points of contact between desk and user.

Chair Mobility

Notice here how the mobility of the chair has increased. This allows the user to adjust his relationship to the desk very rapidly and easily. Because mobility has been introduced to the chair it has not as yet been necessary to make desks more mobile.

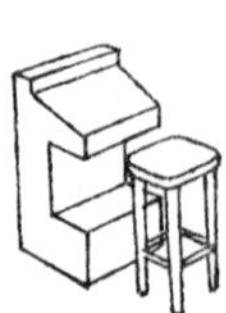
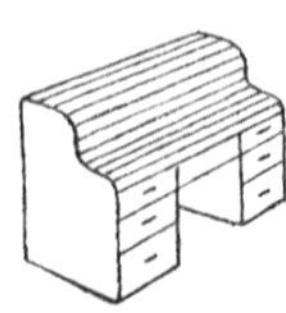

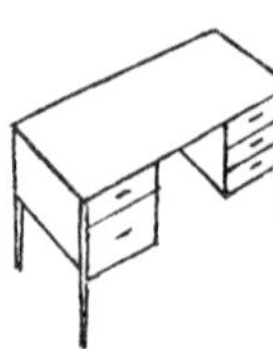

Desk Tops

Note here the reduction of desk top storage and flattening of the desk. The amount of storage beneath the desk top has also been reduced, thus:

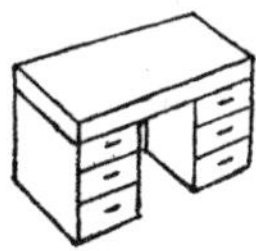

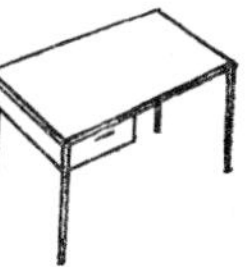

However, there has been an increase in the storage capacity at the side or rear of the desk.

Coupled with the reduction of storage within the desk there has been a more than compensating growth in the amount of 'off-desk' storage in office:

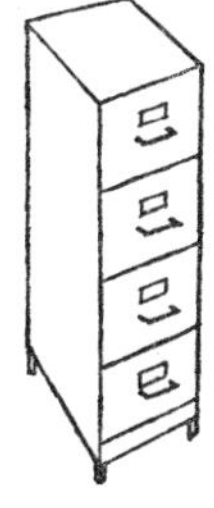
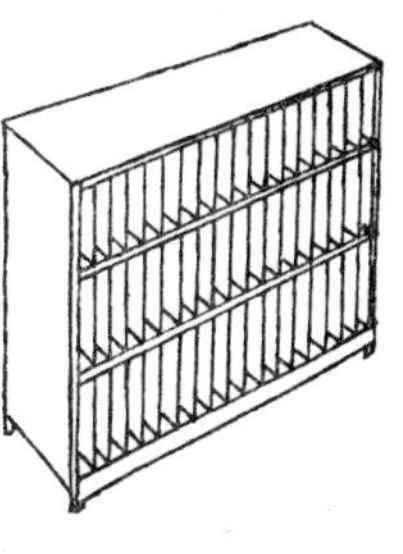

(1) (2) (3) (4)

Apart from the increase in this storage capacity, there has been a change in the type of access to it that is provided. Thus in 3, above, a file is obtained by moving it vertically up out of the drawer of the filing cabinet, while in 4 the access is horizontal.

A similar change in access from vertical to horizontal is evident in telephone design, thus:

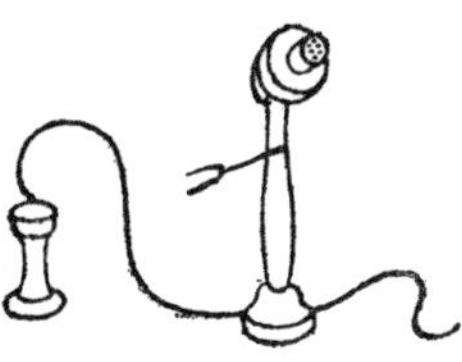

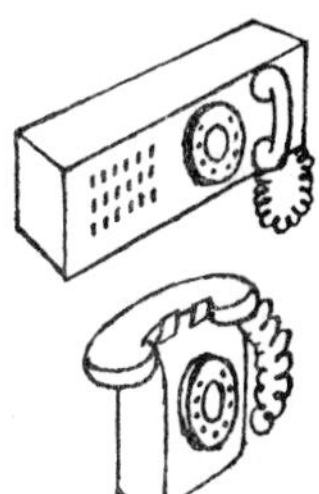

At each stage the user can adopt a more upright posture.

Another trend in telephone design has been the reduction in the number of hands needed to operate the phone, thus:

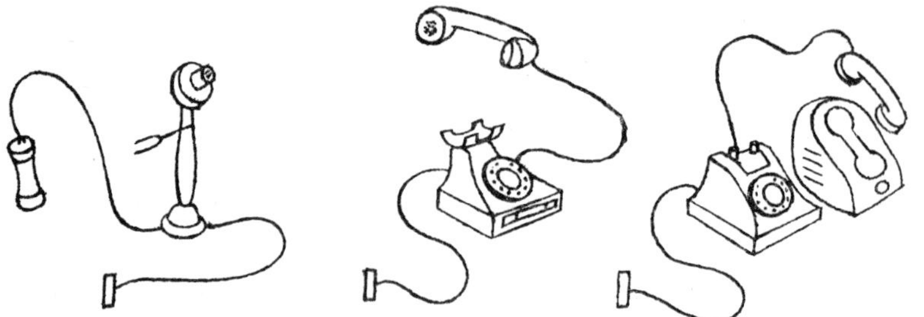

Another feature of many office machines is the way manual versions have been converted to powered models.

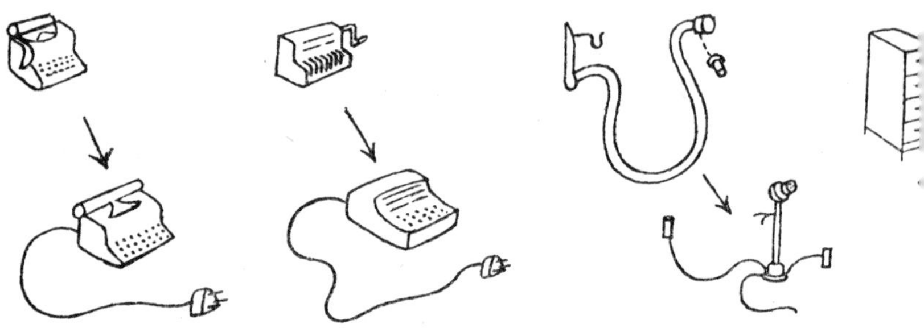

Even though the advantage might be thought to be minimal, the process of electrification has been very clear, and it is quite possible that file access will become powered, instead of remaining a purely human task.

Another trend with machines has been towards decreasing size, thus:

Conclusions from Desk Evolution

The principal changes in the desk have been: a reduction in built-in storage; flattening of the desk top; increased contact between desk and user, by

(*a*) shaping the desk top,

(*b*) making the chair more mobile.

Access both to paper stores and machines has tended to change from vertical access to horizontal access. Both the amount of storage and the number of machines have increased, and efforts have been made to reduce the degree to which a desk user has to adapt himself to the machine. However, no real progress has yet been made towards reducing the work involved in gaining access to paperwork. Both paper stores and machines have tended to move from the frontal position, on the desk, to the side of the user.

This then was the forecast as it was made. The small number of drawings in each example were selected from much larger sets of drawings (Figure 1) which were not contained in the report, but which in some cases showed as many as eight stages of development. However, since the report was intended for people who were already very familiar with the history of desks, the sketches were intended as little more than clues, to remind the reader of well-known aspects of desk design.

I should point out that our conclusions were somewhat tentative. When we started we were anxious not to ignore the efforts of previous desk designers, and we hoped that by attending to previous designs we would be able to form some idea of (*a*) what types of changes in desk design had had a significant effect on sales in the past, (*b*) what range of provision for different activities had been established, and (*c*) what overall trends (or stability) were discernible.

However, although we could see that it would be foolish to ignore the past, it was not immediately obvious how we could use it. The drawings you have just seen are illustrations of the changes that we eventually decided would be useful in the construction of either the design model, or the contextual model, or both.

Because we had not known at the outset just how evolutionary forecasting was going to work, we did not devote much of our available effort to it, but instead hedged our bets by looking at other forecasting and analytical techniques, such as the Delphi method and scenario writing. In one way the successfulness of our report depends on the extent to which it is acted upon, but in so far as evolutionary forecasting itself is concerned we can say that it appears to have the following advantages: (i) speed; (ii) economy; (iii) delegability; (iv) some immunity from the blinkers of current practice.

This last is, of course, the crux of the problem, for it could be that in selecting the significant features of past designs we are in danger of reintroducing the bias of conventional wisdom. However, this method involves data based on designs which have proved successful in their day, and thus can be hoped to have avoided the snags that can threaten an innovation based on one man's view of the problem. Also, by confining our attention to identifiable and discrete features of existing objects we hope to discover data with a validity that will survive even major dislocations in style or technology, for one is forced to seek descriptions of design features that will be applicable to all past designs, and will thus possess a powerful generality.

Reference

J. C. Jones, C. A. Goodwin and B. L. Yaffe, 'Office Desks for the 1970's,' *Confidential report* to S. Hille & Co. Ltd, Watford.

JOHN HAWGOOD

Social Benefit Analysis by Inverse Linear Programming

It is notoriously difficult to quantify concepts such as value, profit, and productivity in fields such as education, health, and welfare economics where the 'product' is not measured directly in financial terms. This paper describes a method for measuring benefit in such fields by inverting the process of linear programming so that known policies are used to calculate the implicit objective functions lying behind the actual decisions taken, which are assumed initially to have been optimal.

The paper is divided into three main sections: first, an introduction to the method, covering the derivation of benefit limits by inverse and iterative programming and of objective functions by ensemble inversion; second, a more detailed examination of the method as applied to the study of university libraries, for which it was first designed; third, an outline discussion of possible applications in other fields and of some mathematical points.

Introduction

The philosophy of this approach is based on the postulate that, taken together, the human mind and the democratic process form a reliable basis for the computing of social benefit functions; that decisions taken by administrators would be 'correct' if there were perfect channels of communication between the electorate, the government, the administration, and the administered. It can confidently be asserted that planners and administrators in most social welfare fields would have a better-defined job if the benefits of the various alternative activities between which they have to choose were explicitly quantified: if they were, techniques such as linear and dynamic programming could be applied to mathematical models of the administrative problems, aiding the decision-makers by presenting to them the optimum solutions of the model problems. Such solutions to model problems would guide the administrator towards that solution of the real-life problem which would maximize net benefits rather than that which would minimize costs, which is the only solution that can be found by calculation in the absence of an explicitly quantified benefit function. The key to the inverse programming method is the undoubted fact that decisions do get made with benefit-maximization rather than cost-minimization as the objective, even though explicit quantification of benefit is not available. Put in a nutshell, the method is to present to a decision-maker information about the benefit-function apparently implicit in his decisions and see if it 'seems reasonable' to him; if it seems unreasonable we will perform an 'iterative programme' which runs through the model with different decisions and different benefit functions until the decision-maker is satisfied that the benefit function corresponding to his decision is a sensible one.

Direct programming. When there is a price mechanism so that the outputs of a system can be measured financially, as is usual in problems of commercial and industrial management, the processes of linear or dynamic programming can be used to determine the optimum combination of activities or the optimum strategy for sequential operations such that profit is maximized subject to the constraints inherent in the organization. The relations between amounts of resources used and volumes of products obtained are expressed in terms of 'technical coefficients', which are the elements of the 'technology matrix' relating the vector of outputs to the vector of inputs. In a linear process with N activities, each constraint defines a hyper-plane in N-dimensional space. The optimum solution to the problem is found at a vertex of the largest convex hyper-polyhedron that can be formed from the constraint hyper-planes. The vertex to be chosen is that which corresponds to the largest value of the objective function. Clearly, there will always be a range of objective functions which will indicate the same vertex of a given hyper-polyhedron, and one of the most important pieces of information obtained from a linear programming calculation is the sensitivity of the solution to changes in costs, prices or technical coefficients (that is, how much the parameters must change before the solution is moved to another vertex).

When there is no quantified benefit function, direct programming techniques can only be used to minimize a cost function rather than to maximize a profit or net-benefit function; the mathematical details are the same, but we would describe the process as being part of a cost-effectiveness analysis rather than of a cost-benefit analysis.

Obtaining benefit limits by inverse programming. Suppose now that an administrator could define and measure his technical coefficients and his costs but not the benefits of the alternative activities; the hyper-polyhedron could be fully defined but he would be unable to choose between its vertices as he would have no objective function to maximize. In such a situation, the most likely result is that though he could, the administrator would not set up the direct programming calculation, despite the useful information that would be available to him by knowing the positions of the vertices though not the identity of the optimum vertex. The decision about policy would be made without quantification of benefits but probably with some qualitative consideration of them.

To determine benefit limits by inverse programming, the analyst would set up the direct programming calculation exactly as the administrator could have, and would assume that the benefit function could be regarded as a function, of known form but with unknown coefficients, of certain parameters of the problem. Then the knowledge of the administrator's policy decision and thus of the corresponding point on the hyper-polyhedron (not necessarily a vertex) would enable the analyst to state that the implicit net-benefit function had a maximum at that point (or on that face, if the point chosen was not a vertex). This fact, implicit in the initial postulate that the administrator's decision was optimal, would give some information about the ranges of values within which the unknown coefficients in the benefit function must lie. We may say that 'benefit limits' can be derived by inverse programming when applied to a single decision.

As an example, consider a very simple problem in library subdivision: a decision has already been taken to buy one copy of each of three books A, B and C, the problem being whether to put all three books in the central library U or to divide them between U and two sub-libraries S and T which are nearer to some of the likely users. Suppose that we have predicted the number of times each book will be used and the cost per use if placed in each alternative position, as tabulated:

	Number of uses at:			*Cost per use at:*		
Book	S	T	U	S	T	U
A	100	10	200	1	1	3
B	10	100	200	1	1	3
C	10	10	100	1	1	3

This indicates that Book A will be used 100 times at a cost of 1 unit per use if placed at S but 200 times at a cost of 3 units per use if placed at U, and so on. (The cost is taken to consist mainly of the cost to the user, so is greater if he has to travel.) If we now postulate that the value to the organization of every use of any book is the same, an unknown number v of cost-units, we can see that the three best plans are

(1) to put all three books at U, giving a net benefit of $500\,v-1500$,
(2) to put A at S, B at T and C at U, giving a net benefit of $300\,v-500$,
(3) to put A at S, B at T and C at either S or T, giving a net benefit of $210\,v-210$.

If we plot these three net-benefit functions against v, we get three straight lines of which that for Plan 1 is highest if $v > 5$, that for Plan 2 is highest if $3{\cdot}22 < v < 5$, and that for Plan 3 is highest if $v < 3{\cdot}22$. The inversion process here consists simply of concluding that if Plan 1 were actually adopted, the implicit valuation of each book use would be at a rate greater than 5 cost-units, whereas the adoption of Plan 3 would indicate that it was less than 3·22 cost-units, adoption of Plan 2 corresponding to the range between these two benefit limits.

With single inversions such as this, we must make some assumption about the form of the benefit function in order to get useful information about limits for the coefficients; if we assume that the function is linear in the parameters, a true inversion of the first programming procedure is possible, but for other types of function we may have to invert by repeating the direct calculation a number of times with different coefficients.

Obtaining benefit functions by ensemble inversion. Because the inversion process is not unique, each individual calculation enables us to derive only coefficient limits, given an assumed form for the benefit function. If we examine a large number of decisions for which the implicit benefit functions 'should have been' the same – that is, for which the price-structures would have been the same if there had been a market mechanism operating – we will obtain decision-points on a corresponding number of hyper-polyhedra. From these, we will be able to get a statistical estimate of the trend of the benefit function itself in the region covered by decision-points, without having to assume a form for it. The information obtained from each decision can be regarded as defining a vector of steepest descent at each decision-point (perpendicular to a face or to a tangent hyperplane at a vertex). The ensemble of such vectors can be made (e.g. by a regression analysis) to yield an estimate of the benefit function.

In the book-siting example, if the cost table remained the same but the predicted-use tables were different for a large number of books, we would obtain a large number of different limits for the ranges of v for which the different siting plans would be adopted, enabling us in the end to derive a single 'average' value per book-use.

Iterative interaction with the decision-maker. The initial assumption made in the inverse programming method is that the decision analyzed was optimal, but we have to face the fact that it was almost certainly not taken with full information and might have been different if the administrator had had more information. The presentation to him of the implicit benefit function derived by inversion may well, therefore, significantly change his information-state and possibly his decision. Depending on the particular situation, the analyst may be able to present the administrator with information about the benefit function before the real decision is made (in the example above, he might say 'If you judge that the value per use of a book is more than five times its cost, my model calculation suggests that you should choose Plan 1'), but in many cases the analysis cannot be made until after the event (the analyst would have to say 'If you had realized that you were implicitly valuing book-use at more than five times cost, would you have chosen Plan 1?').

Almost certainly an interative process is required, with a continual 'conversation' between the analyst and the administrator, with the gradual emergence of a policy corresponding to an implicit benefit function that 'seems reasonable' to the administrator. Another dimension of iteration is involved when we examine the (probably) different benefit functions agreed as reasonable by the decision-maker himself and (*a*) higher ranks in his organization and (*b*) the 'customers' or the electorate, and try to bring the benefit scales closer by improving information-flow.

Applications of Inverse Programming in University Libraries

We can distinguish three levels of planning in the library field, with different time-horizons and different scales of resources to be allocated. The first is the strategic level, at which questions of capital provision, library subdivision and siting are considered; problems which are in principle very like the trivial example of book-siting discussed above will arise. The second is the tactical level, at which the library administrator will be planning the deployment of library funds and staff over a period of a few months, and a simple numerical example is given below of inverse dynamic programming at this level. The third is the personal level, at which a library user plans from day to day his own allocation of time to use of the library and 'competing' activities, according to his own implicit scales of benefit and estimates of cost; a simplified example is also given of the application of inverse programming to this case.

Library tactical planning model. There are two stages to the inverse programming process for this model of library tactical planning: calculation of the benefit function corresponding to current use of library facilities, and calculation of the respective weighting given to current and future benefit. The tactical planning in a library, as in any other institution 'building for posterity' must be regarded as dynamic rather than static – the effect of current activities on future resources must be included in the calculation as well as its effect on current net benefit.

In the simplified and admittedly idealistic model to be described here, we consider the library's resources as consisting of stock, funds, and user goodwill. We take the building space and arrangement as fixed, and assume that all funds (including staff salaries) are transferable. Goodwill, measured in 'man-hours' available for library use, is included essentially as an extra regression parameter to account for that part of demand not well-correlated with the 'internal' resources, i.e. to allow for the effect of user costs both inside and outside the library and for factors such as population changes and emergence of new activities competing for users' time. The library activities on which funds are to be spent may be divided into forced activities, such as maintenance of buildings and stock and the meeting of user demand ('service'), and those to which remaining funds may be freely allocated, such as purchasing books, encouraging and educating users and improving efficiency to cut costs. The unforced activities can be described simply as spending to increase stock, goodwill, and funds respectively (a decrease in costs being taken as equivalent to an increase in funds available for allocation).

The current net benefit is regarded as being determined entirely by library use, both that in the current period and that which would be made of the library in future periods, if its resources were unchanged; we shall write current net benefit as a linear function of stock, funds, and goodwill, though linearity is not essential to the argument. The total net benefit, which will be the objective function to be maximized, will be written as a weighted sum of the single-period net benefit functions for all periods included within the planning horizon. The period weighting coefficients and the three resource coefficients are to be determined by inverse programming, the former by consideration of the part played by investment activities (increase of future resources as opposed to maximization of current net benefit) and the latter by considering single-period policy or cyclic imbedding approximations. Cyclic imbedding is a notion from dynamic programming, and describes the situation, all too familiar to the library administrator, in which he has to run harder and harder to stay in one place – that is, coping with natural decay of stock, the education of new users, and the training of new staff take all the available effort, so that the total value of the library may be regarded as constant.

Numerical illustration of simplified tactical planning model. We consider a number of planning periods, the first starting at time t_0 and ending at t_1, to t_2 and so on. The stock at t_n will be denoted by S_n, the goodwill at t_n by G_n and the funds allocated for spending between t_n and t_{n+1} by F_n. Denoting the increases of resources during the period ending at t_n by s_n, f_n and g_n, we get

$$S_n = S_{n-1} + s_n \qquad F_n = F_{n-1} + f_n \qquad G_n = G_{n-1} + g_n.$$

If we denote by R_{n-1} the funds available for spending in the period beginning t_{n-1} after maintenance and service costs have been deducted, we can write the constraint on total unforced spending as

$$R_{n-1} = uF_{n-1} - vS_{n-1} - wG_{n-1} = af_n + bs_n + cg_n$$

where $u, v, w, a, b, c \geqq 0$ and $u \leqq 1$. The coefficients a, b and c represent the costs of increasing by one unit F, S and G respectively, while $1-u$, v and w represent the unit forced costs. If no overspending is allowed, $R \geqq 0$. All the six coefficients introduced so far should be observable, but the coefficients x, y and z in the current net-benefit function P_n are unknowns, to be found by the inverse programming. We choose to write P_n as a linear function of the resources at t_n, as

$$P_n = xF_n + yS_n + zG_n.$$

The total net benefit function to be maximized for an n-period horizon will be

$$B_n = k_1P_1 + k_2P_2 + k_3P_3 \ldots + k_nP_n.$$

As a simple illustration, suppose that we have observable coefficients

$$a = b = c = u = v = 1 \qquad w = 2$$

and that by a preliminary single-period inversion we have determined the unknowns x, y and z as

$$x = 1 \qquad y = 2 \qquad z = 3.$$

We are now to consider the 'investment versus profit' decision which will lead to an estimate of the weighting factors k_n, and will do this for a two-period horizon, taking P_0 and R_0 as given constants. We have to determine f_1, s_1, g_1, f_2, s_2, and g_2 to maximize B_2 – or, rather, since we do not know k_1 and k_2, we shall have to find them by observation of policy and inversion.

For a two-period time horizon we must optimize the second year's policy to maximize P_2 (by Bellman's Principle of Optimality), subject to the constraints $R_2, f_2, s_2, g_2 \geqq 0$. We soon show that this optimization is effected by $R_2 = s_2 = 0$ and $2f_2 = g_2 = 2R_1/3$, giving $P_2 = P_1 + 7R_1/3$.

Now taking the two years together with this policy in the second year, we can show that if $k_1/k_2 \geqq 5/2$ our best policy for maximizing B_2 is to maximize P_1 at the expense P_2, giving $R_1 = 0$ and $P_2 = P_1 = P_0 + 7R_0/3$. On the other hand, if $k_1/k_2 \leqq 5/2$ our best policy for maximizing B_2 is to use the first period for 'investment', i.e. to maximize, R_1 by choosing $s_1 = g_1 = 0$ and $f_1 = R_0$, giving $P_2 = P_0 + 17R_0/3$ and $P_1 = P_0 + R_0$.

The inversion would be carried out by observing whether or not the administrator's policy has been to maximize future resources or current net benefit. If future 'profits' have been preferred to those in the current period, we would conclude that the ratio of the implicit weighting factors was less than 5/2, as we can show easily that a longer time-horizon would give even less weight to the first year. (Remember, however, that this particular figure was derived from initial data made up for this illustration!)

Library user's planning model. At the personal level, the user has to plan day to day his schedule for library use and other activities, taking into account the constraints on his time and, implicitly, the values and costs to him of the different activities. Suppose that he has already decided how many hours he can spend in library use, and that he has some implicit scales of 'values per hour' of his time as spent in three different libraries BM, UL and DL (see diagrams – supposed to indicate that some time is wasted getting started and that his effectiveness falls off after three hours in the library). We suppose also that there is a definite cost involved in getting to BM and UL, but not in getting to DL (and that all his journeys are made when all libraries are shut!). If he had some such benefit scales, he could draw a cumulative profit diagram like that shown and use it to aid his schedule-making. He would decide on this basis to use BM if he could spare six hours or more, DL is he could only spare less than two hours for library use, and UL with an intermediate amount of time.

Of course, few library users have any such set of benefit scales in mind when deciding their policy – but they do decide! We can therefore observe their behaviour and obtain by inversion cumulative profit diagrams from which value-per-hour diagrams could be deduced.

Conclusion

The inverse programming method could be applied in any field in which a direct programming model can be set up in such a way that it lacks only a benefit function; inverse and iterative programming could then be applied to derive a benefit function agreed as reasonable by actual decision-makers, which could then be used to aid further decisions.

Hospital administration. Planning in the Health Service is even more bedevilled than elsewhere by lack of quantified benefit functions – the obvious emotional content of many of the decisions to be made is one cause for this, but in fact this apparent difficulty is a possible source of strength to an inverse programming approach, for strong subjective approaches to decisions should make for a powerful dialogue in the iterative programming stage.

Consider, for example, the question 'Which patient shall have the only artificial kidney machine?' or, even more topically, 'Which patient shall be deemed dead to supply a heart for transplanting?' These very difficult questions are certainly not answered now by any reference to quantified benefits – the very idea of doing so is repugnant

– but once made, the decisions certainly have great quantitative implications about the value of human life, of keeping a family together, of a breadwinner as against a cripple, etc., and the very drama of the situations involved clarify and hone down the issues involved so that most people would be able to express opinions about them – just what we need to carry out an inverse programming calculation. The results of such a calculation would not be intended for use in making this type of decision, but in answering more mundane questions like 'What is the value of getting a patient back to work quickly?' or 'What is the benefit of opting for childbirth in hospital rather than at home?'

Crime prevention. Similarly, an inverse programming study of the changes in police strategy and tactics that have been taking place and of the insurance market would provide answers to some of the questions that a quantitative planner in a police headquarters would wish to pose, such as 'What is the value of not being burgled' or 'What is the value to the nation as a whole if criminals are chased from one area by police activity, only to commence operations elsewhere?'

Mathematical points. Though most of the discussion has been in terms of linear programming, inversion is just as applicable to quadratic or any other form of mathematical programming, or to dynamic programming: all we require for applicability is a planning algorithm that needs an objective function, and a model which is realistic enough for real decisions to be comparable to model decisions. The constraints can be piece-wise linear in as many pieces as the computer programme can handle (i.e. they can be effectively curved-surface constraints), and the postulated objective function can be of any computable form.

Acknowledgement

The work described above forms part of the Project for Evaluating the Benefits from University Libraries (PEBUL) which is supported by the Office for Scientific and Technical Information. The author acknowledges gratefully the contribution to the development of the method made by the economic expertise of Richard Morley, Joint Principal Investigator, and by discussion and argument with the rest of the PEBUL team and the senior staff of Durham University Library.

Notes added after Conference Discussion, 26th June 1968

(1) The method could be used to analyze implicit benefit scales even in a commercial context if decisions were found not to correspond exactly to maximization of explicitly quantified net benefit.

(2) Though presented above mainly as a tool for retrospective analysis, the object of the method is the definition of benefit functions for use in future planning. Continual checks on validity will be required when the method is so used.

(3) Despite the apparent emphasis placed on quantifying the subjective value-judgments of administrators, the standpoint remains firmly that the consumer's (i.e. the electorate's) scale of values must finally prevail. Ideally, the administrator's and the consumer's scales should tend to coincide as communications and information tend to perfection.

(4) The method can easily be applied to situations of diminishing marginal utility provided their presence is recognized.

MAURICE E. ESCH

Planning Assistance through Technical Evaluation of Relevance Numbers

First Presented to the Industrial Research Institute Meeting in Denver, Colorado, Oct. 13–15, 1965 and reproduced by kind permission

I am very pleased to have the opportunity to discuss Honeywell's long-range planning programme with you. I will concentrate primarily on the technical planning area and discuss in some detail the formal methodology that we have developed, and use to guide our R&D efforts. We feel strongly that long-range technical planning is very necessary, particularly in the Government product area, and that a formalized methodology is a vital cog in this planning process.

During the past decade there have been substantial changes in our National Security Objectives, caused by a rapidly changing military threat coupled with a tremendous explosion of technology. These factors have caused the Department of Defense to continually modify our current and projected military force structure in terms of capabilities, numbers, and types of new weapon systems required to insure our future national security. In most cases there are a considerable number of feasible technical approaches that can be taken to solve any particular problem. As a result, new system development and procurement decisions by the Government are being weighed very carefully in terms of how well a particular system approach supports the overall national objectives with heavy emphasis on a thorough cost effectiveness analysis. In this environment, a tremendous number of interrelated technical political, military, economic, and even social factors affect each system decision by the Government and military officials. Industry, faced with this rather fluid environment, must be highly selective in deciding where to place its R&D dollar in order to continue to grow.

Several years ago, Honeywell's Military & Space Sciences Department (MSSD) addressed itself to the problem of developing an effective tool to aid Company decision makers to identify those critical technology areas requiring upgrading to support the development of viable new system concepts. The process evolved by MSSD is called PATTERN, an acronym for Planning Assistance Through Technical Evaluation of Relevance Numbers. PATTERN was developed and used most extensively for planning in the military arena; however, the methodology is very flexible and can be applied to many decision-making problem areas. For example, Honeywell recently used this planning tool in a comprehensive study to identify present and future technical needs in the bio-medical field.

In developing this tool to assist decision makers in assimilating, analyzing, and evaluating large bodies of data in order to better understand the complex interrelationships between the static and dynamic factors that influence their decisions, Honeywell focussed attention on three fundamental questions. Can large numbers of complex, interrelated variables be broken down into simple decision factors such that these factors can be expressed numerically and stored in a computer? Can these numbers be manipulated to present logical conclusions in such a way that the validity of the initial number assignment process is not biased or destroyed? Can conclusions and extrapolations be made from an analysis of these numbers based on information that was inherent in their assignment?

The formulation of a plan to identify those critical technical programmes which should be initiated today to be ready to meet the needs of tomorrow requires an understanding of the dynamics of the military problem, as well as the capability of industry to develop and maintain an appropriate technology base. In turn, to understand the military problem and assess various weapons systems needs, it is necessary to evaluate the objectives, roles, and missions of the services as they are affected by changes in military, political, ideological, and economic forcing functions. The dynamics of the technology loop must also be analyzed in terms of the changing state-of-the-art relating to new requirements as well as new ideas encompassing pure scientific investigation and innovations that do not support specific requirements.

PATTERN *Methodology*

PATTERN can best be described as a decision aid consisting of three basic parts shown in Figure 1. First, a relevance tree . . . which measures the relative importance to the national objectives of upgrading a particular mission or technical area; second, cross support . . . which measures the degree of technical growth that will result from solving a specific problem; and, third, status and timing . . . which measures industry's capability to solve the identified technical problems. A scenario which projected the world environment (including military, political, and economic factors) that might be expected in the 1968–78 time period, and a comprehensive state-of-the-art technology forecast were used as basic inputs in the evaluation process. At each node of the tree, a team of experts, using matrices, decision criteria, and

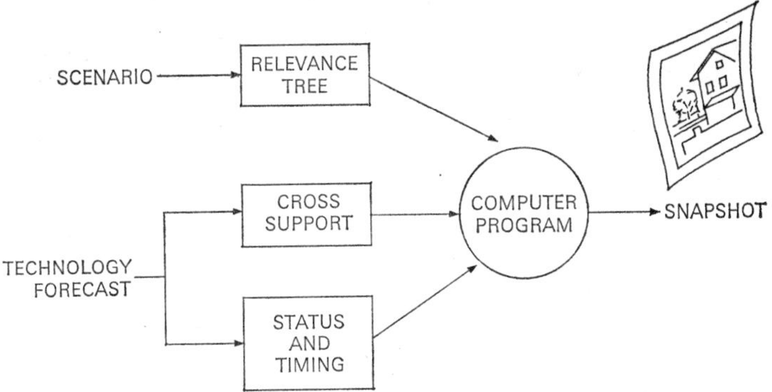

Figure 1. Pattern is a decision aid.

subjective probability techniques, assigned quantitative values relating to the importance of upgrading that item in terms of its contribution to meeting the overall national objectives for the 1968–78 time period. Cross support and status and timing factors were also assigned numerical values. These numerical inputs were fed into a computer programme and the computer readout then gave a snapshot of any particular area of interest in terms of its relative importance to the national military stature as compared to all other areas used in the evaluation process.

Now, let us examine the relevance tree in more detail. It is basically a structured decision network consisting of eight levels beginning with national security objectives and progressing through types of conflicts, forms of conflict, missions, systems concepts, functional subsystems, subsystem configurations, and technology deficiencies, in a tree-like organization. We first divided the structure into three major parts shown in Figure 2. At the top, in the political and ideological area, the President and National Security Council make policy-type decisions. The second level, the conceptual and requirements area, is the level where the Secretary of Defense, the Administrator of NASA, and the individual Service Chiefs make decisions. The third level, the technology area, is where the individual service laboratories and the laboratories of industry make technical decisions. This basic three-part structure was then subdivided into the various levels shown on the right of Figure 2 plus the national objective level, making a total of eight levels. In order to make value judgments in the horizontal plane at each level of the tree, it was necessary to apply rigid definitions to each item on the tree as well as to develop a set of ground rules for the game situation. The ground rules took the form of criteria. Key words representing the various criteria are shown on the left of Figure 2. In

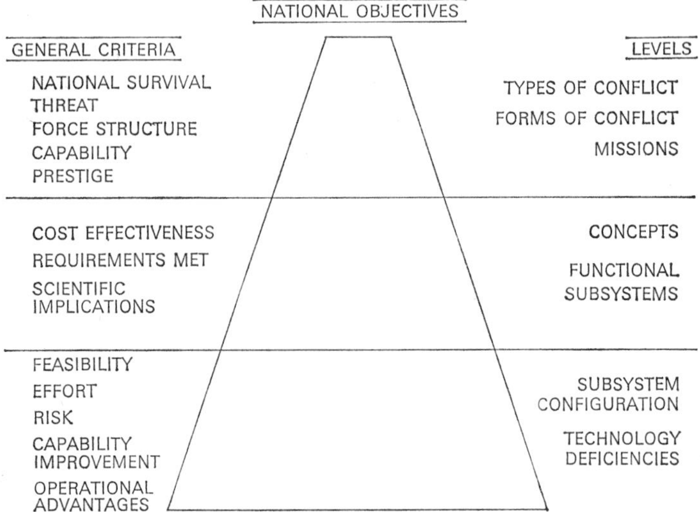

Figure 2. Relevance tree.

developing the criteria, it was necessary to ensure that they were appropriate to the level at which the decision was to be made and that they were mutually exclusive in so far as possible.

A more detailed breakdown of the top four levels of the tree are shown in Figure 3. At the top, we have the National Objectives. Directly below are listed the three national activity areas where we may expect challenges to our National Objectives in the future. The next level, indicates the form that these challenges may take, i.e. various types of limited wars, intelligence, arms control, etc. Under each of these forms of conflict is a spectrum of missions in which we must develop and maintain a capability if we expect to be able to counter the challenge in each specific area of competition. For example, under Limited War II, if we were able to meet all the requirements of the eight missions, shown in Figure 3, we should be able to engage in that type of conflict with a reasonable expectation of winning. Likewise, in non-combat intelligence, if we could perform each of the three missions identified, we could obtain the intelligence information needed to compete in the cold war operation. It is very important that each of the mission areas be carefully defined in order to determine the type of equipment and the technology upgrading required to achieve the specific mission objectives. The advantage of this type of structure is that it divides the large many-faceted problem into small segments and permits us to make comparisons among small numbers of items at any single level. At the same time, we retain the capability of again

NATIONAL OBJECTIVE

- MILITARY ACTIVITIES
  - Limited War # I (Special)
    - Close Combat
    - Fire Support
    - Air Defense
    - Reconn./Surveil.
    - Sea Strike
    - ASW
    - C & C
    - General Support
  - Limited War # II (Small Scale)
    - Close Combat
    - Fire Support
    - Air Defense
    - Reconn./Surveil.
    - Sea. Strike
    - ASW
    - C & C
    - General Support
  - Limited War # III (Formal Combat)
    - Close Combat
    - Fire Support
    - Air Defense
    - Reconn./Surveil.
    - Sea Strike
    - ASW
    - C & C
    - General Support
  - Limited War # IV (Scale Formal with Tac. Nuc.)
    - Close Combat
    - Fire Support
    - Air Defense
    - Reconn./Surveil.
    - Sea Strike
    - ASW
    - C & C
    - General Support
  - General War
    - Destroy Strategic forces and Resources
    - Protect Resources and Retaliatory Forces
    - Military Space Superiority
    - Reconn.
    - C & C
- NON-COMBAT ACTIVITIES
  - Counter-Insurgency
    - Counter-guerilla
    - Civic Action
    - Psychological
    - Unconventional
  - Intelligence
    - Force Deployment Intelligence Collection
    - Force Characteristics Intelligence Collection
    - Target Information Intelligence Collection
  - National Support
    - CC & C
    - Test and Evaluation
  - Arms Control
    - Stockpile/Force Evaluation
    - Test Monitoring
    - Production Monitoring
- EXPLORATION AND CIVIL SUPPORT ACTIVITIES
  - Earth Exploration
    - Hydrosphere Exploration
    - Lithosphere Exploration
    - Atmosphere and Magnetosphere Exploration
  - Space Exploration
    - Environmental Effects Investigation
    - Lunar Exploration
    - Planetary and Solar Body Exploration
    - Solar and Interplanetary Exploration
    - Universe Exploration
    - Space Surveillance and Sweeping
  - Civil Support
    - Weather Service
    - Navigation and Traffic Control
    - Communications
    - Transportation
  - Resources Development
    - Ocean Food and Mineral Development
    - Water and Power Development

Figure 3.

looking at the total package as an entity once the individual value judgments have been made.

Figure 4 shows the lower four levels of the tree on a concept work-sheet used in the study. The postulated concepts represent the fifth level of the tree. At the sixth level, each of the concepts were divided into seventeen functional subsystem areas together with associated requirements needed to meet concept performance goals. It is not necessary that seventeen functional subsystem areas be used. It could be as many as twenty-five or as few as ten. However, it is necessary that each area be defined in great detail in order that everyone working on the study understands precisely what is included in the particular area. In most cases there were several alternative ways by which the functional subsystem requirements could be met. These alternate methods were called subsystem configurations and constituted the seventh level of the tree. Contained within the competing subsystem configurations were the technological deficiencies to be solved. These deficiencies represented the eighth level of the tree. Note on this chart that status and timing is entered at both the functional subsystem level and at the technical deficiency level. Relevance numbers were assigned at each node of the tree by teams of experts using carefully selected criteria as a base for their judgments. The basic procedure was to employ a value judgment matrix using mathematical techniques developed for decision-making under conditions of uncertainty. A typical matrix is shown in Figure 5. For example, at the top level of the tree it is important to assess the relative needs of modifying or upgrading the US posture in the three conflict areas to provide the flexibility of action needed for operation against those forces that may be brought to bear in opposition to our national objectives. The US capability improvements needed can then be evaluated in terms of the following criteria: to assure national survival, to demonstrate a credible posture to our friends and to our potential enemies, and to be in a position to shape and create a favourable world opinion. The same relevance number assignment technique was used at each successive node of the tree. Once the team had assigned relevance numbers to all items at each level of the tree, the numbers were stored in a computer for further use.

The second major part of the study has to do with the status and timing of the technology needs. Once the needs of the Government have been assessed without regard to the nation's ability to perform these functions, it is important to get an evaluation of the capability of industry to achieve the technical solutions to the identified problems. A comprehensive technical forecast was conducted in which an assessment was made of the current status of approximately 300 technologies, as well as of the likely rate of improvement in performance of

CONCEPT TITLE

POSTULATED SYSTEM CONCEPT	FUNCTIONAL SUBSYSTEMS	SUBSYSTEM REQUIREMENTS	SUBSYSTEM CONFIGURATION	TECHNOLOGY DEFICIENCIES
	PROPULSION (S / T)			S / T
	GUIDANCE & NAV.			
	DATA PROCESSING			
	FIRE CONTROL			
	COUNTERMEASURES			
	KILL MECHANISMS			
	VEHICLE			
	COMMUNICATIONS			
	AUX. POWER			
	STABIL. & CONTROL			
	LAUNCHERS & DISP.			
	CHECKOUT & MAINT.			
	LIFE SUPPORT			
	SIM. & TRAINING			
	INSTRUMENTATION			
	ESCAPE AND RECOVERY			
	DETECTION - DISCRIM. & TRACKING			

Figure 4.

	Ensuring National survival	Demonstrating credible posture	Creating favourable world opinion	E(r_i)
	0·6	0·3	0·1	
ACTIVE HOSTILITIES	0·6	0·6	0·4	0·58
NON-COMBAT	0·3	0·1	0·1	0·22
EXPLORATION	0·1	0·3	0·5	0·20

Figure 5. Number assignment technique.

each technology area over time. PATTERN then used this evaluation of the status of technology and its projected rate of growth in determining the time and capability required to meet the identified national technical needs. These data were inserted at the functional subsystem and technical deficiency levels in the tree.

Figure 6 shows the development hierarchy used in assessing the status and timing of a given technology as it moves from research through exploratory development, advanced development, product design, and to the available or off-the-shelf category. These categories are very similar to those used by the Government in defining their development phases. In assessing a given functional subsystem or deficiency, the team put an 'X' in the category where the technology under consideration was determined to be in its development cycle. In the case shown in Figure 6, the committee felt that the technology being discussed was an exploratory development. They were then asked to determine how long it would take a normally prosecuted programme to move the technology from exploratory development to advanced development. This was considered to be three years. Two more years would be required in advanced development before it was

	STATUS	TIMING
AVAILABLE		1
PRODUCT DESIGN		2
ADVANCED DEVELOPMENT		2
EXPLORATORY DEVELOPMENT	X	3
RESEARCH		

Figure 6. Status and timing.

ready to go into product design, etc. So, the total time required for the technology to progress from exploratory development to inventory availability in this case was eight years. Thus, these data in the status and timing section basically indicate the capability of the country, time-oriented, to meet its military/exploration type technology needs.

At this point we have discussed two of the three significant parts of the study; the Relevance Tree and the Status and Timing problem. The third major part of PATTERN consisted of the Cross Support information. Cross support represents the total gain in technical capability, across all subsystem areas, accumulated by working in a specific subsystem problem area. Time was used as the common denominator and a zero to one scale was used in assigning the cross support values. Thus, the subsystem configuration cross support number represented the degree to which solving a specific technical problem on a particular subsystem configuration reduced the effort needed to solve similar or related subsystem technical problems within the same functional subsystem class for other concepts. Judgment factors considered by the technical specialists in the assignment of cross support numbers were the relative reductions in cost, time and man-hours made possible because of the additional knowledge acquired. As previously stated, this was reduced to a single common denominator *TIME* when the number was actually assigned.

PATTERN *Methodology Calculation.* At this point the tree structure and the methodology has been described in some detail. Perhaps the entire study can be put into the proper perspective with a discussion of Figure 7, which shows the total tree structure and contains the fundamental logic equation which expresses the various solutions that can be read out of Project PATTERN.

The first four levels of the tree along with the national objectives level are shown in the first basic term of the PATTERN logic equation as:

$$\sum_{D_0}^{D=D_0} \prod_{i=A}^{D} r_i.$$

These levels were essentially those in which the political, ideological, and cost-effectiveness criteria were used to assign a relevance number at each branch junction of the tree. The relevance-need down to this particular level is calculated by taking the product of the individual relevance number at every level from levels A through D. However, the individual cell relevance number, r_i, was calculated from the assignment process wherein twenty members were used in applying their judgment to the criteria. Since a given postulated concept may be applicable across several missions, the relevance number that it accrues is the sum of the relevance numbers in the specific concept of

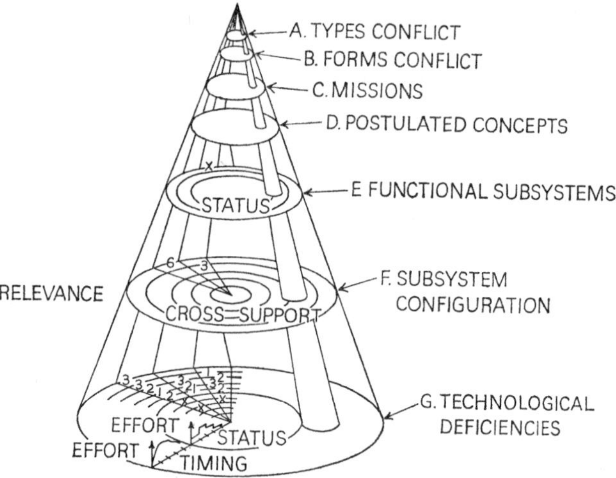

Figure 7. Relevance tree.

PATTERN logic equation =

$$\left[\sum_{D_0}^{D=D_0}\prod_{i=A}^{D} r_i\right]\left[\sum_{E_0}^{E=E_0} r_E f_1(S_E) f_2(T_E)\right]\left[\sum_{F_0}^{F=F_0} r_F x_F\right]$$

$$\left[\sum_{G_0}^{G=G_0} r_G f_3(T_G) f_4(S_G)\right][\delta(r_{A\ldots G}, S_{EG}, T_{EG})]$$

interest wherever it appears under all the missions. So the summations represent the cumulative need for upgrading a given concept area across-the-board in all the missions that it appears. The other terms of the logic equation use the same basic rationale.

The functional subsystem level shows all of the possible building blocks that comprise the design configuration for the given postulated system concept and includes the status and timing numbers of each of the functional subsystems. The outer surface of the tree, comprised of the products of the individual relevance numbers down through the tree, reflect the need or importance of upgrading a given area to meet the objectives as defined at the level above. The supporting evidence that makes up this need are the basic branch levels at any given point within the tree.

The $f(S_E)f(T_E)$ terms represent the density functions that can be inserted by a person to reflect the emphasis he would like to place in a given area as a function of its status and timing.

The next level in the relevance structure shows the various subsystem configurations that were considered under each of the functional subsystem areas. For example, in the guidance area, configurations such as a doppler-type system versus an inertial guidance system versus command guidance, etc., could be used. The technological level supporting the outer surface at this point in the structure is the cross support information that was inserted. Arrayed around the outer surface of the tree are all of the subsystem configuration cells and inside the structure is a ring for each of the subsystem configurations. Inserted within each of these cells is the cross support number for the configuration in terms of the knowledge acquired which can be used for upgrading a similar configuration deficiency on another concept. Here we incorporate the cross support number as a product to modify the relevance number at this particular level, $r_F\ X_F$. This number can either be incorporated to reflect the technical growth that would be achieved through working on this subsystem configuration by its modification of the relevance number, or it can be one, and factored out of the calculation if only the importance or the need of a configuration is desired.

Each subsytem configuration consists of technology deficiencies that must be solved before it can become a reality. These technology deficiencies are reflected as those that are required to solve the needs of the two subsystem configurations above, as represented on the outer surface of the structure.

On the polar plot is shown the structure that makes up the status and timing numbers that were inserted at this level. The various density functions are shown at this level in the tree representing the inquiry that a project manager could request. The other term of the equation $\delta(r_{A} \ldots {}_{G}, S_{EG}, T_{EG})$ reflects our intentions to pursue in much greater detail an evaluation of uncertainties in the assignment of the relevance numbers at all levels through *A*-*G*, and the status and timing numbers at their appropriate *E* and *G* levels in the total structure.

PATTERN *Methodology applied to Bio-Medicine*

As stated earlier, PATTERN methodology can be applied to any problem area where decisions must be made under conditions of uncertainty. In October of 1964, Honeywell Corporate management initiated a study to identify present and future needs in Bio-Medicine' This study was given the acronym Project MEDICINE ((MEDical Instrumentation and Control Identified and Numerically Evaluated), and was to use the decision structuring and relevance number assignment techniques developed in Project PATTERN. The study was conducted by a group of fifteen medical doctors, including Company personnel and external consultants. Study findings and recommendations were presented to executive management early in March 1965.

The team defined the principal national objective in the Bio-Medicine study to be the need to maximize human life span with optimal health and activities in all environments. The generalized tree structure shown in Figure 8 illustrates the thought processes used in going from the national objective down to the actual pieces of equipment that are required to perform the various functions. The number of cells at each level is indicated in parentheses. For example, at the TASK level of the tree, the primary activities necessary to achieve the objective are: (1) diagnosis, treating, curing, and preventing diseases and abnormalities, (2) caring for and nourishing the sick, (3) educating individuals and the community in medicine and hygiene, (4) increasing the body of bio-medical knowledge through research, and (5) prvoiding protection and sustenance for human activity in unusual environments. The APPROACH level contains the procedures to be applied to scientific tasks, such as surgery under treatment. At the SYSTEM level are those bodily activities carried out by several organs operating together under integrated control. (That is, reflexive control of locomotion, circulation of blood, etc.) The SUBSYSTEM, or organ level, contains those units either natural or artificial, which perform a specialized activity. The FACTOR level lists those parameters which need to be measured, analyzed, and controlled to evaluate or cope with the normal or abnormal operation of the organ. The TOOL level lists the devices in the form of hardware or software used to acquire or process data, or to treat, cure, or prevent disease.

After the tree network was structured, the diversified groups of medical doctors used various criteria, as in PATTERN, at each level to assign appropriate relevance numbers. For example, the criteria used at the TASK level measured the need for upgrading of capabilities to meet the Bio-Medical objectives based on: (1) the influence of locale and types of mass threats on population dynamics, (2) the implications of government-directed medical services, (3) the degree to which the task contributes to increased age of modal death and/or reduction of disability time, (4) the psychological impact of world opinion if the task is not accomplished, and (5) the effect on costs of performing various medical functions.

It is beyond the scope of this paper to discuss in detail the complete tree structure and all criteria that were used. Instead, a comparison of the MEDICINE study with the PATTERN military study will be discussed.

MEDICINE *vs.* PATTERN

Probably one of the best ways to compare the two studies is to analyze the differences in data characteristics. The basic data available to the PATTERN and MEDICINE studies offer an example of a rather sharp

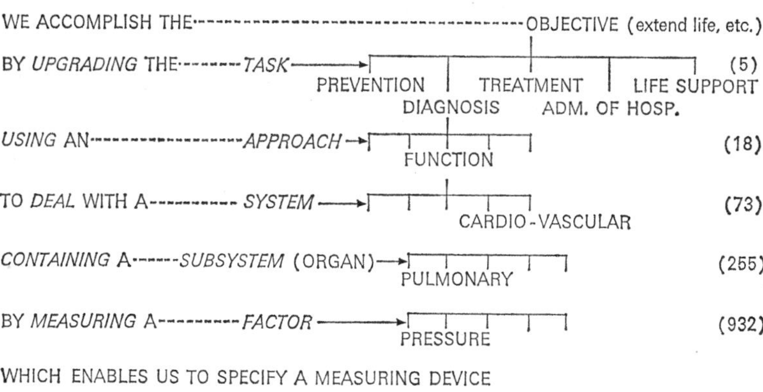

Figure 8.

contrast. In PATTERN, an evaluation of a series of man-originated systems concepts and hardware was made. In MEDICINE, the problem was not to evaluate competing systems but rather to evaluate maintenance and repair methods as applied to the human system. In the case of PATTERN, the systems concept and hardware were well understood by man, in that they were man-originated and we have the reasonably complete development of cause and effect in systems performance. In the MEDICINE study, we are dealing with the human system on which very little hard data is available. Most of that which is available would have to be categorized as associative in nature, where the relationship of cure and effect in the human system is understood very poorly at best.

It may be said, then, that PATTERN is an evaluation of hardware concepts which can be designed and built by men to meet requirements established by man's thought processes in response to world political and economic pressures. This includes the concept design, reliability, cost, and the degree to which a basic national need is met. MEDICINE, on the other hand, deals with an evaluation of the medical instrumentation and control systems, subsystems, and associated hardware that contribute to maximizing the human life span with optimal health and activity. The objectives of MEDICINE are to be met primarily by upgrading the use, maintenance, and repair of the human body. Since we do not, at present, have the options of design or significant modification of the human, the only avenues which appear to be open to us lie in the development of a more complete understanding of the human mind and body and the remedial actions required to correct possible malfunctions thereof.

After the relevance part of the study was completed, and the computer outputs reviewed, the doctors were asked to give their personal opinions of the greatest medical needs in the 1–7 year, 7–15 year and 15–20 year periods. It is significant to note that their individual judgments followed the tree quite closely. It is also interesting that, at the start of the study, none of the doctors could come up with such need listings. This seems to strengthen the validity of the group judgments represented by the study outputs.

In summary, it can be said that the problem structuring techniques and the quantitative evaluation methods developed and employed in PATTERN have been of significant value in aiding the decision making process in that they:

(1) Provided a basic framework within which the many complex interrelated variables which affect today's decisions could be structured, and evaluated on a quantitative basis.

(2) Furnished the results of these evaluations to the decision maker in a form most usable to him.

(3) Provided a relatively simple method of assessing the impact of changing conditions by periodically and systematically updating the inputs which in turn modify the study outputs.

A. V. BRIDGEWATER

Morphological Methods: Principles and Practice

Long-range process design has always provided the designer with his more difficult problems, which are often solved with the help of highly subjective or even hit and miss methods. The main purpose of this paper is to suggest an approach to such problems, employing one of the known design strategies – morphological analysis [1]. This technique is developed from an initial concept to a process designers tool, which is illustrated by detailed reference to the OSCAT project. The design method is regarded by some as a vague and abstract subject. It is hoped that the useful relationship between the techniques embodied in the design method discussed below and conventional engineering is demonstrated through practice.

Design Strategies

The origins of the OSCAT project in relation to the better known design strategies have been discussed by Gregory [1, 2]. He suggests a variety of techniques or strategies that may be used in solving a design problem generally, which together make up what is known as the Design Method. He arranges these in a logical order of application for solving a design problem:

(1) Finding the problem,
(2) The systems approach,
(3) Critical examination,
(4) Morphological analysis,
(5) General problem solver,
(6) Page's strategy,
(7) Gregory's strategy,
(8) Marple's strategy;

which last three may be used at any point to facilitate solution. It is not a prerequisite that the order be followed, nor that all the methods be employed in solving a problem. This is exemplified in the OSCAT project discussed later.

It would be useful briefly to define and expound these strategies to indicate their general usefulness.

Finding the problem: A process may generally be thought of as the transformation of a feedstock into a product. This may be expressed as:

$$Os = f(Is) \qquad (1)$$

where Is = Input
Os = Output
f = Transformation requirements

or in terms of the 'Black Box'. This concept is a very convenient way of simply depicting a complex or unspecified situation whose internal details are of little or no importance at the particular level of discussion. The 'Chinese Black Box' is a development containing small boxes within larger ones to make up the whole.

The idea was used in chemical engineering (without the specific terminology) as long ago as 1932 by Bloomfield [3]; and the black box notion has been developed by Ashby [4], for example.

The systems approach. 'A system is a set of objects (parts or components) with relationships between the objects and between their attributes (properties of objects)' [5]. The systems approach searches for and specifies the effective boundaries or limits of the problem (i.e. defines it), and requires subsequent operations to be performed in the light of these constraints, but not necessarily within them. The boundaries often help to define criteria for evaluation at later stages in the design. See Figure 1.

Critical examination. This is based on the principles of Work Study [6], and has been developed from such requirements to a general design strategy. As the name implies, critical examination involves the breakdown of a problem into constituent parts followed by examination and evaluation. The technique is usually applied to existing problems (e.g. processes, hardware, etc.). When rationalized and performed rigorously, especially under unrestrictive conditions, the method becomes Morphological analysis (q.v.).

Morphological analysis. Morphological generally is the 'science of form' (Oxford English Dictionary), 'a study of the structure or form of something' (Webster's International). In the field of design, morphological analysis is constituted by the rigorous examination and, evaluation of all possible alternatives to each structural part of a problem. This aims to give the optimum solution(s) by virtue of having considered every possibility; and the fewer the restrictions, the more comprehensive and complete are the results. The operation may readily be performed in situations of low information availability using simple, non-specific criteria in the evaluation.

All these points are particularly advantageous to long range process design, as is illustated by reference to the OSCAT project later.

Morphological analysis is developed later from a simple general operation, to a complex process generation – selection procedure.

General problem solver. This is the technique which employs a progressive series of dependent stepwise evaluations to effect solution

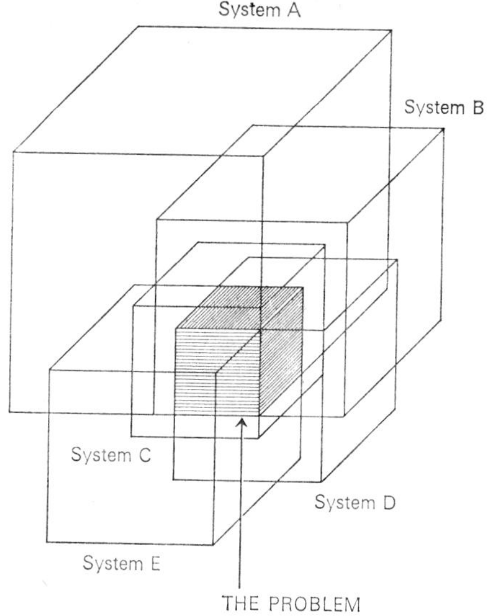

Figure 1.

[10], for example chess [8, 11]. Each step is compared to the final solution, and possibly preceeding and succeeding steps, to effect evaluation.

Page's strategy. The problem is explored in the greatest detail conducive to least expenditure.

Gregory's strategy. The breakage of a closed cycle of dependent relationships is performed with an assumption to facilitate solution. Re-assessment of the assumption may be made later.

Marple's strategy. A solution is found which gives the greatest opportunity for manœuvre afterwards, which may include reconsideration of previous decisions.

Morphological Analysis

The term morphological analysis was coined by *Fritz Zwicky* (in the relatively inaccessible paper 'The morphological method of analysis and construction' in *Studies and Essays*, Courant Anniversary Volume, Interscience 1948). He suggested that if one studies the features of any object they can be set by one into a hypothetical morphological box such that eventually no pigeon-hole in the box contains more than one feature. Some may be empty. Here and elsewhere Zwicky pointed out that by going through this kind of ordered analysis it was possible not only to characterize fully a given object of some kind but also it was possible to set out the list of characteristics which would be expected to hold for any object likely to fall within the same class. From this set of general characteristics it becomes possible by permutation and combination to work out the likely characteristics of objects which do not yet exist but which might be capable of achievement.

Zwicky himself has applied this kind of thinking to fields in which he is interested particularly to the study of possible new kinds of space vehicles (Figure 1) which are *things to be invented*, and to the study of possible forms of existence of stellar bodies which are *things to be discovered.*

Zwicky does not seem to have noted the problems of levels of scrutiny. By this is meant the levels at which one kind of behaviour becomes more or less significant than another. For example, in dealing with the structure of matter, we may observe notable changes of behaviour if we take the atomic level, the crystal level, or the bulk level. Nor does Zwicky seem to have considered the way in which the particular characteristics are interrelated.

The only readily available book on morphological method, *Morphological Creativity*, by M. S. Allen (Prentice-Hall, 1962) is not to be recommended since it is an attempt to use Zwicky's methods outside the field of engineering or science.

Designers have taken up morphological analysis because it offers a number of facilities, one of which is now becoming of great interest among people concerned with technological forecasting. This latter interest is clearly related to the capability of carrying through some kind of rational analysis of alternative but still hypothetical possibilities. But there is the further interest that the morphological analysis gives us light on interrelationships. This is lacking in any clear sense in Zwicky's example but emerges elsewhere in discussions on system design.

It is quite clear that, if we can arrange characteristics within a box or matrix of some kind, we can also set up some relationship arrangement. If we take the primary notion of the morphological box, add to it the notion of level of scrutiny and the notion of interrelationship, then we obtain the essential features of present-day morphological analysis as it is beginning to be practised in this country and elsewhere in the field of design.

Relationships of Morphological Analysis with Other Design Approaches

It is important to emphasize the fact that morphological analysis, while it has values by itself, becomes more important because it can be shown to link up with critical examination and also the use of the system model analogy.

An essential feature of the critical examination approach is to consider what other alternative course of action may possibly exist.

Morphological analysis provides a method of rational analysis. As far as general system models are concerned, it is possible to have characteristics which are interrelated in a way typical of a given system.

It is important to note that the characteristics mentioned may be of many kinds. We are likely to meet basic physical properties such as density, shapes of any geometrical complexity, durations, and, finally, actions of at least two different levels. These are all concerned with hardware or processes. But we still have, as engineers, to consider alternative human or natural occurrences. It is not intended to pay much consideration to these two groups at present.

Relationships between Design and Engineering

So far there might appear to be little relationship between the design method and engineering design. The relatively simple example of a spanner should clarify this:

TABLE 1

A. device for engaging nut	B. device for applying a turning force
open	direct
closed	indirect
box	length
size	shape
square	racheted
hexagonal	torque controlled
dodecagonal	manual
adjustable	mechanical
etc.	etc.

(i) The problems: a device for tightening or untightening a nut on a bolt.

(ii) Boundaries, constraints and values (from systems approach):

cost
material
size
function (which might include: specificity to size/shape of nut, use, user, adaptability, etc.).
These are all interdependent to a certain extent and also help define the selection criteria.

(iii) Critical examination: Who will use it? What is it to be used for? These also help to define the criteria.

(iv) Morphological analysis: This gives all the possible alternatives for making up the spanner, from which selection may be made according to specified criteria from (ii) and (iii).

The final solution will comprise one or more alternatives from each part A and B; selected by application of criteria arising from (ii) and (iii) (see also criteria selection in the OSCAT project below).

The problem is clearly defined. The systems approach and critical examination are closely related and interdependent, and may in fact be reversed. One or more of the three named strategies (Page, Gregory and Marples) may also be necessary to help make decisions prior to morphological analysis. The criteria for this latter operation are very dependent on the previous ones. It is not intended to work through this example, but to indicate the range of possibilities. For example, a specialized versatile motor mechanic's tool for removing wheel nuts may be required – a 'spider', or a general purpose handymans tool – a small 'adjustable'. Let us consider the normal valve used for shutting off or controlling the flow of fluids. What are the general features it must have? What are the kinds of ways in which these general features may be brought into actuality as far as shape is concerned? There are also, of course, other possibilities of alternatives, e.g. in respect of materials of construction. In Table 2 are listed some of the likely possibilities. This list is not set up as complete and any suggestions for further alternatives will be welcome.

A feature of valves and many other devices is that they have to be operated. They may be operated by hand or by some device. Frequently we wish to make them compatible both for hand operation and device operation. Let us just consider hand operation. This need for rotation or some other kind of movement is a common feature of engineering. It brings us directly in contact with a man-machine interaction problem and with system boundary problems.

A similar procedure may be carried out on process design, but in such relatively complex problems, one strategy may frequently dominate. In the case of OSCAT, morphological analysis is the main technique employed in solution, and the term used to describe this approach to solving a design problem is called the Morphological approach.

The Morphological Approach

The principles of morphological analysis have been outlined above. In its simplest form, all possible alternatives to a given problem are found, followed by evaluation to give the optimum solution. In order to treat the alternatives in the manner described below, each must be regarded as a distinct entity, which may be a unit operation (as in OSCAT), or a physical feature (e.g. the handle of a spanner – see above) as examples. It is this assumption of complete independence that permits relatively rapid and straightforward evaluation of many alternatives. In design practice after this stage the clear definition may be slackened for more detailed study.

TABLE 2 *Features of a Valve* (does not cover full product profile; omits e.g. fabrication, assembly, effect of orientation)

---

(1) *Flow system function* (note: single channel, multiple channel, and compounds)
- *a.* inlet
- *b.* gap change device (see further details)
- *c.* exit

(2) *Flow system embodiment*
- *a.* materials
- *b.* inlet(s) junction (s)
- *c.* exit(s) junction(s)
- *d.* enclosure (note relationship with closure motion device, etc.)
- *e.* support

(3) *Gap change device*
- *a.* function (on-off; control, rough, sensitive, wide range, etc.)
- *b.* gap seal (metal-to-metal, i.e. 'material-self', rigid, deformable, liquid, etc.)
- *c.* gap change geometry
- *d.* closure motion
- *e.* closure motion device

(4) *Gap change geometry*

i. *closure geometry*	ii. *motion geometry*	
plane-plane	slide parallel	
	slide (disc or sector)	
	normal parallel	
	flap	
cylindrical piston-cylinder	slide axial	combination
	slide rotary	
cone-cylinder	axial	
cone-cone	axial	
	rotary	
ball-cylinder	axial	
ball-cone	axial	
ball-spherical body	rotary	

(5) *Closure motion device*
- *a.* Energy source: manual, gravity, mechanical, pneumatic (including line pressure effect), hydraulic (including line pressure effect), electric, etc.
- *b.* motion train
- *c.* seal device operation
- *d.* location of motion device
- *e.* enclosure seal

Figure 2 depicts a simple analysis, where there are nine alternative solutions to the problem, all but one being excluded by application of criterion 'A'. The first part of the operation is termed divergence, where the alternatives are generated, and the second part convergence, where selection or evaluation takes place. This approach may be further complicated in two ways:

(1) by applying several criteria consecutively to converge to a unique solution

(2) by splitting the initial problem into basic parts or functions, followed by a search to generate the alternatives for each part.

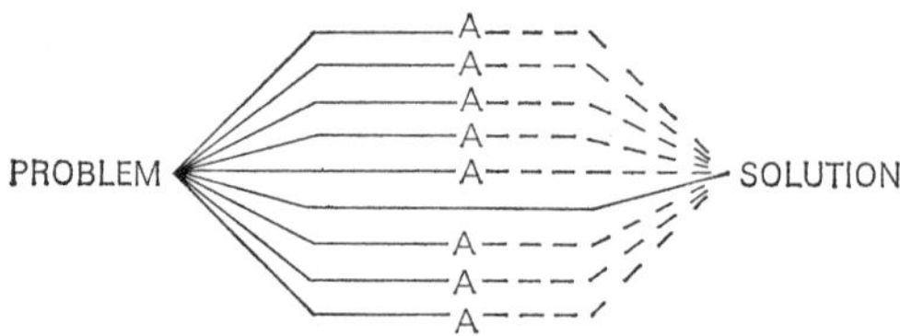

Figure 2. Application of criterion ' A ' eliminates most of the alternatives.

These effects are depicted in Figures 3A and 3B respectively. The problem in Figure 3B is divided into three functions, and one alternative from each makes up the solution, e.g. a three-stage process. The divergence-convergence concept is also apparent with a maximum of $5 \times 5 \times 5 = 125$ three-stage route alternatives.

Conventional morphological analysis as reported severally in Gregory [2] usually employs a pre-set sequence of operations diverging in a combinatorial manner and converging to a unique solution. The rest of this paper is devoted to showing how the method outlined above is developed into a useful technique for improving long-range process design.

Process Design

It may often prove difficult to translate these design method concepts into conventional process design. This may be due to a variety of reasons, including the time element of competition, necessity of using existing plant, ease of buying 'off the shelf', and high specificity to feedstocks, products and other boundaries. In such cases morphological analysis, considerably restricted, may still be carried out on certain parts of the process. This may be described as a 'tight' morphology; when constraints are imposed, due to interrelationships (number, sequence, etc.) and dependence on external variables. An example is illustrated by Figure 4. At point X–X there is a maximum of twenty alternative routes involving all four basic parts arranged in order from

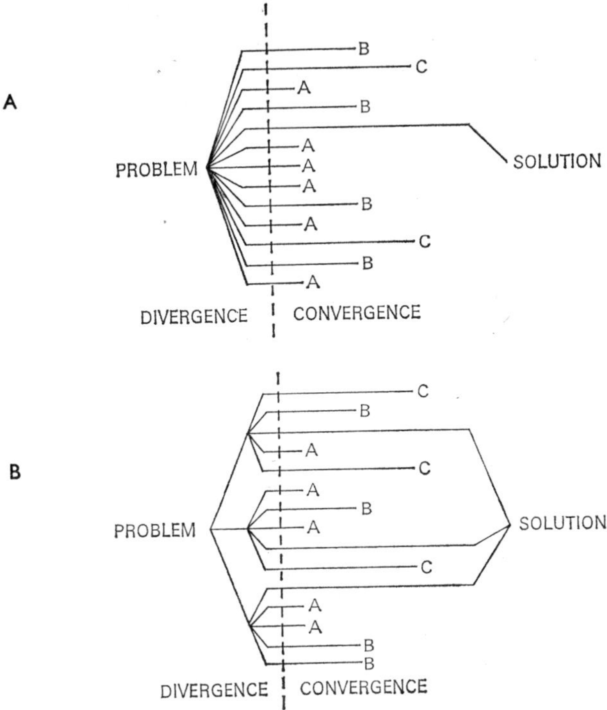

Figure 3. (A) Successive application of criteria A, B, C; (B) A, B, C are criteria The solution is made up from each initial group of five.

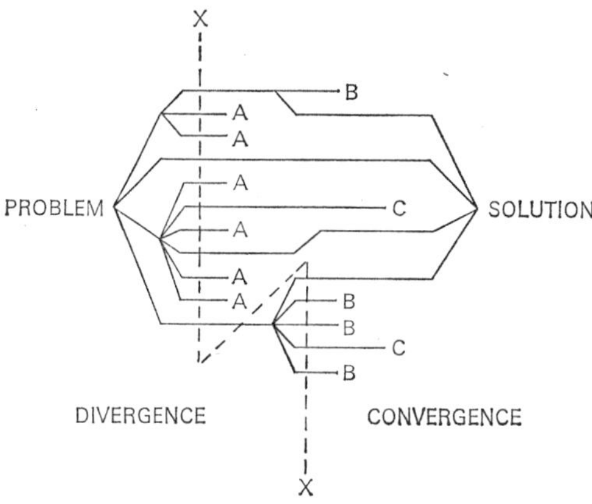

Figure 4.

top to bottom. Complete permutation gives over 400 alternatives of four stages.

When undertaking long-range process design, there are usually fewer, if any, restrictions. It becomes possible, therefore, to diverge not only as outlined above in a combinational technique, but also by including complete permutational interchange between the alternatives. This is best illustrated by diagrams. Figure 5A shows how this may be applied to a simple two-stage process, with three alternatives per stage giving a total of eighteen alternative processing routes. The route starts with an alternative from the top set followed by an alternative from the bottom set; or vice versa. When depicted in this manner, each route may be traced through from feedstock to product. Figure 5B is a further development.

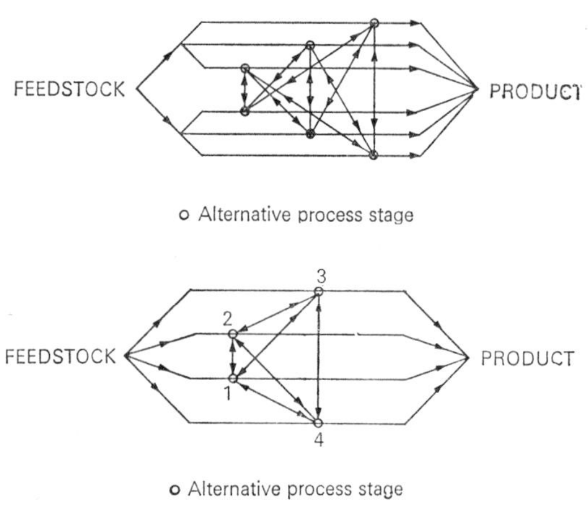

Figure 5, A and B.

In this second example there are four processing routes of one stage, twelve of two stages, twenty-four of three stages and ninety-six of four stages without repetition of any stage. Elimination may be achieved by interposing criteria at suitable points as in previous examples. Figure 6 shows how complex such diagrams may become. This very complete approach may be seen as analysis of a slack morphology and is particularly suited to long-range process design as it permits consideration of every possible alternative with evaluation in successive retractable steps. It is relatively simple to backtrack in the light of technological advances and repeat parts of the analysis (Marples' strategy), particularly where computerization has been introduced. It will be more useful to discuss the application and long-range aspects of this technique in terms of work on the OSCAT project.

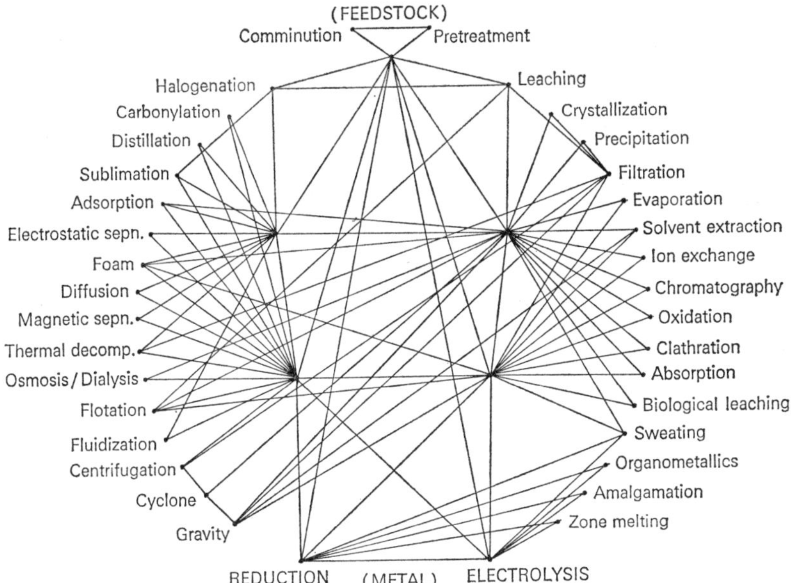

Figure 6.

OSCAT *Project*

The origins and aims of the OSCAT project have been discussed (above, 1 and 9). The 'best' processing route or routes from an iron-bearing feedstock to a shaped pure iron product is found by applying morphological analysis as described above.

Any metallurgical operation of extracting metal from an ore involves three basic steps:

(1) Separation – extracting and purifying the metal values from the gangue.

(2) Reduction – reducing the metal compound to metal.

(3) Shaping – forming the metal into a useful and acceptable shape.

Although most processes have these steps in the order given above, theoretically any arrangement is possible. This has been discussed at length [9] and is beyond the scope of this paper.

It is possible to construct a system similar to Figure 3 where the problem is split into the three basic parts and alternatives found for each part, but allowing total permutation of the alternatives. A simplification may be introduced, however, by considering Reduction as a separation method, and by the fact that generally Shaping is a direct result of the reduction step and need not therefore be regarded as a distinct operation. (See [12] for complete discussions of these simplifications.) The problem thus reduces to one of finding all possible alternative separation methods (including reduction), permuting these to give processing routes, and selecting optimal routes by application of criteria.

At a relatively early stage in the project, the workload was split into two major parts – 'wet' and 'dry'. The former covers those processes in which the iron always stays in the liquid or solid phase, while the latter covers those processes in which the iron is vapourized as a volatile compound. In order to clarify the procedure, only the 'wet' processes are discussed.

A comprehensive list of all known separation methods was compiled from the literature, which is summarized in Table 3. This was cross-checked for completeness against similar lists drawn up by other members of the project from different sources. These methods were classified by phases, and those peculiar to 'dry' or gaseous processes are in parentheses and not considered further. However, to give an idea of the complexity of the problem, the network of alternatives is shown in Figure 6 based on Figure 5B.

There are a number of separation methods in Table 3 which are termed 'Mechanical aids' and labelled 'M'. These are standard mechanical (i.e. non-mass transfer) separation methods which are well documented and generally applicable. In some cases they may be understood to be an integral part of another separation method; for example filtration with precipitation. Filtration may also be replaced by centrifugation, cyclone, gravity settling, etc., depending on circumstances. As such, therefore, these methods are not considered in the following processing route planning and selection.

There are thus twenty-seven possible separation methods which might be used in a chemical process for the separation of iron. Theoretically therefore, as far as morphological analysis is concerned, these may be combined together in any order to give a 'process'. In view of the large number of alternatives, it was decided that preliminary selection should be computerized. Complete permutation gives:

27 routes of 1 stage
729 routes of 2 stages
19,683 routes of 3 stages
531,441 routes of 4 stages
14,348,907 routes of 5 stages
387,420,489 routes of 6 stages, etc.

Of course, many of these alternatives are highly improbable, if not impossible, technically; and may therefore be easily eliminated.

Before an evaluation of the alternatives could be attempted, it was important to list the boundaries that apply, and also any assumptions that need to be made in generating the processing routes. Since OSCAT

TABLE 3

(Absorption		G–L)
Adsorption		G–S, L–S
Amalgamation		L–S
Biological leaching		L–S
(Carbonylation		G–L, G–S)
Centrifugation	M	G–L, G–S, L–L, L–S
Chromatography		G–G, L–L
Clathration		L–S
(Condensation		G–L, G–S)
Crystallization		L–S
Cyclone	M	G–L, G–S, L–L, S–S
Dialysis		L–L
(Diffusion		G–G)
Distillation		G–L
Electrodialysis		L–S
Electrolysis aqueous		L–S
Electrolysis fused		L–L, L–S
Electrophoresis		L–S
Electrostatic separation	M	G–L, G–S, L–S, S–S
Evaporation		G–L
Filtration	M	G–S, L–S
Flotation		L–S
Fluidization	M	G–S, L–S
Foam		G–L
Gravity	M	G–L, G–S, L–L, S–S
(Halogenation (non-aqueous)		G–G, G–L, G–S, S–S)
(Ion beam		G–G)
Ion exchange		L–L, L–S
Ion exclusion		L–S
Leaching		L–S
Magnetic separation	M	S–S
Organometallic		G–L, L–L, L–S
Osmosis		L–S
Oxidation		G–G, G–L, G–S, L–L, L–S, S–S
Precipitation chemical		G–S, L
Precipitation electrodeposition		L–S
Precipitation electrostatic		G–S, L–S
Reduction (chemical)		G–G, G–L, G–S, L–L, L–S, S–S
Solvent extraction		L–L
(Sublimation		G–S)
Sweating		L–S
Thermal decomposition		G–S, L–S, S–S
(Volatilization		G–G, G–L, G–S)
Zone melting		L–S

Stage 1 is a paper study (Page strategy), all information is obtained from the literature.

Boundaries

(1) Knowledge – information availability, and feasibility for iron separation.

(2) Compatibility.

(3) Economics.

These boundiaries in fact formed the basis for the selection criteria (see Figure 7).

Assumptions

(1) Feedstock – this may be scrap, ore, superbeneficiated ore, mill-scale, fume or pickle liquor; of which only the first two deserve serious consideration [13].

(2) Comminution and Pretreatment – these are almost certainly necessary for ore feedstock, and to a certain extent are dependent on the first stage of a process. The two steps are not included in the route generation.

(3) 'Mechanical aids' – as stated earlier these are not included.

(4) Recycle steps – not included also as these would depend on reagents employed.

(5) Number of stages – these are restricted to four. There is strong evidence [12, 13, 14] that the number of stages is related to capital cost, which constitutes a major part of the total cost of operation [13]. As ancilliaries such as mentioned above and below are not included in the routes, this decision appears reasonable for a first trial (Gregory strategy). (Full justification was, in fact, obtained on completion of the analysis.)

(6) Impurities – any impurities that may contaminate the iron, are ignored at this stage – only iron-bearing streams are considered. Additional purification stages may be added if more detailed investigations later proves them necessary. Any credit that may benefit from selling byproducts is likewise ignored.

(7) Compatibility – this is based on the phase compatibility of successive separation methods, and forms the basis of the computer programme for elimination.

(8) Repetition – no method shall occur more than once in any processing route.

It is possible to generate all the processing route alternatives within a computer. At the same time, the above assumptions may be applied as rules to effect the elimination and complete the first step towards finding the optimal processing routes. This is represented in Figure 7. There are, however, two ways of approaching this particular problem:

(1) Generation of all possibilities following by elimination according to the assumptions set out above gives about 10,000 alternatives for closer study, particularly the first boundary.

(2) Elimination of separation methods by the first boundary initially, followed by generation and elimination as for (1), gives less than 100 alternatives.

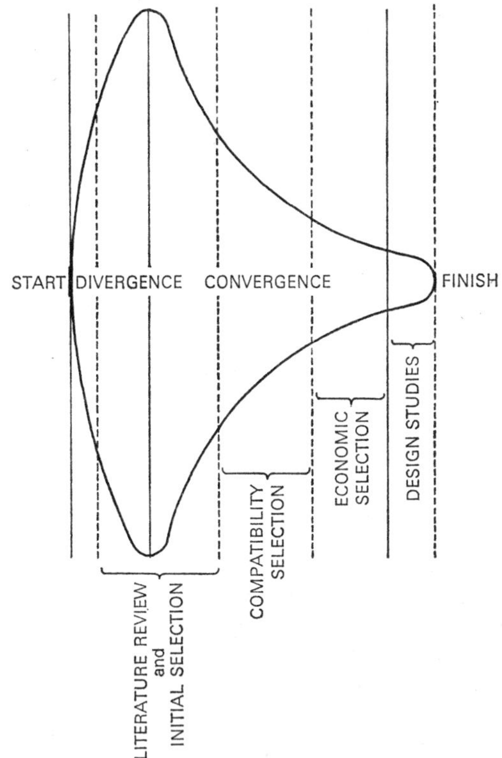

Figure 7. The maximum number of alternatives is represented by the widest part of the figure between ' Divergence ' and ' Convergence '. The OSCAT evaluation described in the text is taken up to line A.

Assessment of knowledge and feasibility is a relatively straightforward manual task, and is more easily performed on twenty-seven separation methods than 10,000 processing routes. The second alternative was therefore accepted.

A very comprehensive literature survey of all twenty-seven separation methods with particular reference to iron separation was carried out [12]. Table 4 indicates how methods are eliminated on the grounds indicated. Fuller details have been published [12] but are beyond the scope of this paper.

TABLE 4

Acceptable	*Not Feasible*	*No Information*	*Not Applicable*
		Adsorption	Adsorption (?)
	Amaglamation		
	Biological leaching		Chromatography
		Clathration	
Crystallization		Dialysis	Dialysis (?)
			Distillation
			Electrodialysis (see Electrolysis)
Electrolysis aqueous			
Electrolysis fused			Electrophoresis
Evaporation to dryness		Flotation	
		Foam	
Ion exchange		Ion exclusion	
Leaching			Organometallic compound
		Osmosis	
Oxidation (leach or precipitative–q.v.)			
Precipitation chemical			
Reduction chemical			
Solvent extraction		Sweating	
Thermal decomposition			Zone melting

In order to distinguish between the very different reductive systems, electrolysis was divided into aqueous and fused, and reduction into reduction of a solid phase and of a liquid phase. The possible stages then became:

Crystallization
Electrolysis aqueous
Electrolysis fused
Evaporation (to dryness)
Ion exchange
Leaching
Precipitation
Reduction–L (of a liquid phase)
Reduction–S (of a solid phase)

Solvent extraction

Thermal decomposition

'Compatibility' rules were devised for two-, three- and four-stage routes made up of combinations of the above eleven methods; and subject also to the assumptions and rules laid down above.

(*a*) As the feedstock is a solid, the first stage can only be leaching.

(*b*) The last stage is reduction or electrolysis, and no further purification is required. This may be expressed as:

Electrolysis aqueous cannot be followed immediately by: crystallization, electrolysis aqueous, electrolysis fused, evaporation, ion exchange, leaching, precipitation, reduction–L, reduction–S, solvent extraction, or thermal decomposition. In other words, electrolysis aqueous cannot be followed by any other method. The same applies to electrolysis fused, reduction–L, and reduction–S.

Similar expressions were derived for the other separation methods:

(*c*) Crystallization cannot be followed immediately by crystallization, evaporation, leaching or precipitation.

(*d*) Evaporation by: crystallization, electrolysis aqueous, evaporation, ion exchange, precipitation, reduction–L, solvent extractions.

(*e*) Ion exchange by: electrolysis fused, ion exchange, reduction–S, thermal decomposition.

(*f*) Leaching by: electrolysis fused, leaching, reduction–S, thermal decomposition.

(*g*) Precipitation by: crystallization, evaporation, precipitation.

(*h*) Solvent extraction by: electrolysis fused, leaching, reduction–S, solvent extraction.

(*i*) Thermal decomposition by: crystallization, electrolysis aqueous, evaporation, ion exchange precipitation, reduction–L, solvent extraction.

The above 'compatibility' rules are based on the phase relationship of adjacent stages, and with no repetition of any method. These rules were made the basis of a computer programme for generating and selecting processing routes, but space does not permit reproduction here. A salient feature is that each alternative route is generated, checked for acceptance or rejection according to the rules set out above, and if accepted is printed out on a lineprinter simultaneously with computation in the form given in Table 5. Thus a large memory

TABLE 5

Leaching	Electrolysis aq.			(2)
Leaching	Crystallization	Electrolys aq		(14)
Leaching	Crystallization	Thermal decmp.	Reduction–S	(40)
		Processing routes Total:		56

is not required, only that necessary for the programme itself. This was designed to calculate firstly two-stage routes, then three-stage and finally four-stage routes. Table 5 shows the first route in each category as an example, and the total number of routes.

Economic evaluation followed based also on the conclusions of the literature survey [12]. Each method concerned in the fifty-six routes obtained from the computer programme was individually examined. In order to make a selection it was necessary to fix arbitrarily a maximum operating cost per stage of £10 per ton of iron produced (Gregory strategy). This figure was chosen because at any stage of operation it is substantial in relation to the value of the iron or steel product, which may be worth £30–£80 per ton. Clearly any stage costing much more than this would have to be automatically excluded from consideration. In fact this crude economic evaluation could be included in the previous operation, but has been separated for clarity. The following methods were judged uneconomic from information available [12]:

Electrolysis fuses
Ion exchange
Precipitation (except oxidative)
Solvent extraction (in fact a 'borderline' case).

After applying this criterion, only the following six processing routes remain.

LEACHING	ELECTROLYSIS AQ		
LEACHING	CRYSTALLIZATION	ELECTROLYSIS AQ	
LEACHING	CRYSTALLIZATION	REDUCTION–S	
LEACHING	CRYSTALLIZATION	THERMAL DECOMPN.	REDUCTION–S
LEACHING	PRECIPITATION	THERMAL DECOMPN.	REDUCTION–S
LEACHING	EVAPORATION DRY	THERMAL DECOMPN.	REDUCTION–S

Thus by applying three sets of criteria, 551,880 theoretical processing routes have been reduced to six.

Discussion

While the processing routes set out above are by no means complete, they do represent the essential steps in a process and provide the framework for more detailed study. The importance of regarding each step as a clearly defined stage is also apparent, especially as evaluation is carried out under conditions of low information availability. It is only after the possibilities have been reduced by a large factor, as for example on the OSCAT project, that necessary ancilliaries and details may be added.

This is well illustrated by reference to the RCA Process (Research Council of Alberta, Canada) [12, 15], which is an investigation into the hydrochloric acid leaching of ore or scrap to produce pure iron powder. The process is in fact included in the final six routes which provides a useful cross-check that no unreasonable assumptions have been made, and also provides justification for the assumptions made earlier. This is represented by:

Leaching
Crystallization
Reduction–S
3 steps

The complete process stepwise is:

Ore preparation
Ore reduction
Leaching
Filtration and washing
Evaporative *Crystallization*
Crystal separation
Crystal drying
Briquetting
Reduction
Gas separation (HCl recycle)
Hydrogen production (3 steps)
Total 13 steps

It is clear that the basic routes generated and selected by the computer completely define the processes. Subsequent design studies employing possibly one or more of the techniques described earlier establish additional secondary process steps and conditions. Morphological analysis was also effectively employed in the manual selection of leaching acids using knowledge availability, feasibility, compatibility and economics once again as criteria. The operation resembled Figure 6A. These techniques may be applied to process design right through to the design of the hardware as discussed by Gregory [16], which is very near the 'Finish' of Figure 7.

Although the overall number of alternatives may in theory reach astronomical proportions, the selection may be carried out in stages and/or with the help of a computer. Cross-checks may be made at intervals, therefore, and new information, or variations, or developments in technology fed in at any stage in the process design. Criteria may be checked and adjusted, and alternatives re-evaluated. All these may be carried out at any time in the life of a process design project, which may be in excess of fifteen years, and considerably simplifies the task of reassessing alternatives, particularly when the selection has been computerized.

Conclusions

The suitability of morphological analysis for long-range process design of large-scale projects has, it is hoped, been made apparent.

It is a method which considers every known alternative to a problem in order to find the 'best' overall process(es), which in fact may be completely defined from feedstock to product using this technique. Although the solution(s) may be obvious and very likely to be those found intuitively, the technique ensures that the designer covers all possibilities, leaving no method unconsidered and also that he is conscious of all relevant (and usually irrelevant also) developments and possibilities. It is the examination of the fundamentals of a process in this manner that create favourable circumstances for radical innovation to occur, not necessarily as a direct result of rigorous analysis, but possibly sparked off by well-disciplined thought.

This appears likely to happen in forecasting the results of the OSCAT project. Against these advantages and possibilities, the question of 'does it pay?' must surely be answered favourably.

Finally, it is believed that this paper provides one of the first rationalizations and theoretical treatments of morphological analysis applied to chemical processes; and that within the OSCAT project is one of the first chemical process designs to be carried out from conception using this technique both in substantial depth and rigorously. It is to be hoped that development does not stop here, but that designers will become increasingly aware of the usefulness of this tool and use it to their advantage.

References

1 S. A. Gregory, in *Symp. Europ. Fed. Chem. Eng.* (I. Chem. E. to be published).
2 S. A. Gregory (Ed.) *The Design Method* (Butterworths 1966).
3 A. L. Bloomfield, *Trns. I. Chem. E.* **1** (1932), 95–103.
4 W. R. Ashby, *An Introduction to Cybernetics* (Chapman and Hall 1956).
5 A. D. Hall, *A Methodology for Systems Engineering* (Van Nostrand 1962).
6 R. M. Currie, *Work Study* (Pitman 1963).
7 F. Zwicky, in *Courant Anniversary Volume* (Interscience).
8 H. A. Simon and P. A. Simon, *Behavl. Sci.* **7** (1962), 425.
9 E. A. Feigenbaum and J. Feldman (Eds). *Computers and Thought* (McGraw-Hill 1963).
10 A. Newall and H. A. Simon, Ref. 8 pp. 279–96.
11 A. Newall, J. C. Shaw and H. A. Simon, Ref. 8 pp. 39–70.
12 A. V. Bridgewater, *A Preliminary Evaluation of New Processes for the Manufacture of Iron by way of Liquid/Solid Phase Systems*, M.Sc. Thesis (University of Aston in Birmingham 1966).
13 OSCAT Project, *Final Report Stage* 1.
14 W. H. Gore, *A Study of Capital Cost Estimating for Preliminary Process Evaluation*, M.Sc. Thesis (University of Aston in Birmingham 1967).
15 C. P. Gravenor, G. J. Govett and T. Rigg, *Can. Min. Met. Bull.* **624**, 4 (1964), 421–8.
16 S. A. Gregory, in *European Conference on Technological Forecasting* (Glasgow 1968).

J. A. HOBBS

Trend Projection

The interest that a company has in technological forecasting depends on its marketing policy. An industrial leader must be interested in the first applications of a technological change. The military and space organizations are similarly interested in knowing when a new facility or a change will become possible. Many companies, however, will be interested not in first applications but in knowing how a declining technology may be affected by innovation, or how soon a new technology will achieve sufficient volume for action to be needed.

In the case of the latter type of organization their principal requirement is a forecast of the behaviour of a market resulting from the penetration of a new technology. Four pieces of information are needed:

(1) The introductory date of an innovation.

(2) Its maximum penetration of the market of which it is a part.

(3) The time it will take to build up to its peak rate of annual sales.

(4) The pattern of growth before and after the peak year.

This requirement is greater than that needed by the organization wishing to know only the introductory date, but on the other hand it is likely that in some cases the introductory date is either past or is much closer than it was for the forecaster who had to predict it for the industrial leader or the military. Under these conditions it is likely that the forecaster will have much more information available on which to estimate items 1 to 4.

If the pattern of growth conforms to a known shape, then it becomes easier to predict item 4 once items 1 to 3 are known. We have found, particularly in the example of world shipping fleet composition, that the proportion of new items in a population does follow a predictable pattern. Biologists have also observed this pattern in the growth of subpopulations with distinct characteristics. The curve which describes the pattern of growth is variously called the logistic, the epidemic curve, or the S curve. We will use the latter term.

We will show first what information is needed to describe the S curve and what information it in turn provides. The first case will be for a fixed population and only two types, the new and the old. We will then generalize to the more common case of an increasing population, and finally deal with the general case of several succeeding innovations in an expanding population. The concepts which we will develop were used to forecast the demand for several categories of shipping and can be applied to forecast the annual penetration of new technologies once certain key predictions are made about timing and maximum penetration. We will then show how this approach will be applied to an investigation in the electronics industry.

Suppose we plot, year by year, the proportion of new items in a fixed population of N items, which consists only of the new type and the old type which it is replacing.

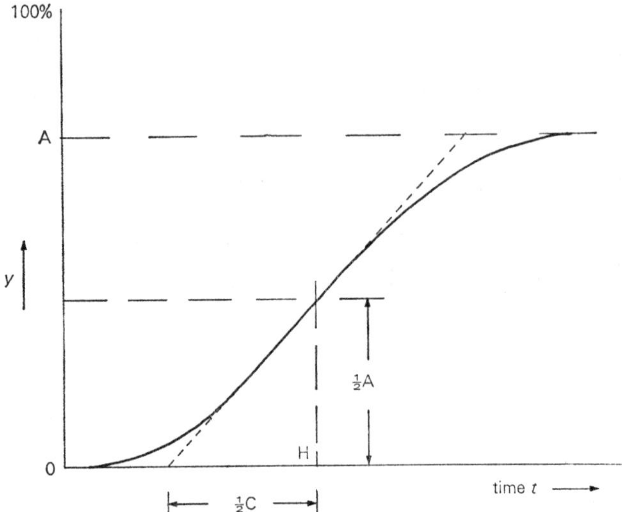

Figure 1. The S curve.

$$y = \frac{A}{1+BC^{-ct}}.$$

The curve shown in Figure 1 would represent the way in which the proportion of new items rises from 0 to A per cent. It can be described by a mathematical equation which involves knowing three numbers; A, the maximum proportion of the population that the new item will reach; C, a constant which depends on the slope of the curve at the halfway stage. If the time (t) is measured from the present, then a constant, B, takes account of the position of the halfway point (H). The proportion of new items to be expected by year t is given by equation 1 below.

$$y = \frac{A}{1+Be^{-ct}} \qquad \text{...(1)}$$

The actual number of new items will be obtained by multiplying the total population by y. Another way of describing the S curve is to write down the expression for the rate of increase in the proportion y each year.

This expression turns out to be:

$$\frac{dy}{dt} = \frac{1}{A} cy(A-y) \qquad \text{...(2)}$$

In words, this means that the rate of increase in y depends on the proportion of new items in existence (y) and on the remaining proportion of old items which the new item can replace ($A-y$). This is intuitively sound. Thus if we know A, B, and C we can make forecasts for the proportion of new items year by year throughout the product lifetime. If we know the total population (N) we can also convert the proportion (y) into the actual number of new items in use. The number of new items introduced each year is also found by multiplying N by the change in y in any year.

If we are correct in our assumption that a product will develop along the S-shaped curve, then a forecast of its total sales each year is obtained from only three statistics. There remains the problem of estimating the values of A, B and C, and this is dealt with later.

It can be seen, however, from Figure 1 that the smaller the value of C the more rapid is the development to maturity.

The assumptions of a fixed population over the years is restrictive and a more general case is one where the population is itself growing. We will discuss the case where there is an exponential rate of growth although more strictly it is likely to be a small part of a very much larger S curve. Over the period considered we will represent the growth of total population by:

$$N = N_0 e^{kt} \qquad \text{...(3)}$$

N_0 is the current population at time $t=0$; k is a constant which depends on the rate of expansion of the population as a whole. Clearly other expressions can be used to represent the population growth.

The total number of the new item in year t is still given by $N.y$, but the expression now becomes:

$$N.y = N_0 e^{kt}\left(\frac{A}{1+Be^{-ct}}\right) \qquad \text{...(4)}$$

What industry is interested in is the annual sales in year t which are found by differentiating equation 4. This becomes complicated looking and from now onwards we will deal in terms of two ratios which are of interest.

The first is the ratio of the rate of innovation of the new item (c in equation 1) to the rate of increase in the total population (k in equation 3). Call the ratio $c/k=m$.

A large value for m can arise either because c is large, implying a slow rate of penetration into the market, or because k is small. A small value of k implies a slowly expanding total market.

The way in which the annual sales of the new product vary with time depends on the ratio m. Figure 2 shows that the value of 4·8 is a cross-over point. If m is greater than 4·8, then there is a definite peak as the new product is rapidly sold, followed by a trough after which sales pick up again as the total market continues to expand. If m is less than 4·8, then sales rise without coming to a peak. The final rise in each case is due to the assumption of an expanding population.

The second ratio of interest is that of sales of the new item as a proportion of total expansion sales of the new and the old product. Call this ratio R and we see that in Figure 3, R rises to a peak value and eventually drops to A, its long-term proportion of the total population. The value of the peak proportion that new sales form of all expansion sales is calculable in terms of m and is:

$$\frac{A}{4}\frac{(m+1)^2}{m} \quad \text{or} \quad \frac{Am}{4} \quad \text{if } m \text{ is large.}$$

Perhaps this theoretical curve helps explain how your own products' market shares have risen and fallen in the past? The time of the peak market share is close to the halfway point H, shown in Figure 1.

Before moving on to the case of successive innovations we will incorporate the effect of scrapping of worn-out old products. The scrapping age will vary, but it can be shown that if it is assumed to be constant at p years and if the population of products has been expanding exponentially over the p years at the same rate as now, then the total market for new and old products instead of being given by ke^{kt}, which is the demand due to expansion, is increased to:

$$\frac{ke^{kt}}{1-e^{-kp}}$$

The ratio of replacement sales to total sales can be shown to be e^{-kp}, based on the assumptions made above about a fixed scrapping period and a smooth expansion rate.

It is now worth looking at the phenomenon of premature replacement or scrapping. Premature scrapping of old products must be occurring if the demand for the new product exceeds the total needs for expansion and for normal replacement.

Whether the premature scrapping caused the extra sales or whether the extra sales caused the premature scrapping depends on the product. With shipping, sales of a new type to one operator can force premature scrapping of less-efficient old vessels to would-be other operators. With other products which are replaced on a one for one basis, then a decision about premature replacement must precede an order for the new item.

To see whether one's forecasts about market shares assume premature replacement is going to take place, the expression for the old type of product's share of total sales can be plotted.

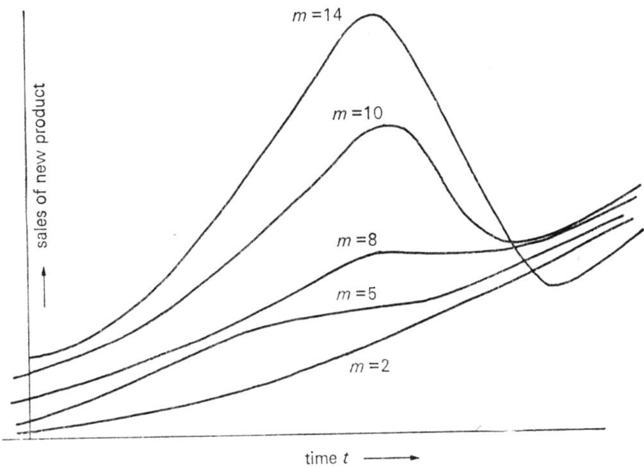

Figure 2. Annual sales of the new product in competition with the old product in an expanding total market.

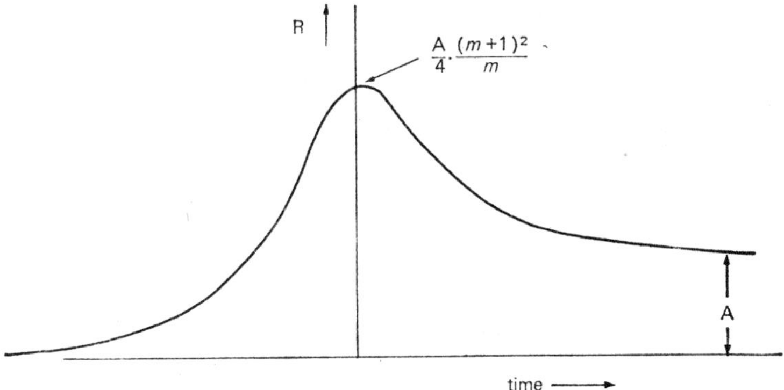

Figure 3. New products' sales as a proportion of all expansion sales (The ratio R).

Figure 4 gives three examples of the way in which this might behave. In the first case, 4.1, the new type's sales, expressed as a proportion of the total annual market for expansion and normal replacement, rise to a peak then tend towards the long-term proportion *A*. In the second case, 4.2, the new product sales are greater than the expansion and normal replacement requirements and this indicates premature scrapping must occur otherwise the proposed market share for the new product is unrealistic. However, if the new type's eventual share of the market is not 100 per cent, then sales of the old type will eventually rise again as a proportion. For this reason, in the shipping world ships

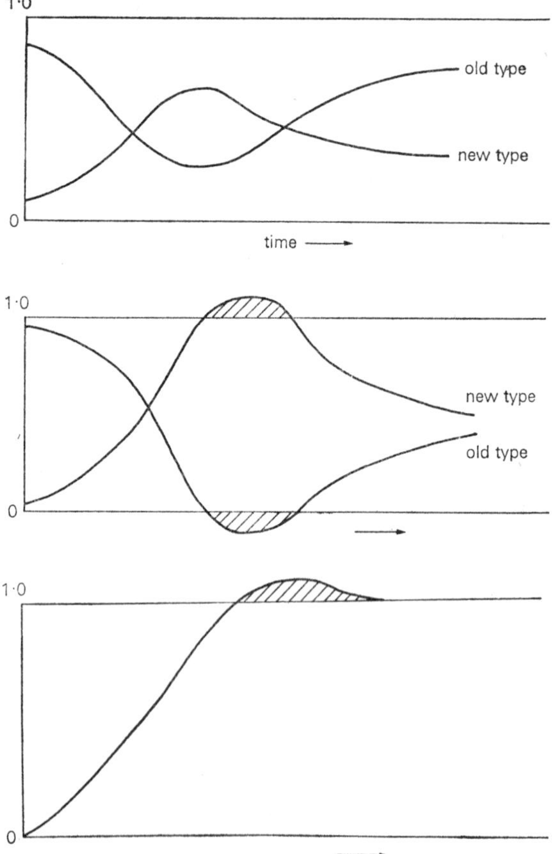

Figure 4. Market shares of old and new types, expressed as a proportion of expansion and normal replacement. (i) no premature replacements implied; (ii) implied premature replacement; (iii) eventual 100 per cent market share.

are often laid up rather than scrapped so that they obviate the need for some replacement sales later.

Figure 4.3 shows the more restricted case when the new type will eventually take over 100 per cent of the market. The sales of the new product will exceed those required for normal expansion and replacement – indicating that premature replacement of old items must occur if the S curve is followed. If premature replacement is thought unlikely, then this analysis shows the rate of penetration assumed in the S curve to be unrealistic.

These somewhat idealized cases will not be followed rigidly in practice because there are fluctuations in sales about the smooth trends shown in the figures. But the phenomenon of a drop in sales of the old type, followed by a picking up, can be predicted if the interactions of market expansion, replacement sales and the S curve for the new type are investigated. The important thing is not to become bemused by the arithmetic but to see broadly what the effect of a number of assumptions about parameters will be on sales over the years.

Successive innovations of progressively improved types can be analyzed by again considering that there are two classes only. The new type is one class and all inferior types are the other. One then has to estimate a long-term proportion (A) of the population for each new type, and a time and rate at which it will reach the halfway point (estimating B and C). Figure 5 shows an example of this based on ships of progressively diminishing sizes.

The behaviour of demand for any individual class of ship is found by taking the difference between two successive classes. An interesting phenomenon which emerged from our study of ships was that if the population is composed largely of a single type, then rapid innovation can only take place if the old type is scrapped prematurely. If there are many other types, each steadily penetrating the market, then premature scrapping of the less-efficient classes is not necessary.

It is clear also that in a rapidly expanding total market a new item can penetrate rapidly without needing or causing premature replacement.

Prediction of Parameters

It is not possible to make a good forecast of the final proportion (A) of an item in a population based on an inspection of penetration to date, unless penetration has already reached 50 per cent of maximum.

However, if one can anticipate what the eventual proportion will be – based on experts' knowledge of the function of the new type – then it becomes possible to forecast both B (timing) and c (rate of penetration) once the proportion of the new item has reached some 20 per cent of its final value.

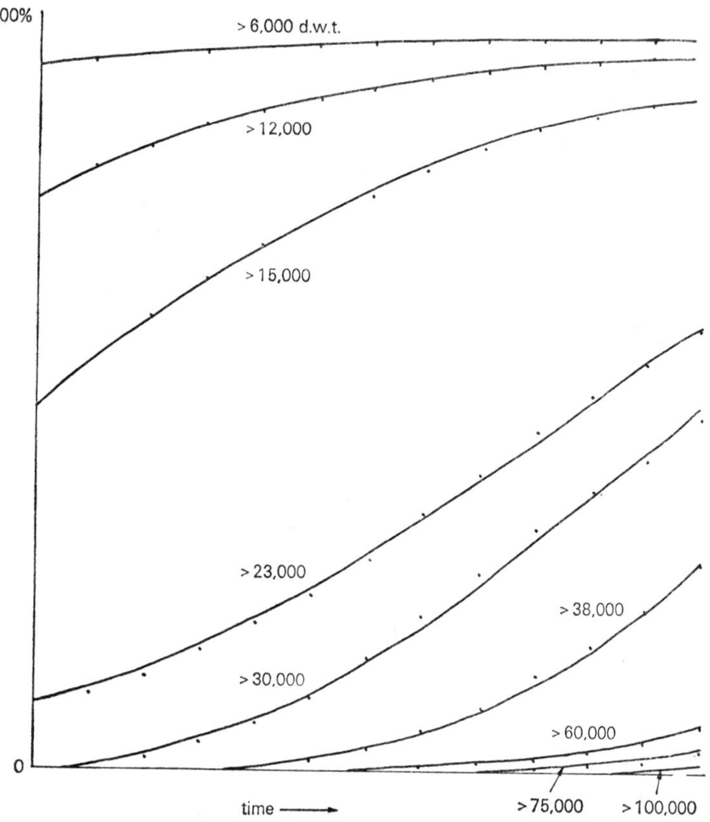

Figure 5. Population composition by size categories for the world tanker fleet.

The value of *A*, *B* and *C* all depend on the commercial incentive to introduce a new product. Additionally *B* and *C* (the speed factors) must depend on the characteristic structure of the market being supplied and of the industry supplying it. Neither can change more rapidly than they can generate money for capital from previous products or production lines.

For a technological forecast of *A*, *B* and *C* before the new product is marketed it is essential to have expert knowledge of the role of the new products, and an understanding of the normal replacement periods for equipment in the industries concerned. Given broad estimates of these replacement rates one can explore the consequences of different assumptions about *A*, *B* and *C* and about the expansion rate of the whole market as typified in our examples by the constant *k*.

The S curve discussed so far is open to criticism, but we submit that the important thing in forecasting is to use the simple first in order to prevent any difficulties with the calculations from obscuring the forecast.

An Application of the S Curve

The concepts behind the use of the S curve will be used in part of a forecast of the demand for printed circuits over the next seven years. Electronics is a rapidly changing field both with regard to the expansion in demand for equipment of various types and with regard to the components used to make those equipments.

One major change in components is the trend to miniaturization as a result of the use of integrated circuits. Integrated circuits can give lower cost per circuit provided the number of items to be produced is high enough. The break-even number will drop as technology develops and the starting point of the forecast must be predictions of the times at which different circuit applications become amenable to integrated circuit techniques. Manufacturers have two incentives to change; the first is cost and the second is size reduction. Actual changeover will depend on the time at which a certain cost-performance function reaches the right level – this fixes the starting date for the S curve.

The changeover rate then depends on the manufacturers production line policy. He may make modifications to his line, or he may wait to redesign completely to take advantage of the new technology. We will make forecasts of this rate of switching in order to fix B and C in the S curve representing the proportion of sales using the new technology.

The next requirement is to predict the ultimate role of the new technology in each application. Not all circuitry can be made by integrated techniques. The actual proportion depends on run length, cost, the importance of size and the performance characteristics demanded.

For our particular exercise we will be interested in the consequences of these changeovers to new technology in terms of their effect on printed circuits. The effect in the individual case will be estimated from a knowledge of current sizes and projected dimensions of circuit boards using the smaller components. This effect will then be converted into a trend in area per equipment as dictated by the S curve for the old types and new types of each category of equipment investigated. The level of detail will vary from industry to industry, but computers and television are examples which are worth categorizing in detail. There is also a need in some categories to project an increasing trend in the number of circuits per equipment. This will correspond to the expansion coefficient k in the previous argument.

Final demand for printed circuits, by square footage, will be calculated from forecasts of annual demand for equipments combined with the projected trends in area per equipment. Some of the equipment demands will be predicted on the basis of S curves, notably that for colour television; it is well known that it will follow an S curve, but the paucity of data, so far does not yet permit a good forecast for individual years because the long-term trend is being upset by economic conditions. There is also some uncertainty about the final proportion (A) of households that will own one, since this depends on the ultimate cost and consumer attitudes to the luxury of colour.

E. P. HAWTHORNE AND R. J. WILLS

Forecasting the Market for Certain Machine Tools, 1974-1999

The purpose of this study is to examine the technological factors affecting the potential market available to a company considering entering the metal-turning machine-tool field. Since this is a study made as part of a long-range planning effort, the period of interest has been chosen to be 1974 to 1999. Two constraints which have been specified are that, first, only machinery for the light and medium metal-working industries is to be considered and, secondly, machinery for producing 'one offs' or very small quantities is to be excluded.

Some of the background questions which the forecast is intended to answer are:

(*a*) What is the rate of diffusion of new technology into the metal working industry?

(*b*) Will this diffusion be fast enough to create profitable new market opportunities?

(*c*) If these markets are to be pursued, what scale of research and development effort will be necessary?

(*d*) What R&D facilities and skills would be required and can guidelines be given to aid the setting of R&D strategies?

The scope of such a forecast is wide and of necessity it is therefore limited to metal parts, although it is appreciated that in market terms there is a need to consider the impact of the use of non-metallic materials as a substitute for metals in such parts.

This paper is concerned with methodology of the technological forecast and not with results. We would expect that as the forecasting procedure itself is followed through, refinements of the methodology will become necessary.

Forecasting Model

Two of the main purposes of this study are: (i) to relate the development of new technology in metal turning to the changes in the demand for turned parts, and (ii) to relate changes in turning machine users products to the demands for new turning machinery.

Thus, we are concerned with the influence of research and development on the uses and design of equipment using turned parts as well as that underlying the metal turning equipment itself.

Our basic model attempts to take both of these main groups of factors into account, by building up a related series of matrices following the

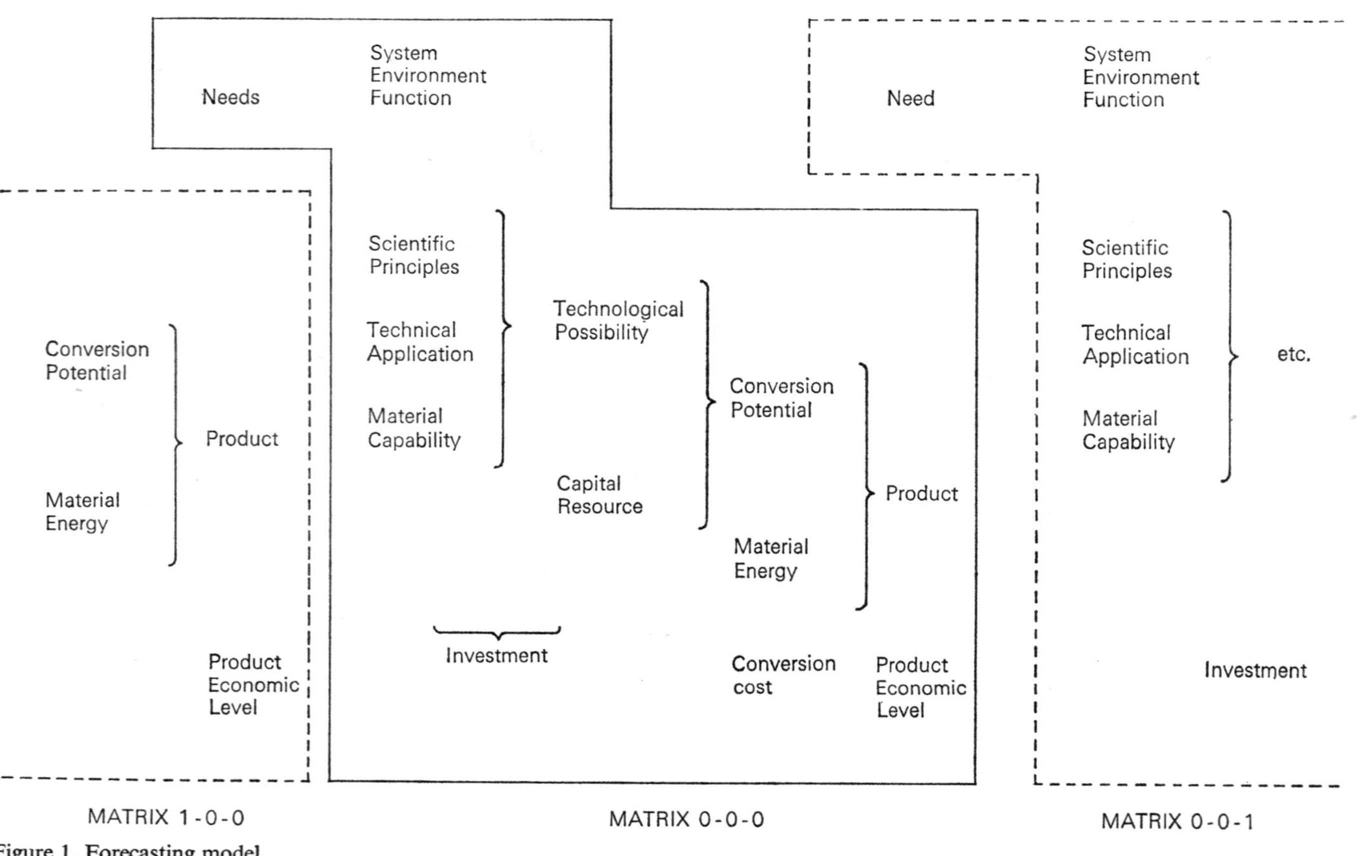

Figure 1. Forecasting model.

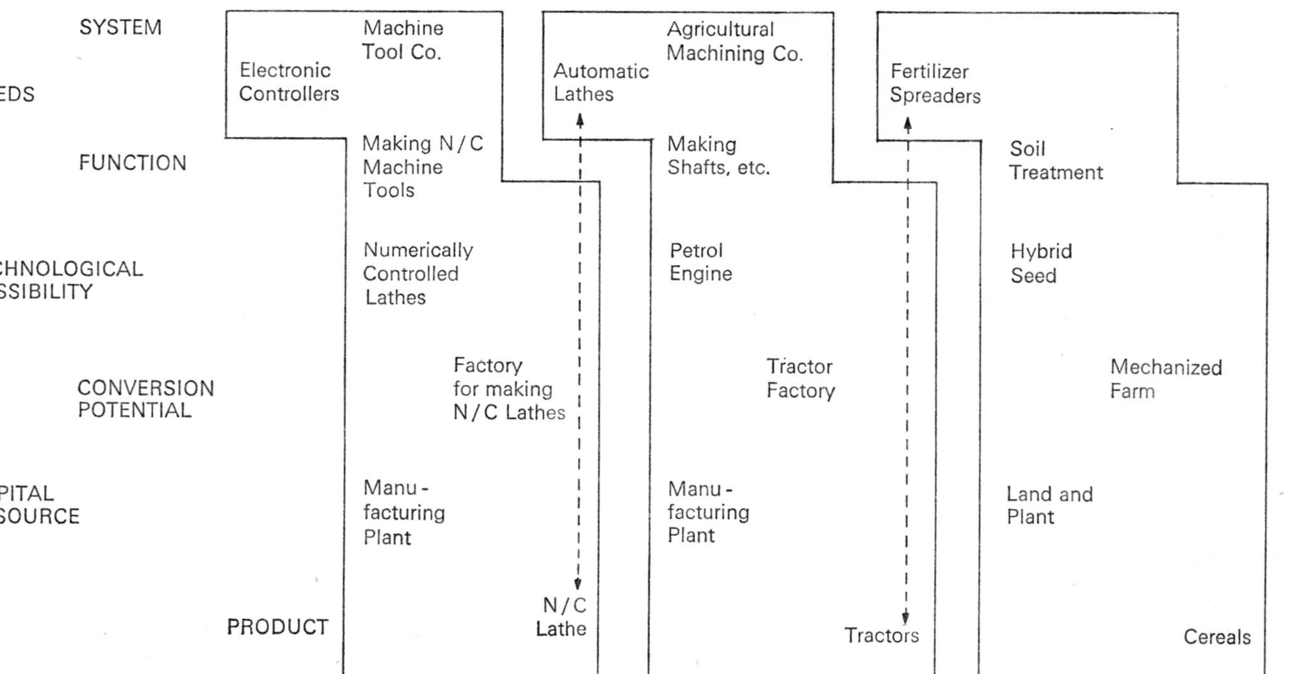

Figure 2. Related matrices.

pattern shown in Figure 1. These two separate aspects of the overall problem form interrelated parts of a closed cycle: new production techniques eventually affect the design of the goods produced but the design of the goods also helps to shape the development of the production techniques. Alternatively this can be viewed as a leap-frogging situation where, in turn, a certain section of machine tool users demand improved machinery, and following its introduction the remaining users go through a process of catching up and effectively utilizing the new machinery.

An example of such a related matrix series is shown in Figure 2. For simplicity some of the headings of Figure 1 are omitted, the remainder being listed on the left-hand side of the diagram.

The model comprises three sections. The top section refers to the *System* under investigation. This system operates under certain environment conditions and constraints and is concerned to carry out certain general *Functions*. Each general function can in turn be split down into a series of more specific functions. The system creates certain *Needs*. In the diagrams shown, the needs are shown as those which can be satisfied by a *Product*. Other systems will, of course, throw up needs requiring satisfaction in other ways, such as by services, etc.

The centre portion of each diagram is concerned with the technological basis of the activity of each system in carrying through its functions. It is particularly concerned with the mechanisms available for innovating, developing and manufacturing the products which will satisfy the systems needs.

Technological innovations arise from three sources:

(*a*) An increase in knowledge about scientific principles.

(*b*) A putting together of knowledge and ideas in a 'technical application' through design or know-how of construction, etc.

(*c*) An extension or new development of materials capability.

A combination of events in these three categories can give rise to the *Technological Possibility* of meeting a need in a better or original way – that is, we have an innovation.

However, the means for making use of such an innovation may not be available or may not even exist. Thus, only if a *Capital Resource* is available can we then have the *Possibility of Conversion* of materials into products.

Finally, of course, the need-product relationships exist only below a certain economic level of product cost. The costs corresponding to this level are dictated firstly by the potential market for the product (because this governs production quantities to which manufacturing costs are strongly related), and secondly by the costs of conversion and by the capital investment in all manner of resources including knowledge. Hence the lowest section of the matrix covers the relevant economic aspects of the activities in the other matrix sections (Figure 1).

This is a very simplified approach to the complex real-life situation. Related matrices can be built up to show other activities in the given system. Nevertheless, such a framework is necessary to ensure that the maximum number of relevant factors are considered during the study, and to provide an appreciation of the way in which these factors relate to each other.

Methodology of Forecast

(A) *Types of change.* Changes in the market for equipment for producing turned metal parts will arise from the following factors: (*a*) Growth (or decline) of the use of current types of equipment by current users; (*b*) Growth of the use of current types of equipment by new users; (*c*) Growth of the use of new types of equipment and processes by both users of current equipment and new users entering the market.

This paper is concerned with the methodology underlying the forecast of item (*c*), but it is obvious that a complete forecast would take note of items (*a*) and (*b*).

The methodology of the forecast includes the following steps:

(1) An analysis of the fundamental reasons for making turned parts.

(2) An analysis of technological possibilities.

(3) An assessment of the impact which such technological possibilities may have in the first-level matrices – those covering the machine tool manufacturing industries.

(4) The development of a series of second-level matrices – those covering the users of the products of the machine-tool industries – to assess the possibility of technological change affecting their needs.

(5) An assessment of time scales of significant changes.

(B) *Step 1 – Fundamental reasons.* The purpose of this step is to inquire whether users require turned parts because of their intrinsic merit or because it happens to be easier and/or cheaper to utilize a solid of revolution rather than some other shape.

The intrinsic qualities of a solid of revolution in engineering design are:

(1) *Rotation.* The part is required to rotate relative to, and in near contact with, another part, e.g. shafts, bearings, wheels, etc.

(2) *Strength/weight ratio.* A cyclindrical shape has the highest strength/weight ratio, e.g. jacks, shafts, etc.

(3) *Uniform stress.* A smooth surfaced part will have uniform transverse and longitudinal stress distributions, e.g. shafts, pressurized components.

(4) *Sealing.* It is easier to provide a seal against a cylindrical surface than against an irregularly shaped surface, e.g. hydraulic jacks, piston valves, etc.

On the other hand, a round shape may be chosen because of:

(5) *Practicability and cost of manufacture*. Because existing metal working equipment is readily available and well understood, it may be easier and cheaper for a designer to specify turned or bored parts. As in all design work, this represents a compromise between the ideal design and commercial common sense, and there is no reason to suppose that such compromises will not continue to be reached in the future.

By raising these points we are attempting to test the strength of the relationship of circular shaped components to the particular method of manufacture employed. If parts are made circular for fundamental engineering reasons then the designer is unlikely to be swayed from circular parts to parts of a different shape which might be more suitable for a new manufacturing method. On the other hand, if there are no fundamental reasons for making a particular component circular but it is made so simply because an economically acceptable manufacturing process is available, then these parts are liable to change in response, for instance, to a new cheaper technique for making equivalent square parts.

The simple example of domestic electrical plugs and sockets will illustrate this. The change from round pins to rectangular pins which accompanied the use of ring mains was made primarily to ensure that the new plugs would not be interchangeable with the old-style sockets. Round pins were originally used because at the time of their introduction they were cheap and easy to make. Round pins did not possess any intrinsic engineering merit, and therefore they were liable to be replaced by other pin shapes whenever the right economic or standardization pressures existed. This particular product would not, therefore, have been a stable one to use as a basis for planning the long-term demand for turning machines.

(C) *Technological possibilities*. A technological possibility (see forecasting model) exists when a combination of knowledge and ideas are available within the three stems of scientific principles, technical application and material capability. The production of metal solids of revolution can arise from one or a combination of the processes of:

Metal formation
Metal removal
Metal deformation.

Confining our attention to the process of metal removal only, we can say that the scientific principles involved are of the type:

Scale:	Atomic	Molecular		Particulate
Removal process:	Dislocation	Vaporization		Dissolution
Energy form:	Force	Heat	Chemical	Electromagnetic

This process can be continued in a series of steps to whatever detail is considered necessary. For instance, the concept of removal by vaporization in particulate structures would lead to the notion of a concentrated energy source such as that provided by the controlled application of electromagnetic energy. The laser could be one example of such a process.

Technical Application and Material Capability need to be considered together since the one is dependent upon the other. The parameters to be considered in material capability could be:

Hardness:	Soft	Hard	
Characteristic:	Strength	Shape	Conductivity, etc.
Utilization:	Disposable	Renewable	

The parameters involved under Technical Application increase rapidly as the analysis grows more detailed. For instance, we may have the following:

Method of removal:	Surface removal		Sectioning	
Form of motion:	Stationary	Translatory	Rotary	Oscillatory
Element of motion:	Tool	Workpiece		
Period of energy application:	Steady		Intermittent	
Control:	Manual		Automatic	

and so on.

If one considers all the possible combinations of the above forms of motion referred to the tool and workpiece, we find that the combinations can be summarized as follows:

Combinations of Forms of Motion

Translatory	
Stationary	1
Continuous (in any three dimensions)	7
Oscillatory (in any three dimensions)	7
Continuous and Oscillatory	12
	27
Rotary	
In the combinations given above	27
Total number of combinations given above	729
Hence number of combinations applicable to tool and workpiece together	531,441

This number of combinations can be increased considerably by including motions consisting of an oscillating component superimposed on a continuous level.

Clearly, if this analysis is to be carried out some means of rapidly eliminating the non-useful motion combinations must be found. This can be done in three ways:

(*i*) by studying the motion needs of the particular basic metalworking process chosen earlier in the relevance pattern,

(ii) by eliminating motion combinations which produce non-circular parts, and

(iii) by making a judgment on the correct balance between complexity and cost on the one hand, and the operating flexibility which might arise from an increased number of motion axes on the other.

By means of these analyses a complete series of relevance patterns can be built up as shown in Figure 3. This traces through to the notion of a numerically controlled lathe using throw-away tools. Another example which can be traced through is the simple hand-saw (although one could arrive at that without such an elaborate procedure!).

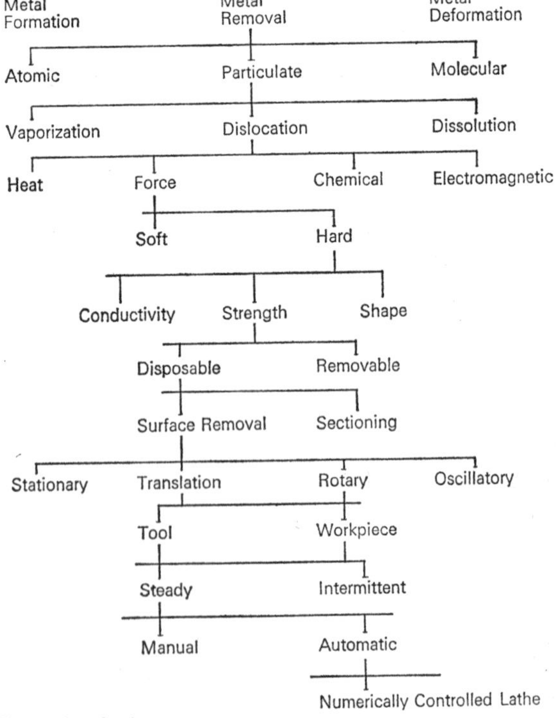

Figure 3. Example of relevance pattern.

The approach described above is tedious and it is desirable to eliminate early on both the known and the totally impracticable or unduly long-term solutions. A possible approach here is to consider the development of technological possibilities as a combination of streams of scientific and technological development rather than as a combination of specific and unrelated events.

By way of illustration Figure 4 shows (in elementary fashion) how four streams of individual developments come together to provide the technological possibility of numerically controlled machine tools. For many years each of these streams proceeded independently of the others until eventually they could be combined to form a major improvement in basic metalworking machinery.

In applying this approach, it is necessary to determine which is the basic process and then to seek other streams of technical developments which can be allied to it.

(D) *Time scales.* The essential art in any forecasting study is to ascribe an accurate time scale to the forecast. This is undoubtedly the most difficult aspect of forecasting simply because it involves the most variables and imponderables.

The process of exploitation of an innovation involves two overlapping phases; the technical development of the innovation and its diffusion throughout its potential market.

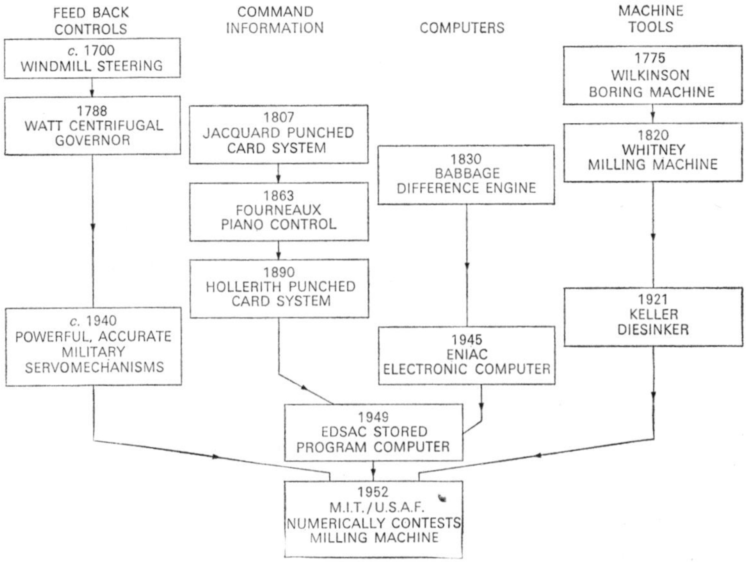

Figure 4. Four-line development of numerical control.

It is very difficult to assign time scales to these periods because new processes develop continuously. Diffusion periods, in particular, are difficult to define because the development of an innovation usually results in a widening of its range of application so that one can only define the end of an innovation period and the beginning of the diffusion period as that point in time when the product is beginning to gain commercial acceptance. Historically, when the innovation and diffusion cycle is completed it is possible to define this point as, say, the time when 1 per cent of the total market had been penetrated [1].

Thus, in the metal removal field a notional indication of the state of the art in the UK may be given by the following time scales:

Numerically Controlled Metal-cutting Machines		
Innovation period	*c.* 1947–65	18 years
Electro-chemical Metal Removal		
Innovation period	*c.* 1948–62	14 years
Spark Erosion Metal Removal		
Innovation period	*c.* 1941–58	17 years

The above figures may be broadly classed as the development period. The diffusion period for these examples is not, of course, known yet, but Figure 5 shows an estimate we have made for the rate of replacement of certain types of conventional machine tool by their numerically controlled counterparts. Broadly speaking, we have estimated a period of twenty years from 1 per cent diffusion to 90 per cent diffusion. If this is borne out in practice the overall time scale for the complete development and diffusion period is some thirty-five years.

The implication of a total time scale of the order of thirty years or so for such capital goods is that the ideas for equipment in common use at the end of the century are already in existence now or will appear during the next five years. Even if the ideas are not yet known, the trends leading to such ideas ought now to be present, and therefore it is unlikely that any metalworking machine having a major share of the 1999 market will be based on scientific principles not now known at least in the laboratory.

Another factor which can give some guidance in the consideration of time scales is the rate of obsolescence common within an industry. For instance, the survey reported by Metalworking Production [2] shows that the age of the UK turning machine-tool population in 1966 was:

Percent under 10 years old	39 per cent
Percent between 10 and 20 years old	36 per cent
Percent over 20 years old	25 per cent

If this pattern was maintained into the future, then something less than 25 per cent of the machine tools in use today would still be in use in 1999. This gives a good first indication of the time constant associated with machine tool replacement, but such figures obviously need to be treated with caution.

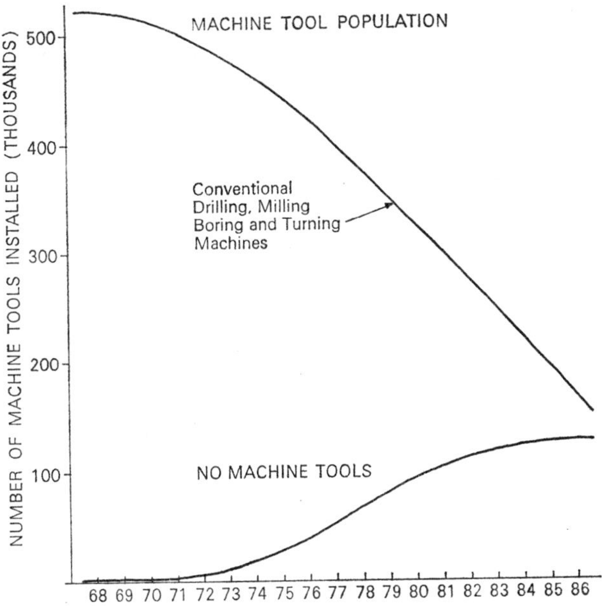

Figure 5. Estimate of UK machine tool population.

Conclusion

This paper has not set out to forecast the precise type of metal-removal equipment for producing cylindrical parts to be used in 1999, but to illustrate one method of tackling such a forecast. Emphasis has been placed on the normative approach rather than on the extrapolation of present trends. The study is still at an early stage, but the following conclusions may be useful.

It is fairly easy to arrive at broad indications of new processes and changes in demand. To go into detail requires the building up of a very complex model and a method of closing the loop of the model without becoming involved in a degree of labour which may not be justified in the event.

A very fruitful general approach can be that of studying the streams of developments in science and technology, and considering how these might interact when applied to certain basic processes.

A much greater understanding is required of the factors affecting time scales and rates of diffusion. Some of these are unconnected with the technology itself – as for instance the effects of money interest rates on obsolescence replacement.

Despite the difficulties, however, we remain convinced that technological forecasting of this nature is an essential ingredient in the development of more refined and balanced judgments in the selection of fields of interest for exploratory research and in the setting of strategies for company development and growth.

References

1 Edwin Mansfield, 'Intrafirm rates of diffusion of an innovation', *Review of Economics and Statistics* **45** (1963).

2 *Metalworking Production*, **110**, 3 (July 27, 1966).

ROMAN KRZYCZKOWSKI

Total Systems Analysis. Case Study, Nuclear Marine Propulsion

Total System Analysis

Total system analysis is a way of solving complex problems. The essence of the method is to consider all relevant facts, to establish appropriate criteria of effectiveness and to use these criteria for rigorous examination of the major elements of a problem.

Total system analysis is an embodiment of common sense. While no superhuman talents are required, a pedestrian follow-up of basic principles will not do either. Those who aspire to undertake this type of work should have, apart from sound training in a scientific discipline, sound judgment, a broad-thinking horizon and lots of intelligence.

What separates the men from the boys in the profession in the long run is the ability, almost a sixth sense, to foresee the unexpected. Technological forecasting which concentrates only on the existing state of the art, which does not concern itself with the likelihood that something better will be invented is not forecasting at all; it is extrapolated history.

I will first of all outline the usual sequence of activities comprising a total system (often also called 'complete system') study. Then I propose to give a specific example illustrating this sequence as well as the main difficulties encountered in studying large, technological, and future-oriented problems. The illustrative example is taken from a study made for the General Electric Company (USA) concerning the future of nuclear ship propulsion for merchant ships.

Total System Study Sequence

A complete system study entails three steps:

(1) an analysis of demand (market analysis),

(2) examination of alternative ways of satisfying the demand (supply alternatives),

(3) an analysis of interactions between demand and supply (analysis).

Frequently the client may also require a recommended plan for action to be included in a complete study. Such a plan is based on conclusions arising from the joint analysis of demand and supply.

Figure 1 shows this sequence. As the figure indicates, it is only logical that formulation of a plan for action be followed by the client's decision (should he, or should he not, act according to the plan for action recommended and if so 'how and when'?) and the eventual implementation of this decision.

Most think-tanks, especially those academically oriented, are inclined to stop their work after the analysis step. Those better versed in business problems will not hesitate to present practical plans for action. Such plans can take the form of a fully documented appropriation request to the board, a detailed sales plan, a set of engineering drawings or a combination of these.

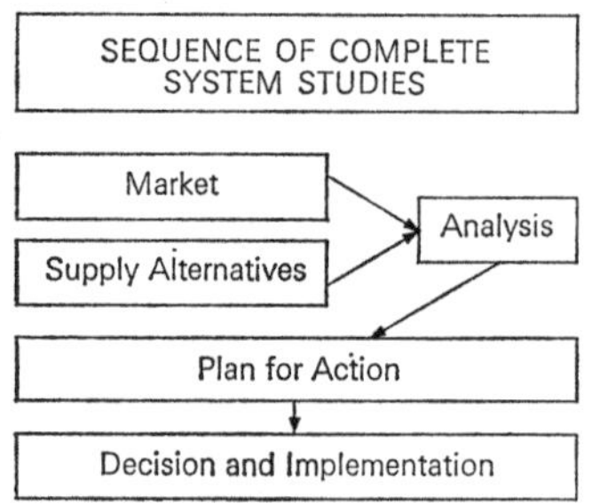

Figure 1.

Under no circumstances will a think-tank move below the dotted line in Figure 1. Decision is a prerogative of management. Professional planners, i.e. the staffs of think-tanks, have no right to encroach upon this prerogative. It is also up to the decision-maker to initiate the required implementation action.

Analysis of demand. In a total system study it normally makes good sense to begin with the market analysis step. If there is no demand for whatever we intend to do, there is no valid business reason to do it. Scientists, engineers, and production people may have excellent ideas on how they will design and manufacture a dream product. If the market analysis step of the study indicates, however, that no one is likely to buy this dream product at a price commensurate with engineering, manufacturing, and distribution costs, then the dream product had better be shelved and the study terminated.

Supply alternatives. The next step should be embarked upon only after the study team is satisfied that there is a marketable product. This step constitutes a search for the best way to satisfy the proved demand. The analysis of supply alternatives should determine the technical and operational possibilities, select the most promising solutions (not forgetting the ones that will be, or are likely to be invented) and then it should present complete cost estimates for all feasible solutions.

Often difficulty is encountered in this step in obtaining accurate enough estimates of required general overhead, especially for research, development, and testing of the product before it enters production. Experience in cost estimating, sound judgment, and adequate technical training of analysts seem to be the only cure. Short-cut solutions or 'guesstimates' normally end in disaster.

Analysis of supply-demand interactions: cost effectiveness analysis. In the modern business world – and this includes the design and procurement of defence equipment – the 'best' solution is often the one which is the most 'cost-effective'. Cost effectiveness, as the name implies, relates the effectiveness or value of the product or service to its cost. The cost-effectiveness analysis thus aims at determining which particular product, selected from alternatives gathered in step two, will best satisfy market demand consequently resulting in the most advantageous pay-off.

How many miles can I get out of my tyres per dollar spent on their purchase? How big a territory can I annihilate per one billion dollars spent on a nuclear offensive system? Both questions are practical examples of cost-effectiveness measures.

Economies of scale, the shapes of learning curves, market penetration costs, and price elasticities have to be carefully examined at this stage. The work requires the close co-operation of market analysts, scientists, engineers, economists; and possibly other specialists depending on the specifics of the case. It is at this stage that the notion of an interdisciplinary approach really becomes meaningful. It is also the work area where the science and the art of making a truly complete system study merge.

Non-economic factors. The analysis step of Figure 1 comprises not only the determination of the cost-effectiveness of the contemplated product or action, but also the investigation of important non-economic factors pertinent to the problem. An outline of such factors, often called imponderables, is given later in this talk.

The three steps of such a complete (total system) study now will be described in some detail with the aid of a specific example.

Market Analysis: Basic Requirements

The essence of market research is perhaps defined best in the statement of Lord Kelvin: 'When you can measure what you are speaking about and express it in numbers you know something about it. But when you cannot measure it your knowledge is of a meagre and unsatisfactory kind.'

It is not sufficient to say that 'there is a demand for a product' or even that 'there is a great demand'. It is absolutely essential to quantify the adjective 'great' and to compare the quantitative measure obtained with relevant terms of reference.

The second important point in Market Research is to understand at the outset of the analysis the time-nature of demand. For example, the total system study team must clearly understand that the future horizon of interest to its client is, say, ten, twenty, or thirty years. A 'quick-fix' job requires a different approach from the one concerned with the next generation of equipment from forthcoming state of the art.

In a long-term study it is also important to examine the future of the basic demand. Otherwise the essence of the problem, the long-term cycle, may be missed altogether and the client completely misinformed.

For instance, in our example to be described, the apparent demand seems to be for ship-propulsion systems. A moment's reflection enables one to realize that ship propulsion is only one part of a ship so that the 'real' demand is for shipping: no ships, no propulsion system! However, further reflection will reveal that the basic demand is for transportation service. It is conceivable that for many products in the future the service may be satisfied by other means, say by pipes for bulk liquids or large cargo airplanes for miscellaneous dry cargoes.

It is interesting to observe that there is no basic difference between demand analyses in defence and commercial fields. The military question of 'what will the enemy do to me?' becomes, in the commercial field, the one of likely competitive actions. If I, Mr General Electric, do *this*, what is Mr Westinghouse likely to do? The commercial concept of market penetration corresponds to the target penetration in analyses of offence systems.

The need to foresee the unexpected was mentioned in the introduction. The study may completely miss its objective if the study team fails to foresee and present its foresight in quantitative terms; that a competitive product will be invented, that the public taste will change or that the enemy will invent a better antimissile defence.

The above remarks on the essence of market analysis are summarized in Figure 2.

Nuclear ship-propulsion market analysis. Let us now come to the market analysis for nuclear ship-propulsion systems to illustrate the above points.

The need for the study arose when the ship-propulsion division of General Electric Co. (USA) designed a novel, nuclear propulsion system and desired to know how many of such systems are likely to sell, as well as when and at what price levels.

After my appointment as the study manager, I quickly realized that in order to answer our client's question much more than a market research study would be required. The dream product of the propulsion division would have to be compared with other propulsion systems, both current and those which will be invented. Since a ship, once built, lasts at sea for fifteen to twenty-five years, our time frame would be until approximately the end of this century. Thus, we were faced with a full-blown total system study and I organized it along the three-step sequence outlined in the introduction to this talk.

THE ESSENCE OF MARKET (DEMAND) ANALYSIS
1. Defense and industrial–no difference
2. Define NATURE of demand
3. Quantity and time-schedule
4. Foresee the unexpected

Figure 2.

The essence of our quantifications and the time scheduling of the specific shipping problem we had in hand is shown in Figure 3.

THE MARKET
Transportation SERVICE 1965 -2000
WHAT needs transportation?   1. Bulk liquids   2. Bulk dry cargoes   3. Miscellaneous dry cargoes
WHEN? 1970-2000
HOW? Ships   Pipes   Airplanes

Figure 3.

From the outset, due to technological constraints, we thought it wise to limit our study only to large ships – tug boats and coastal tankers appeared, on a common-sense basis, unlikely customers for expensive nuclear reactor systems. Setting the lower limit of the ship's size at 10,000 DWT, the remaining population of large ships in the world in 1965 came close to 12,000 ships.

From the voluminous statistics on the subject we were able to elucidate the following broad picture of the 1965 market for shipping:

The Shipping Market: 12,000 Ships

Kind of work	*How many (%)*	*Amount of work*	*Percentage built 1957–65*	*Rate of growth (%)*
Bulk carriers	10	1/4	70	5
Tankers	25	1/2	50	3
Freighters	65	1/4	25	0

It can be seen that 10 per cent of the total world's fleet (bulk carriers) was doing one-quarter of the total work in terms of ton-miles carried. Every fourth large ship on the globe is a tanker and they do one-half of the total work.

The observed rate of growth in ship construction confirmed that these two categories of ships account for the largest share of the total world demand for shipping. This was, then, the area of primary interest for our study. We could foresee that many types of general cargo freighters or specialized ships will be replaced either by large cargo aircraft or by a small number of container ships. But the big-volume growth-business was represented by bulk carriers and oil tankers.

SIZE OF SHIPPING MARKET 1970–2000	
Existing World's Fleet	12,000
PLUS annual increase in demand	xxxx
LESS annual mortality	yyyy
World-wide shipbuilding program	zzzzz

Figure 4.

Before estimating how many of these will go nuclear, we obviously had first to find out how many large ships will be built during the next thirty years. We thus had to construct a future world-wide shipbuilding programme. Figure 4 shows the essence of our calculations.

From the existing 12,000 ships, using experts' opinions on the longevity of specific categories of ships, and knowing the 1965 age distribution of the world's fleet from the *Lloyd's Register of Shipping*, we could subtract, year by year, over-aged ships using standard actuarian distributions.

Then we had to add, year by year, the number of ships likely to be built. In order to estimate this parameter, the following analytical steps had to be performed:

(1) estimate the quantity, location and time for demand for oil and oil products,
(2) estimate the quantity, location and time of crude oil production,
(3) estimate demand and supply patterns for key bulk cargoes (coal, metal ores, wheat) carried by ships,
(4) assume reasonable sizes and speeds for future bulk carriers and tankers,
(5) simulate the world's pattern of ship's movements between 1960 and 2000 from estimates obtained in items 1–4.

The above sequence was performed for the three decades 1970–80, 1980–90, and 1990–2000. The sensitivity of assumptions such as the speed and size of ships was checked.

We also carefully examined possible competitive methods of transportation, especially pipelines for crude oil. It was concluded, with the help of expert advice from outside-the-study-team consultants that it is most unlikely that transoceanic pipelines will be built before the year 2000, i.e. within the time frame of our study.

The resultant calculations indicated that great numbers of ships will be built during all three decades and specially between 1990 and 2000. In our forecast of demand for large ships we were not concerned with the exact number of ships to be built. This clearly would be impossible. Our interests were in correctly determining an order of magnitude for shipbuilding so that our client would gain an appropriate understanding of the size of the market awaiting him. In essence, we were attempting to tell him whether his sales potential should be measured in units, dozens or hundreds. Our conclusions were that hundreds of large ships will be constructed annually between now and the end of the century.

Supply Alternatives

Simulation model. Having ascertained that strong demand for shipping services will continue until at least the end of this century, in the total system study outlined here we proceeded to analyze the ways in which this demand could be satisfied. At this point in our work we had to remind ourselves that the basic purpose of our endeavours was to advise the General Electric Company's management whether or not the Company should invest in nuclear ship propulsion.

The two months spent on the demand analysis taught us that not only are there three basic kinds of ships, but also that they operate in a variety of ways, on different length voyages, and at different speeds. In order to fit feasible future ship-propulsion systems into this maze of variables representing the annual movements of 12,000 ships, it was necessary to construct a model to enable us to understand the basic features of world shipping. Without such a model, we felt, we could easily get lost in details and, therefore, lose the ability to present the 'big picture' to management.

The model that was constructed is shown in Figure 5. It distinguishes between eight different world markets (or 'operational requirements') for shipping. To arrive at this simplified representation of movement of large ships, we divided all voyages into 'long' and 'medium'. A long voyage would be from the Middle East to the West Coast of the United States or to Japan; a medium voyage would be from the Middle East to Europe. A second distinction made was between large and medium ships. The boundary was arbitrarily set at 70,000 DWT. The third distinction was that of speed: fast or slow. In using the model, we actually varied the ship's speed from eleven to twenty-six knots in intervals of one knot.

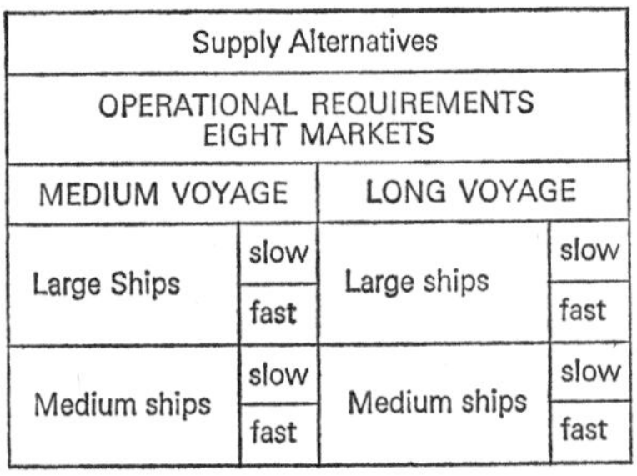

Supply Alternatives			
OPERATIONAL REQUIREMENTS EIGHT MARKETS			
MEDIUM VOYAGE		LONG VOYAGE	
Large Ships	slow	Large ships	slow
	fast		fast
Medium ships	slow	Medium ships	slow
	fast		fast

Figure 5.

The question before the study team then became, 'What will be the best propulsion system to meet the operational requirements of, say, a high-speed large ship on a long voyage? Would the same system also be the best for medium ships on medium voyages and plying at "slow" speeds?' In order to answer such questions, we had to know more about the technical and economic characteristics of future ship-propulsion systems.

Present and future technology of ship propulsion. We began with existing, conventional systems. They are all based on steam turbine and diesel engines, and while both have their proponents, either one seems to satisfy a wide range of present requirements. In addition, at the time of the study, the Nuclear Energy Division of the Company had a fully-engineered design for a nuclear boiler coupled to a conventional steam turbine. Aside from this design which other competitors were known to have, no other designed types were in existence. Thus, the starting base for current, competitive ship-propulsion systems consisted of three systems:

(1) conventional steam turbine,

(2) diesel,
(3) nuclear steam turbine.

In the opinion of the study team, however, only three systems were inadequate in view of the time frame of thirty years imposed on us by the longevity of ships' hulls. We felt that something new, or possibly better, would be likely to be invented before the year 2000. This feeling is of great importance in any total system study. It is useless to model history. Excellence in technological forecasting lies in not overlooking what is likely to be invented. That is why the art of foreseeing the unexpected is so essential to professionals in the field.

We sent many questionnaires and solicited hundreds of individual opinions from experts in fields related to our problem in an attempt to forecast other possible future propulsion systems. Their replies were analyzed by engineers on the staff of the study team. Two conceptual systems emerged. They were: (i) advanced bunker 'C' fuel gas turbine, (ii) nuclear gas turbine.

The first system was based on advanced thinking associated with aircraft propulsion technology, and the second on inert-gas, closed-loop nuclear system concepts.

The originality of the first system was in the adaptation of aircraft-type gas turbines to low quality shipping fuel (i.e. to black oil, or bunker 'C'-type fuel). The feasibility of the second design would depend on the successful construction of a leak-proof joint, the present Achilles' heel of all gaseous-type nuclear reactors.

The combination of cheap fuel (either bunker 'C' or nuclear), high thermal efficiency of gas turbines and the small size of either system presented a most attractive package. We decided, therefore, to test these two against the three known systems. Before such a comparison could be made, however, we had to acknowledge the existence of and account for serious technical problems that would occur with the two future possibilities. For instance, corrosion from bunker 'C' fuel will cut the life of a conventional aircraft-type gas turbine to a few hours. The study team, therefore, had to estimate the cost of a research and development programme which would solve the corrosion problem (and a legion of other problems) and spread the estimated cost of the entire R&D effort over the number of systems likely to be supplied.

The result of the analysis of supply alternatives was a description of technical, operational, and cost parameters for the following five competitive, candidate ship-propulsion systems:

(1) conventional steam turbine,
(2) diesel,
(3) nuclear steam turbine,
(4) advanced bunker 'C' fuel gas turbine,
(5) nuclear gas turbine.

Cost-effectiveness Analysis

Use of simulation model. The simulation model (Figure 5) had been constructed to observe the behaviour of our five candidate ship-propulsion systems under the eight operational requirements. We decided to run our candidate systems through a one-year operation cycle. This meant that each system (e.g. a steam turbine) was conceptually fitted into a ship (e.g. large) and then the ship was run on a long or medium voyage at speeds varying from eleven to twenty-six knots. All costs of operation for each system incurred during the year were observed for each operational requirement. These included capital amortization, crew wages, fuel, canal, and harbour dues, insurance and many others (Figure 6).

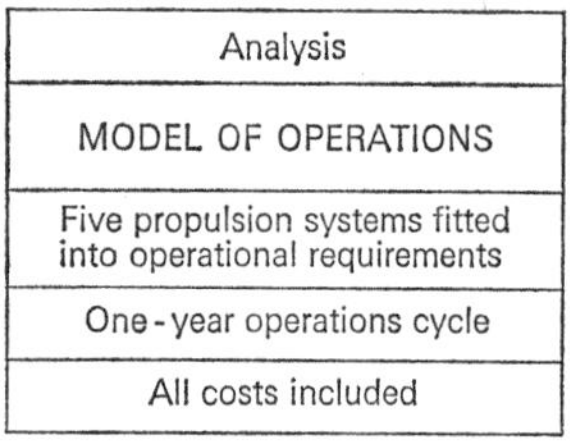

Analysis
MODEL OF OPERATIONS
Five propulsion systems fitted into operational requirements
One-year operations cycle
All costs included

Figure 6.

The total number of candidate systems, ship sizes, voyage lengths, and speed variations (and consequent engine sizes) was such that the model warranted programming for a computerized solution. In order to make the cost and operations parameters as realistic as possible, two ships logs were secured which gave us hour-by-hour details and costs for typical and long medium voyages for a sample large and medium ship, respectively. True to operations research principles, study team members also accompanied a ship on one voyage, standing watches on the bridge and in the engine room in order to gain first-hand familiarity with operational problems, and thereby realism in the model.

Measure of cost-effectiveness. The common denominator in our calculations was the cost to ship one-ton of cargo (crude oil, or bulk-ton) either on a long or medium voyage. Such a simple measure of cost-effectiveness was selected because the fundamental demand requirement for transportation service is to lower cost (of transport) and also because it enabled us to account for the advantage of non-conventional fuels, i.e. when no bunker-fuel space is required, more cargo space becomes available. In a similar manner the advantage of compact gas turbines over cathedral-like conventional steam turbines and marine diesels could be accounted for.

For conventional systems the faster the ships move, the more fuel is consumed by the propulsion system, and more bunker space is required. On the other hand, at high speeds, all competitive systems enable a ship to complete more voyages per year, and consequently carry more cargo. The construction of the model permitted us to account for these and other similar parameters, e.g. crew leaves, duration of annual overhauls, time wasted in canal crossings and in harbours, and others. Reliability of machinery was based on historical data supplied by shipping companies. It was assumed that novel systems would have to be at least as reliable as the existing ones in order to be competitive.

Results. The general results of our simulation of shipping operations can be summarized in the following three statements:

(1) Excessive speed does not pay.

(2) There are great advantages in increasing the size of the ship.

(3) Bunker fuel cost is the greatest single expense in the annual operations cycle.

The first two results confirmed, scientifically if you wish, what is apparently well known already in the shipping world. Actually, our model indicated that today's tankers operate within one-half of a knot of their theoretical optimum speeds. The current trend towards giant super-tankers confirms our forecast of 1965. It may be of interest to note that advantages of size are so great that we predicted in 1965 that for Middle East oil operations, *it would pay* sufficiently large tankers to by-pass the Suez Canal.

What we did not expect was the importance of fuel cost. It far overshadowed the capital charges of the expensive nuclear reactor systems. The old wisdom of total system studies, 'beware of the unexpected', was fully reaffirmed.

Since the problem was thus largely reduced to a competitive battle between costs of conventional and nuclear fuels, our immediate aim was to forecast the trend of prices for uranium and the costs of nuclear fuel delivered to small-sized ship-borne reactors. This change in emphasis of the study well illustrates another difficulty in the job of completing such studies successfully. Because the unexpected result arrived at the three-quarter point in the study duration, we had to delay the final presentation until we were quite sure that our supplementary and unexpected calculations of future fuel prices were reasonable.

The final result of the foregoing cost-effectiveness analysis was a classification of the five competing ship-propulsion systems with their advantage under different operational requirements. We were, for example, in a position to advise our client that strictly from the cost-effectiveness point of view, a system, say, No. 3 on our list will be best for medium voyages by large ships within the range, of say fourteen to eighteen knots.

Some systems were proved clearly superior to others for most requirements. Some speeds were found to be of particular interest to certain special interests like special-cargo shippers, or certain types of naval operations. For such special uses we were able to advise on the best foreseeable systems and specify, in quantitative terms, why, and by how much, a specific system is superior to others.

Matching the data obtained in the market analysis (Step 1 of the total system study) with the above-outlined results, we could predict how many ships in each propulsion category are likely to be built during the next thirty years.

If the world were completely rational, and as simple as our model, the results obtained would have corresponded to reality within our limits of accuracy and technological foresight. Since the world is not that simple, a great deal of work remained to be done.

Non-economic factors. Convincing evidence that one system is superior to another on a cost-effectiveness basis supported by realistic and quantitative data is only the first, albeit important, stage in total system analysis. As pointed out in the introduction, its essence is a rigorous examination of the major elements of the problems under scrutiny. Economics and technology are only two elements of many. These two are most amenable to quantitative analysis and can be somewhat routinized and formalized. However, when the client makes the decision, he is apt to consider other non-technical and non-economic factors. Very often, these other factors are of significant importance and will actually prevail in the course of the final decision.

It follows, therefore, that a realistic total system analysis must account for such 'other' factors. In our case study we could think of eight principal groups of such factors which, by and large, were beyond our capability for quantitative evaluation. We labelled them 'imponderables' and they are listed below:

(i) attitude of shipping industry,
(ii) interests of oil industry,
(iii) psychology of nuclear safety,
(iv) trade and labour pressures,
(v) insurance considerations,
(vi) political prestige,
(vii) technical capabilities of shipyards,
(viii) defence considerations.

Our approach was to invite experts in each group of imponderable factors (say a trade union when we dealt with trade/labour pressure groups), and discuss with them at some length the likely impact of their factors on the future of nuclear shipping. These round-table, brain-storming sessions were held in an attempt to understand and consequently to incorporate into our analysis the impact of imponderables. The method is obviously unscientific, it relies on study team judgment and its ability to translate opinions into figures, but it is the only way known at present in 'think-tanks' to account for apparently nonquantifiable factors. We listened to experts, asked questions, posed problems, exposed our informants to other views and approaches. When all was discussed, expert opinions were categorized, and numerical weights assigned to each. Rudimentary sensitivity analysis was then performed in order to judge how important the imponderable in question was on the overall result. The quantified opinions were then superimposed on the results of the cost-effectiveness analysis and the number of nuclear ships likely to be built modified accordingly.

The team felt confident enough to present the study results to our client, only after the completion of this last portion of our analysis. A formal, oral presentation was organized, supported by visual aids (some of them being reproduced in this talk). A written report was issued. Many supplementary questions were asked. Then for quite some time, there was a complete silence.

Epilogue

After an interval of several weeks, the client informed us that the approach and methodology of our study were convincing enough, and the results sufficiently interesting to warrant extending the study. A plan for action was called for.

Preparation of a practical plan for action required an entirely different type of working team than the original study group. Problems like 'where are those ships likely to be built?', 'should we license or build them ourselves?', or 'how should we finance the venture?' had to be examined in realistic detail, and this required different expertize.

The preparation of the plan for action, aimed at world-wide market penetration and a twenty-year time period (1965–85) took several months. At the conclusion of it, results and recommendations were examined in detail by appropriate task forces of the Company. Then, and only then, a decision to implement certain recommendations *was* taken. The total system study was completed.

In conclusion it may be pointed out that the approach described here with the aid of a specific example is applicable to a great variety of complex problems. In my own experience I have successfully applied the total system study technique to such different questions as:

(i) How should the American gold-mining industry be reorganized?

(ii) What is the future of world telecommunications through the use of satellites?

(iii) How should the North American continent be supplied with electric power and water until the end of this century?

As Figure 7 shows, in every case we had to examine the demand for the proposed action first; then we evaluated the supply alternatives; and finally we performed the supply-demand interaction analysis.

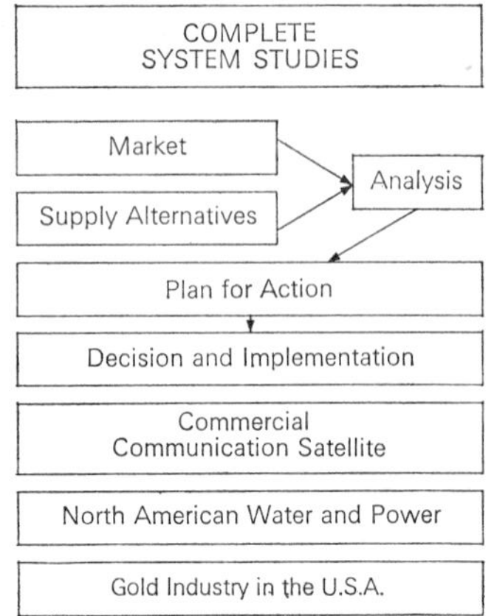

Figure 7.

Note. This paper was first presented at a meeting in London organized by the Science of Science Foundation.

R. D. MEDFORD

Some Remarks on the Application of Technological Forecasting

The efficiency of technological forecasting is critically dependent upon the goal an analyst is trying to achieve. In consequence it is worth while to reiterate here the functions of the Programmes Analysis Unit [1, 2] so that participants of this Conference obtain a reasonable perspective of the critique contained in this paper. The relevant functions of the Unit are:

(*a*) To develop technical and economic criteria and techniques of analysis by which the potential benefits of R&D programmes can be assessed.

(*b*) To apply these criteria and techniques to the assessment of current and proposed R&D programmes.

(*c*) To provide a focal point of expert knowledge about R&D evaluation techniques on which the Ministry of Technology and the UKAEA can draw for their own purposes.

Our experience of technological forecasting has mainly been of exploratory techniques, i.e. the extrapolation of present trends into the near and far futures; and these techniques have, in general, been used for assessing potential markets for the end-products of proposed R&D programmes. More recently, however, we have concerned ourselves with normative forecasting [3] and relevance techniques in order to formulate procedures for selecting and evaluating portfolios of R&D programmes.

This paper describes our recent experience, airs some of the unsolved problems which the author considers important and warns against some of the pitfalls awaiting the technological forecaster.

Experience of Technological Forecasting in the PAU

Since it was formed in March 1967, the PAU has evaluated a fairly wide spectrum of R&D proposals which, generally speaking, have fallen into two categories:

(i) those concerned with a relatively narrow range of R&D activity – explicitly directed towards an end-product which should yield a national economic or social benefit;

(ii) those concerned with broad important areas of R&D activity such as marine technology, or areas of computer application.

Both kinds of proposal have necessarily involved exploratory forecasting in the form of temporal extrapolation from a base of retrospective facts. But exploratory forecasting, on its own, has not been sufficient for the second kind and we have been forced in addition to consider normative forecasting – which assesses future goals, needs, desires, missions, etc., and works backwards to the present (see Reference [3]).

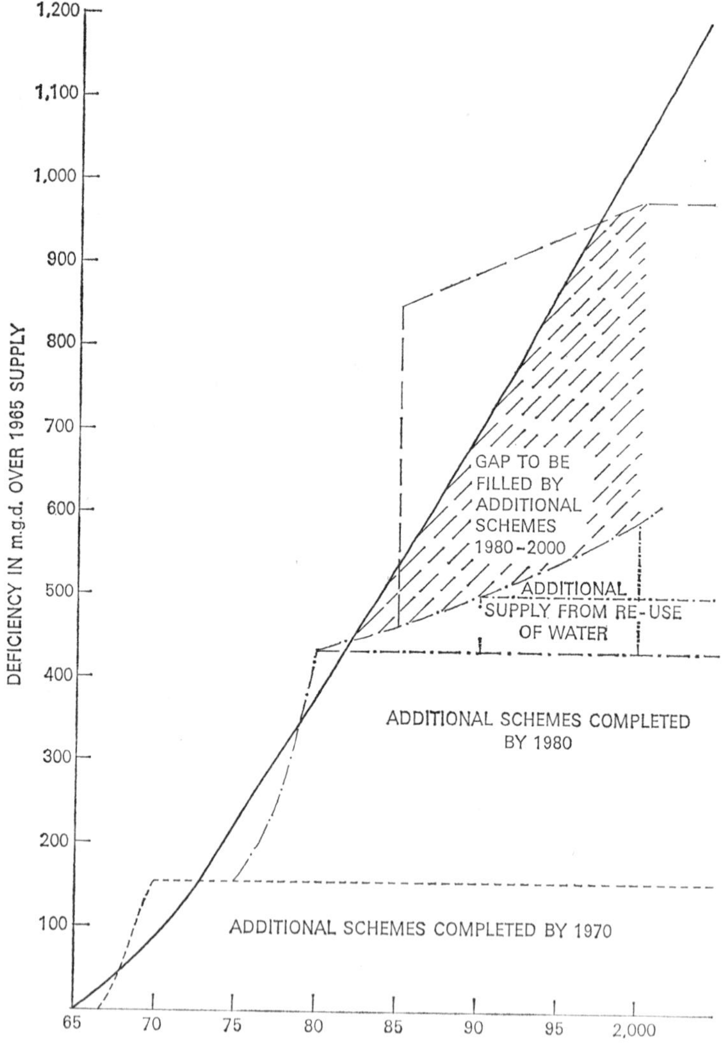

Figure 1.

Exploratory forecasts. Typical examples of exploratory forecasting arising from explicit R&D proposals are the estimation of cost per BHP of diesel engines from 1968 to 1974 and of the UK production of steel by electric-arc furnaces from 1968 to 1990. Very often the accuracy of such extrapolations into the 'far-future' is not of critical importance because in discounted cash flow calculations the contribution made to Net Present Value, or Benefit/Cost ratio, by benefits forecast twenty or more years ahead is often not appreciable. There are techniques universally in use which fit logistic curves to observed data, in the form of time series, by using the method of least squares and then extrapolating into the 'near-future'.

For an illustrative example of extrapolation without numerical analysis we select forecasts arising from the evaluation of a desalination programme where the research is aimed at satisfying the potential demand for fresh-water between 1980 and 2000:

The first step is to forecast the need for technological innovation and for this purpose we used the study carried out by the Water Resources Board, which shows that by the end of this century the excess of demand, in SE England, over 1965 supply will amount to 1,100 million gallons per day (thick line, Figure 1). A number of schemes in hand or proposed (see Table 1) will augment supplies to meet estimated demands up to about 1980, and these have been superimposed on Figure 1.

TABLE 1 Proposed additional water schemes for South-East England

Scheme	*Total increase m.g.d.*	*Total capital expenditure £ millions*	*Phased expenditure from 1966*			
			66/70	*71/80*	*81/90*	*91/00*
Authorities	130	19·5	17·0	2·5	—	—
Local schemes	15	16·0	8·0	8·0	—	—
Diddington	15	4·7	4·7	—	—	—
Ely Ouse	22	8·5	8·5	—	—	—
Great Ouse	90	29·0	1·0	28·0	—	—
Thames G. W.	125	14·0	3·4	10·6	—	—
Welland and Neve	20	7·0	—	7·0	—	—
Re-use	215	15·6	0·7	3·3	5·1	6·5

To meet the excess potential demand between 1980 and 2000 various alternative schemes have been suggested:

(*a*) A barrage across the Wash which would provide about 380 million gallons a day. Supplies of fresh water would not become available from it, however, until the completion of the whole scheme (which would take about fifteen years). This sudden large influx of additional supply would inevitably result in a period of years when demand exceeded supply, or vice-versa, depending on the time of its introduction.

(*b*) The introduction of a number of smaller schemes from 1980 onwards such as diversion of water supplies from other parts of the country, the artificial recharge of aquifiers or the provision of desalination plants. The commissioning of desalination plants of 100–150 million gallons per day at four-year intervals from 1985 onwards would provide increases in supply broadly matching increases in demand.

(*c*) Increasing the utilization of recirculating water by new methods of purifying water. This could help to bridge the gap but would probably not in itself be sufficient.

This illustrative example is, of course, much simplified – it takes no account of relative economics nor offers any solution to a complex

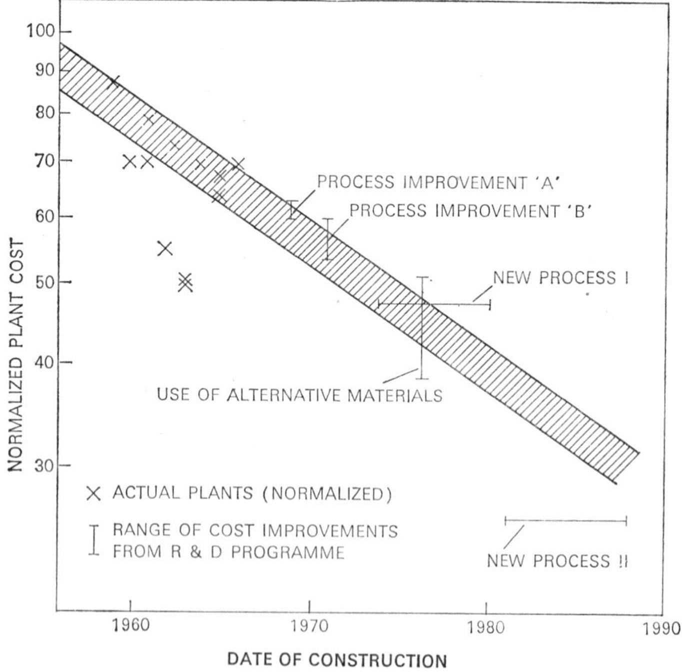

Figure 2. Anticipated capital costs of Desalination Plants normalized to 2 MGD units with P.R. 8:1.

problem. It does, however, help to define boundaries to the problem, identifies possible solutions and estimates the effect of these. In this case recognition of the very important part re-use of water had to play drew attention to the possible application of desalination techniques to sewage treatment.

In order to estimate the financial return from a desalination R&D programme it was clearly necessary not only to discount the value of future benefit with time but also to allow for future reductions in price of desalination plants and in desalinated water. Again, extrapolation was used of the normalized capital cost of actual plants with respect to time. The result is shown in Figure 2. Estimates of cost reductions resulting from improved technology together with the timing of its implementation were consistent with the extrapolated trend and are shown as bars in Figure 2.

Exploratory forecasting by analysis of precursive events is recognized as an acceptable technique when there is a causal relationship between the known, earlier, development and the expected future development. R. C. Lenz gives a good example of this [4] in which the precursor is the maximum speed of military aircraft and the development to be forecast is the upper speed of transport aircraft.

If we consider, however, a completely new field of human endeavour without any obvious precursor, are there any situations in which this method is applicable? A perhaps lighthearted and certainly speculative exercise would be to estimate the future growth rate of a human undersea population. A comparison might be drawn with the development of land cultivation beginning with the neolithic period when 'slash and burn' farming enabled our ancestors to extend their activities from the hills to the wooded valleys.

The growth of population [5] is plotted (Figure 3) against time from which the rate of growth of agricultural population, from the end of the mesolithic period to Domesday, is found to be exponential with an e-folding time of 1,100 years.

Can anything meaningful be deduced from this about the development of the submarine environment? Even though pioneer aquiculturalists will be equipped with technological and medical aids and means of communication and environment control which were unthought of even fifty years ago, they will face unknown hazards and possible catastrophe no less severe than their pre-Domesday agricultural forebears. The differences in kind, however, may be regarded as too fundamental for an analogy of this kind to be valid but at least we have a starting point for debate and a means of concentrating attention on some of the factors which seem relevant. Rather provocatively, therefore, we estimate that the rate of population growth of

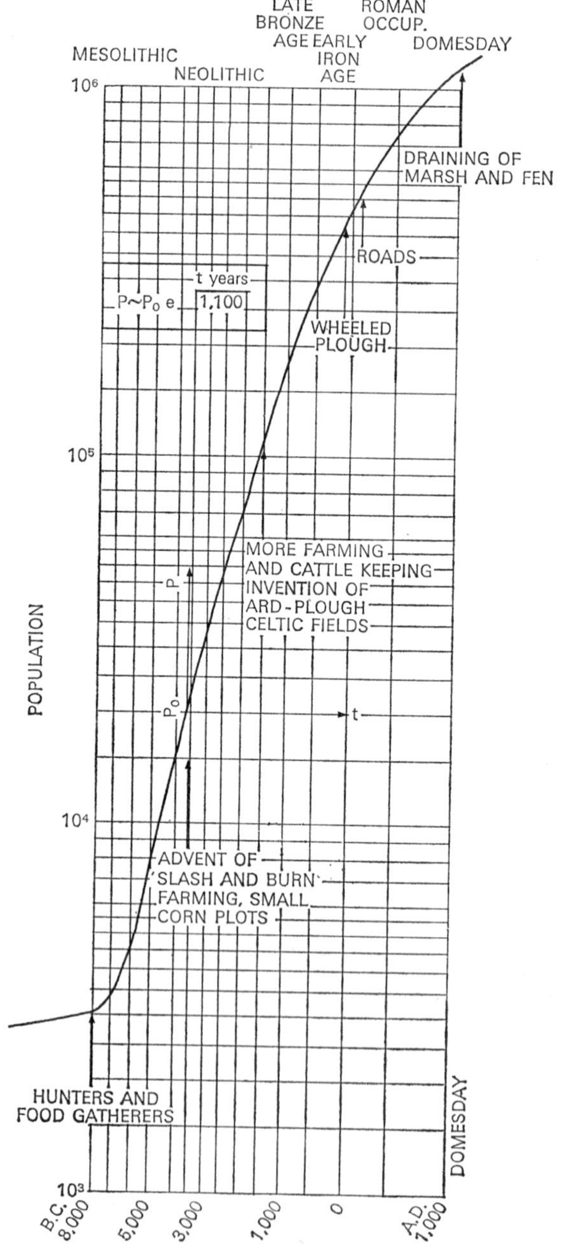
LATE BRONZE AGE
EARLY IRON AGE
ROMAN OCCUP.
DOMESDAY
MESOLITHIC
NEOLITHIC
10^6
10^5
10^4
10^3
POPULATION
DRAINING OF MARSH AND FEN
ROADS
t years
P~Po e 1,100
WHEELED PLOUGH
MORE FARMING AND CATTLE KEEPING
INVENTION OF ARD-PLOUGH
CELTIC FIELDS
P
Po
t
ADVENT OF SLASH AND BURN FARMING, SMALL CORN PLOTS
HUNTERS AND FOOD GATHERERS
DOMESDAY
B.C. 8,000
5,000
3,000
1,000
0
A.D. 1,000

Figure 3.

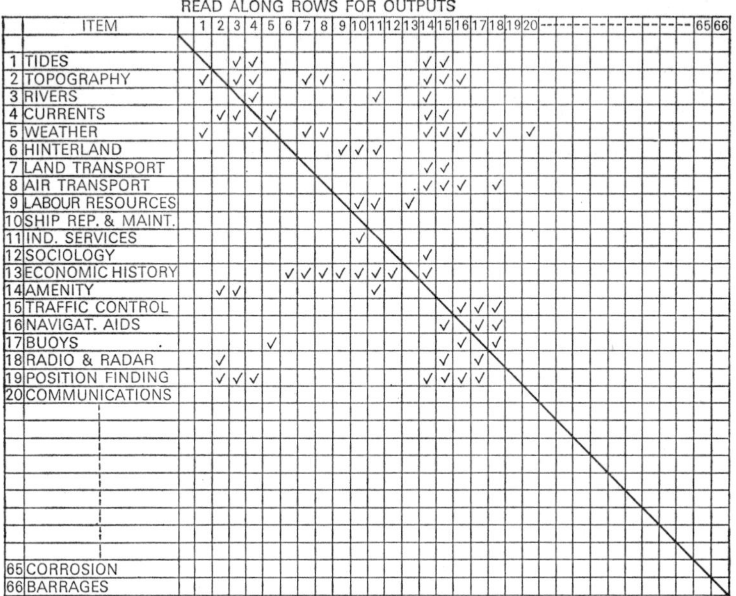

READ ALONG ROWS FOR OUTPUTS

	ITEM	1	2	3	4	5	6	7	8	9	10	11	12	13	14	15	16	17	18	19	20	---	65	66
1	TIDES			✓	✓										✓	✓								
2	TOPOGRAPHY	✓		✓	✓			✓	✓						✓	✓	✓							
3	RIVERS				✓							✓			✓									
4	CURRENTS		✓	✓		✓									✓	✓								
5	WEATHER	✓			✓			✓	✓						✓	✓	✓		✓		✓			
6	HINTERLAND									✓	✓	✓												
7	LAND TRANSPORT														✓	✓								
8	AIR TRANSPORT														✓	✓	✓		✓					
9	LABOUR RESOURCES										✓	✓		✓										
10	SHIP REP. & MAINT.																							
11	IND. SERVICES										✓													
12	SOCIOLOGY														✓									
13	ECONOMIC HISTORY						✓	✓	✓	✓	✓	✓	✓		✓									
14	AMENITY		✓	✓								✓												
15	TRAFFIC CONTROL																✓	✓	✓					
16	NAVIGAT. AIDS															✓		✓	✓					
17	BUOYS					✓											✓		✓					
18	RADIO & RADAR		✓													✓		✓						
19	POSITION FINDING		✓	✓	✓										✓	✓	✓	✓						
20	COMMUNICATIONS																							
65	CORROSION																							
66	BARRAGES																							

Figure 4. Relevance Matrix No. 6, Ports, Docks, and Harbours.

human aquiculturalists will not exceed 250 per cent per millennium.

Matrix techniques. Our experience of the so-called matrix techniques[1] of technological forecasting has not been particularly encouraging; two different matrix techniques have been investigated and found to be inadequate for a normative analysis of marine technology; these are:

(i) square Leontief-type relevance matrices; and

(ii) morphological matrices.

In making our technological forecasts we were particularly concerned to find those areas of technological activity which could be crucial to the growth of the whole field of marine technology. The initial expectation was that the crucial growth areas would be clearly revealed as points of communality in a square relevance matrix; we therefore made tabular presentations of particular sectors of marine activity such as transportation, marine-mining, recovery of sand and gravel etc. (Figure 4).

1 Although the phrase 'matrix techniques' has become part of the nomenclature, it is usually a misnomer because matrix algebra is rarely applied to the original table or 'matrix'. For most cases 'tabular techniques' would be a more accurate description.

Unfortunately, the multiple facets of each sectorial marine activity lead to extremely large matrices. Sizes of 50×50 were not uncommon. This necessarily meant that thousands of coefficients, denoting the relationships between pairs of matrix parameters, had to be quantified – either rationally or subjectively. Not surprisingly, therefore, the exercise degenerated into a system whereby quantitative coefficients were replaced by qualitative 'ticks', similar to the method developed in France by DGRST. We were also forced to conclude that even with sufficient effort available to evaluate coefficients, these would at best have been the coefficients of linear relationships, relating matrix parameters and therefore unreliable for extrapolation beyond a small percentage change. The exercise did, however, force the analysis team to order systematically their thoughts on marine technology and it can truly be said that the effort did produce indirect benefit to the study.

An interesting by-product of our first exercise on relevance matrices is that we discovered a technique, based on the mathematical formula for the total variation of a function of many variables and the solution of simultaneous equations, which enables properly quantified matrices to be standardized so that EDP techniques may be easily used to calculate the effect of varying a matrix parameter. A few notes on this technique are contained in Appendix 1.

Zwicky's morphological method was adopted after the Programmes Analysis Unit realized that the marine technology team had not got sufficient information gathering capacity to implement fully the relevance matrix technique. The original intention was that we should:

(*a*) use morphological matrices to derive objectively all the conceptual systems which together comprise marine technology; then

(*b*) examine the derived systems (including existing, immediately feasible and speculative systems) for common features. An example here would be the 'communality' of sonar devices used for fish detection and sub-bottom marine survey instrumentation; then

(*c*) attempt a technological forecast of the ubiquitous features to determine areas of possible economic benefit which would determine normative goals for marine technology.

The first part of the exercise (*a*) was an exacting but stimulating task. For each sector of marine technology a master matrix (see Figure 5) was constructed from which sub-matrices were derived, each representing a conceptually possible marine system within the sector. Each sub-matrix was then related to the environment by using a specially constructed system of denoting regions within the environment. See Figure 6, which is self-explanatory.

Two typical sub-matrices abstracted from the communications and fishing master matrices are:

Satellite Communication System

$[I_a;\ C_r;\ G_s;\ \check{A}\hat{E}]$

Fishing for Demersal Fish in a Tropical Ocean

$[L_{EE}+L_{SE};\ H_N;\ C_{BT};\ W_M;\ P_{DF};\ B_{CP};\ D_{PM};\ T_C;\ \check{D}\hat{K}]$

where
I_a denotes analog communication
C_r radio carrier
G_s guided transmission – via satellite
$\check{A}\hat{E}$ environment region
$L_{EE}+L_{SE}$ denotes shipborne and externally based fish location equipment
H_N naturally occurring fish shoals
C_{BT} bottom trawls
W_M mechanical preparation of fish inboard
P_{DF} fish preparation by deep freezing
B_{CP} fish stored in consumer packs
D_{PM} waste disposal by conversion to fish meal and pulverising
T_C transport by catcher vessel
$\check{D}\hat{K}$ region undersea.

COMMUNICATIONS – MASTER MORPHOLOGICAL MATRIX

$I_d I_a$	INFORMATION: digital or analog
$C_r C_i C_o C_\alpha$	CARRIER/TRANSDUCER: radio, infra-red, optical or acoustic
$T_r T_i T_o T_\alpha$	FREE TRANSMISSION: radio, infra-red, optic, or acoustic waves
$G_c G_n G_i G_o G_\alpha G_s$	GUIDED TRANSMISSION: cable, waveguide, heatguide, lightguide, soundguide, and satellite

Figure 5.

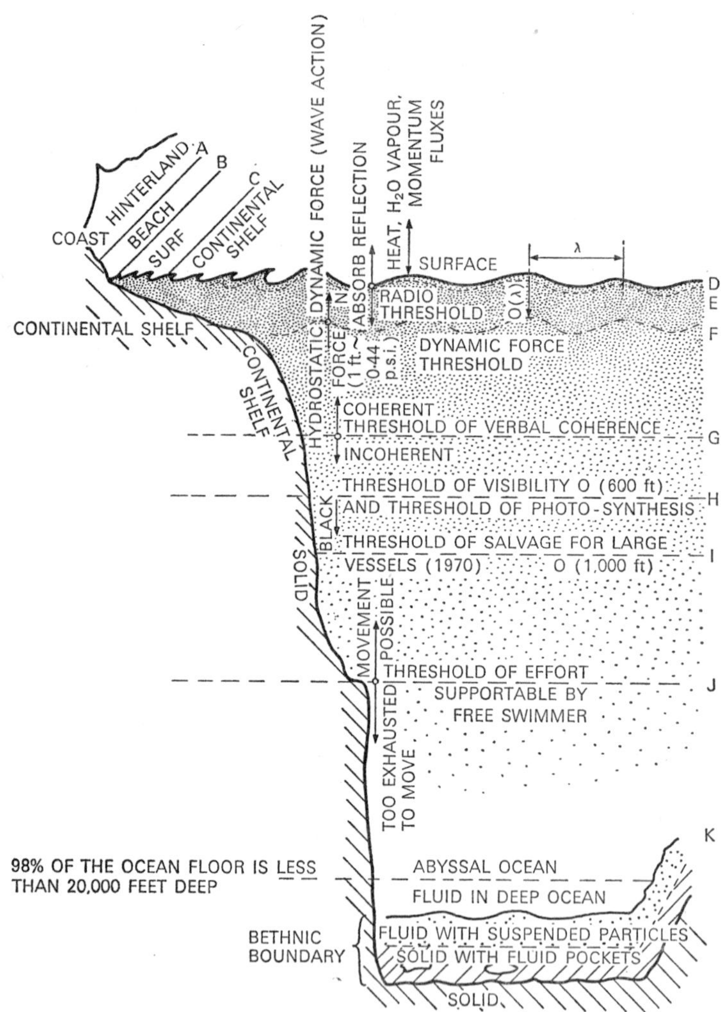

Figure 6. Environmental regions are labelled $\vee$ and $\wedge$. *Example*, DI denotes the region above threshold I and below boundary D.

The first part of the exercise yielded about twenty marine systems for marine transport, twenty-two distinct systems of marine communication and many thousand possible fishing systems. Despite the large number of possible combinations of sub-systems to be examined an attempt was made to discover common features. But unfortunately the sheer weight of the problem handicapped the analysts and it was impossible to achieve objective (*b*) in the allocated time. Some retrieval of effort was, however, possible. It was discovered that in some sectors, particularly communications, the parameters forming the sub-matrices could be quantified to show what had currently been achieved and what was physically possible – thus providing a base from which scenario-type technological forecasts could be made; an example (not to be taken too seriously) is:

Technological Forecast for Marine-Communications

(This is a technological forecast for the state-of-the-art of marine communications in 1985. It is based on extrapolation of quantified morphological sub-matrices and a mixture of intuition and pure speculation.)

Sonar systems will by 1985 have almost reached their full potential. Cheap non-linear narrow beam systems will be in common use at sea for search, identification and fishing; beam widths narrower than 1/10th of a degree will be possible, and bit rates up to a maximum of 104 over distances of about ten kilometres will have been achieved. Signal/noise ratios will also have been increased by parametric amplification techniques.

Three-dimensional submerged objects will be visibly reconstructed from holograms made with visible and/or ultrasonic beams; but, even with the use of computers to 'smooth out' the coarse resolution (few lines per millimetre), the poor reconstruction of ultrasonic holograms will not be entirely satisfactory for fine scale work. However, the deterious effects of turbidity will be considerably reduced by the use of holographic techniques.

Radio transmission via satellites will be in use for navigational fix, automated steering and ship routing. Communication satellites will also be used, in conjunction with weather satellites, for facsimile transmission to vessels of meteorological data, thus assisting course selection, even for pleasure craft.

Optical communication with submersibles will be well established and the functions outlined above for radio satellites will be performed in some cases by optimal carriers. An experimental satellite lens aquiculture system of induced photosynthesis will be field tested.

Rig and survey ship positions will be more accurately controlled by satellite fix and radar. Seismic information will be fed from rigs to shore by microwave links on-line direct to computers for processing. Geological decisions will thus be made within computing time and prospecting costs minimized.

Free-divers will have their work areas illuminated by visible radiation with small superimposed depth of modulation to allow one way communication and will acknowledge signals via 'donald duck' compensated acoustic links.

There is a distinct possibility that an impressive increase in the output power of transmitters and improvements in the detection threshold of receivers (achieved by solid-state and cryogenic innovations) will lead to greater use of shorter wave radio communication under sea.

To summarize our experience of matrix techniques used in technological forecasting, we make the following points:

(1) The tabular stage of relevance matrix analysis, where correlation between activities in a selected set are located, is of use in ordering thought processes.

(2) The meaningful quantification of large relevance matrices is beyond the capability of a moderately sized team working to a deadline – say four men for six months for a complete project.

(3) Methods for quantification of relevance matrices are usually based on linear relationships and are not of much use to the forecaster, who is vitally concerned with rates of growth.

(4) Morphological techniques organize thought processes and may reveal unexpected possibilities; but they tend to swamp the instigator of the analysis with an ever increasing number of possibilities.

(5) Finally, we have a suspicion that most matrix techniques described in the literature of technological forecasting have grown from simple, but useful, tabular aids to a state of useless sophistry.

Modelling. This conference will not be surprised to hear that the PAU (which contains an effective mix of generalists, engineers and scientists) has devoted some time to modelling real world situations. Work has ranged from conceptual analysis of *technological diffusion*, through applications of probability theory, to more practically orientated quantitative models for benefit/cost ratio of R&D programmes and qualitative models of causal relationships in particular industries.

Conceptual models. It is relevant to say something here of our speculative work on technological diffusion because the distribution of technological capability must radically influence the future. A useful starting point is to consider whether the ubiquitous physical law of diffusion (Fick's Law) is applicable to the diffusion of technological capability in environmental space:

Hypothetically we assume that technological capability T flows from regions of highest capability[1] to regions of lowest capability [6] and the flow per unit time is proportional to the negative of technological gradient, where we define technological gradient as the slope of the technological capability curve in environmental space (see Figure 7).

Let us consider an isolated neighbourhood of superior technological

[1] Excluding the immediate consequences of the 'Brain Drain'.

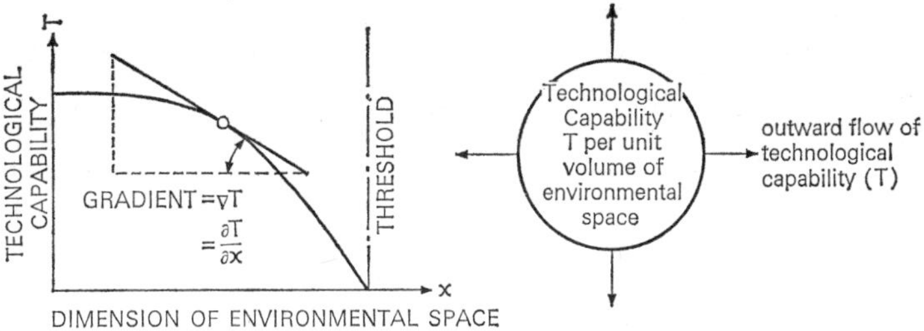

Figure 7. Technological-Diffusion.

capability. Then the rate of loss of technological capability must equal the outward rate of flow of technological capability across the boundary, i.e.

$$-\frac{\partial}{\partial t}\int_V TdV = \text{Constant} \int_A (-\text{Gradient of } T)\,dA$$

which reduces to

$$\nabla^2 T = K\frac{\partial T}{\partial E}. \qquad ...(1)$$

∇^2 represents the divergence of the gradient within environmental space. For example, in marine technology ∇^2 could be the second derivative with respect to depth below the surface of the sea, i.e.

$$\frac{\delta^2}{\delta x^2}$$

K is, of course, the technological diffusion coefficient and varies for different kinds of technology and environmental space.

Equation (1) has only been used once, to predict the growth of a technological capability – the ability to see underwater objects – as a function of time and depth under sea. The results were instructive but inconclusive since we had no previous data against which to check the procedure. We therefore pose the question: 'Does technological capability diffuse in accordance with Fick's Law – and, if not, how should forecasters handle problems which contain a large element of technological transfer?'

If any members of the audience have statistics relating to the diffusion of technology we would very much like to meet them in order to check our hypothesis and/or formulate a new one.

Qualitative models. Qualitative models of causal relationships in industry are of importance in technological forecasting. An example of this is our own experience in trying to allow for interaction and competition between terrestrial and marine mining when prognosticating on the future of marine technology.

Causal relationships in the mining industry are complex; it is not possible, for example, to substantiate the simple hypothesis that continual consumption of minerals leads to depletion of finite terrestrial resources which eventually establishes the economic viability of marine mining.

One objection to the depletion hypothesis is that, although the reserves of ore with an acceptable percentage of tenor (determined by current mineral prices and costs of exploitation) are indeed finite, the terrestrial resouces could become 'infinite' given a sufficient demand. Lasky, of U S Geological Survey, has demonstrated [6] how dependent the quantity of reserves are upon the acceptable tenor of ore; and, in particular, he has shown that a reduction of $\frac{1}{2}$ per cent in tenor leads to a three-fold increase in the U S Copper Reserves.

Another objection, if taken in conjunction with Lasky's work, arises from the assertion made by Herfendahl, that low-grade ore may be less costly to mine because of its easier accessibility and the fact that low quality ore usually possesses admixtures of other minerals. Whether Herfendahl's statement is correct depends upon the mineral under discussion but it is a relevant fact that deteriorations in copper ore quality have not boosted real costs in the past.

To carry any discussion of the interaction between marine and terrestrial mining beyond the elementary level of expertize provided by a simple 'depletion hypothesis' it is necessary to use a superior hypothesis which is more cognisant of the existing relationships in terrestrial mining. Unfortunately it has not yet been possible to produce a quantitative model and because of the exigencies of mining (the large gambling element, for example) it may never be possible to do so. However, Figure 8 is a qualitative model, in the form of a flow-diagram, which forms a useful basis for discussion.

Each block of the diagram represents one link in the chain of causal relationships. The middle block contains a Lasky-type relationship and shows the effect of varying tenor on the available reserves, i.e. a reduction of tenor creates an increment in reserves. Selling price is influenced by the available reserves and the demand, thus we obtain a functional relationship of the kind depicted in the right-hand block. Selling price and the cost of exploitation determine the grade of ore which it is profitable to mine, i.e. the tenor, and this relationship is shown schematically in the left-hand block. Tenor determined in the left-hand block feeds into the middle block and thus completes the chain.

As a demonstration of the use to which the diagram can be put we

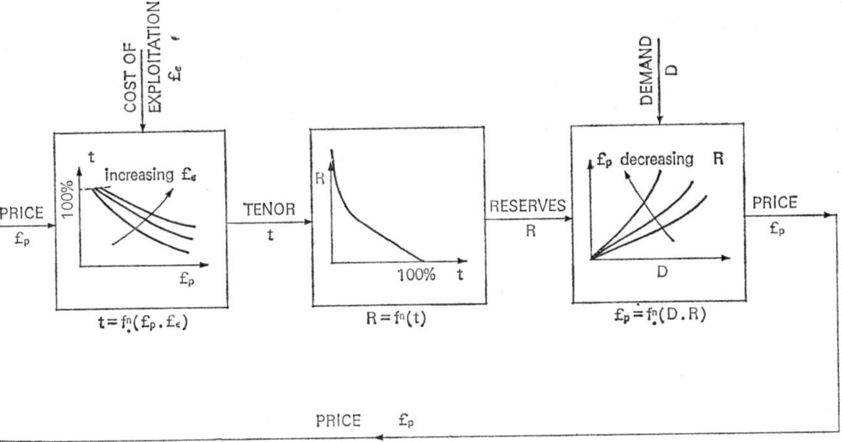

Figure 8. Causal relationships in mining.

discuss the consequences of various likely perturbations in the mining industry:

Suppose that the demand for a mineral increases suddenly so that existing mineral reserves are not adequate. (This could well happen with Columbium, i.e. Niobium, if there is an unprecedented demand for superconductors.) The consequences will be an increment in the selling price of the mineral (see right-hand box); which will lead to attempts at substitution and greater efforts to reduce wastage, but mainly to the utilization of lower grade ores (see left-hand box) available in the neighbourhood of existing reserves – and also the commissioning of additional prospecting surveys for the discovery of new deposits of all tenors down to the new minimum tenor. This inevitably leads to an increment in existing reserves (see middle box) and a nullifying effect, with time lag, on the tendency of selling price to increase. The situation thus tends to stabilize price as suggested, for other reasons, by Herfendahl.

Consider another possibility which is also pertinent to marine mining. Let us suppose that a national programme for marine technology leads to a deliberate, or hidden, subsidy of prospecting and underwater engineering which leads to the inception of marine mining of nonfuel minerals. During the R&D period of marine mining the terrestrial mining cycle is operative, as in the first example, and stabilizes prices against increase of demand. But the marine activities, if they are of significance, tend to increase the overall reserves which leads to a reduction in selling-price (right-hand box); this reduction makes it necessary to work a higher tenor or seek even cheaper methods of exploitation (left-hand box); an increased search for higher grade deposits is also likely, because existing high-grade reserves are not large enough to maintain economic viability (see middle box). The marine miner is thus forced into a prospecting/technological competition with his land based colleague but he works under more stringent conditions.

Thus paradoxically, the more successful a marine miner is, the harder he must work in comparison with the terrestrial miner, to maintain his viability. We conclude from this that only those marine mining operations which are currently viable without subsidy can hope to compete with terrestrial operations. Future marine mining operations may be continually successful but need an exceptionally high tenor or superlative technology which *is not* available, or of use, to terrestrial mining. Marine technology would be particularly suited to increasing the depth of commercial working of terrestrial mines because this is often limited by the economics of pumping water from the workings.

Quantitative models. Certain critical parameters control the benefit/cost ratio of proposed R&D projects and it is usually possible to assess objectively economic viability, and technological consequences, without recourse to complex mathematical formulation – when there are a few parameters. When a large number of parameters is involved it is often better to build a mathematical model which describes, in simplified form, the crucial aspects of the problem.

We now describe a model for the benefit/cost ratio of off-shore mining operations which reveals the juxtaposition of the parameters involved and provides a useful focus for analysis of the future of marine mining:

The parameters which control the viability of off-shore mining operations are:

- A Area of sea bed prospected, in thousands of square miles.
- χ Attainable throughput of processed mineral, obtained from A, in thousands of tons per annum.
- p Probability of achieving throughput χ from area A.
- M Market price of mineral in thousands of pounds sterling per ton.
- λ Mineral content extracted, per mining vessels, in thousands of tons per annum.
- R Cost of recovering mineral from the sea bed, in thousands of pounds sterling per ton. (Derived from the cost of recovering gaugue and ore and the average tenor, see below.)
- T Transport cost, in thousands of pounds per ton of mineral.
- L Cost of 'mineral rights', in thousands of pounds per ton of mineral.
- r Discounting factor, i.e. $r\% - 100$.

The first step in the exploitation process is to submit the designated area A to saturation prospecting. Such a process is inevitably painstaking and will obviously be a major time-consuming factor in the exploitation of undersea mineral wealth. We have found no accurate guides which enable the rate of prospecting to be estimated but our informed guess is that sub sea bed prospecting will not proceed faster than terrestrial prospecting in the Yukon [7] (1,660 square miles per annum at an annual cost of \$1M).

After $t = 0{\cdot}6\,A$ years, therefore, it is assumed that area A has been satisfactorily prospected and that costs have been incurred at a rate of approximately £0·5 S million per annum, where S is a multiplier which allows for the additional difficulties experienced by marine prospectors. It is currently equal to 10 for the UK continental shelf and somewhat smaller for calmer waters.

Each region, within area A, possessing geophysical portent will be submitted to drilling evaluation and the cost of this will be proportional to the expectance of throughput $p\chi$. Drilling costs are, therefore, put equal to £$p\chi . k$ million, where k is a factor which allows for the type of drilling required (shallow or deep, etc.) and can also include an allowance for technological improvements in drilling (e.g. turbine drills).

A mining system will be required to work the deposits revealed by drilling and, for the purpose of analysis, we divided such systems into the following categories of use: extensions of dredging technology, undersea shaft mining and mining by drilling (i.e. oil, gas, sulphur, etc.). On the assumption that the engineering of the mining system will be akin to shipbuilding, the capital cost of the mining system is assumed to be proportional to (expected throughput) $^{0{\cdot}6}$, i.e.

$$C = C_s \left(\frac{p\chi}{\chi_s} \right)^{0{\cdot}6}$$

where C and C_S are capital costs in millions of pounds of annual throughputs χ and χs respectively, Appropriate values of C_S for current throughputs have, of course, been calculated.

It is incorrect to assume that the basic system cost will not vary significantly with the environmental severity of the operating zone. The major cost induced by environmental severity is on the utilization rather than capital costs and an adjustment for this is made. The production of the mining system will be highly dependent on outage, i.e. days on which production is low or zero. This will depend on both mechanical viability and environmental conditions; these have been considered and a factor q combining both of these parameters and related to the environmental zone has been derived.

These considerations result in the following cash flows:

(i) The rate of flow of cost will be approximately constant over 0·6 A years and equal to

$$\pounds\left(0{\cdot}5S+\frac{p\chi k}{0{\cdot}6A}\right)\text{ million per annum.}$$

(ii) At time $t = 0{\cdot}6A$ years, $\pounds C_s\left(\frac{p\chi}{\chi_s}\right)^{0\cdot 6}$ will be spent on mining systems.

(iii) After 0·6 A years benefits will flow at approximately

$$\pounds q(\chi_p)(M-[R+L+T])$$

million per annum.

Incorporation of these flows into a benefit-cost ratio gives, after simplification, the following model of the economics of marine mining:

$$\frac{B}{C}=\frac{q.(M-[R+L+T])}{\left(\frac{C_s}{p\chi}\right).\left(\frac{p\chi}{\chi s}\right)^{0\cdot 6}r+\left(\frac{0{\cdot}5S}{p\chi}+\frac{1{\cdot}67k}{A}\right)(\exp[0{\cdot}6rA]-1)}$$

This model has been checked against the known economics of existing off-shore operations for the extraction of sand/gravel, oil and gas, and found to be sufficiently accurate. It is now in use to compute the sensitivity of benefit/cost to improvements in marine technology.

A Subjective View of Technological Forecasting

Historically scientific prognosis of the course of technology has a respectable record. But each prognostication has, in the long term, been subject to error because forecasters of the calibre of H. G. Wells – or the actual inventors – are required if we are to foresee future discontinuities that act as 'branch points' in the growth of science and technology.

It is extremely doubtful whether any systematic effort can be made to solve the problem: '*How do we foresee technological innovations*?' Therefore forecasters should not willingly become twentieth-century alchemists by exclusively attempting to turn statistics of retrospective events into an allegorical telescope through which they hope to perceive the future. Possibly we can learn from the fact that the setting up of think-tanks and techniques like Delphi and Scenario Writing are simply attempts to use the psyche of known innovators more effectively.

The aims of technological forecasting are worth while. We should, therefore, devote effort to examining the worth of many different approaches which have been put forward. When decisions have to be made which affect our future it is appropriate that effort be put into forecasting, particularly working backwards from social goals by means of normative analysis. But where technological forecasting is regarded as an amorphous subject which constitutes a rich source of pseudo-scientific theorems and an open field for dilettante exercise, effort should be savagely restricted. Let us not be carried away by the present popularity of some, apparently logical, numerate techniques of forecasting in which the analyst abdicates his responsibility to the computer ascribing hastily chosen numbers to relevant facets of the problem.

Finally I hope that our academic colleagues can devise some method of orientating all 'decision makers', and advisers, towards the future without introducing dichotomy between 'future thinkers' and people handling present problems. Democratically we should all try to be members of one giant think-tank and not a majority of the uninspired awaiting the word of a few 'Kahn-like priests'.

Conclusions

Most members of PAU have reservations about the effectiveness of technological forecasting in all situations; nevertheless, it is generally accepted that the increasing need for objective evaluation of new R&D projects makes the use of technological forecasting essential.

The Unit is experimenting with, and debating the use of, most of the known techniques – and this is a continual process whereby we improve our knowledge of the subject. Members of this Conference may judge present prospects from the foregoing examples – but they should be warned that the selection of examples is the author's and other members of PAU might have selected differently.

References

1 K. G. H. Binning, 'The Analysis of R and D in the Ministry of Technology' (PAU M3/67).

2 R. L. R. Nicholson, 'Programme Evaluation in the Programmes Analysis Unit' (PAU M/67).

3 Erich Jantsch, *Technological Forecasting in Perspective* (Organisation for Economic Co-operation and Development, Paris 1967).

4 R. C. Lenz, Jr., *Technological Forecasting*, 2nd Edition (*Report ASD-TDR*-62-414, 'Aeronautical Division' Air Forces System Command, US Air Force, Wright Patterson Air Force Base, Ohio, June 1962).

5 Eric S. Wood, *Collins Field Guide to Archaeology in Great Britain.*

6 Landsberg *et al.*, *Resources in America's Future*, 1960–2000 (John Hopkins).

7 Chisholm and Black, 'The Application of Saturation Prospecting Techniques to Yukon Exploration', *Canadian Mining Journal*, **88**, 4 (April 1967).

APPENDIX I

STANDARDIZATION OF MATRIX PROCEDURES

1. *Introduction*

It has been suggested that the matrix technique, presently used by PAU Group A be standardized so that EDP techniques may be more easily used to evaluate the effect of an increment (or a decrement) in any of the matrix parameters.

This memorandum describes a method of standardization based upon the mathematical formula for the total variation of a function of many variables and the solution of simultaneous equations by determinants.

An implicit assumption is that all relationships between pairs of matrix parameters can be quantified, either rationally or subjectively. Without quantification of the relationships between parameters we can only hope to display the initially derived relevancies in another form, e.g. flow diagram; we cannot expect a computer to insert numeracy into an innumerate system.

2. *Existing Matrix Technique*

This appears to be a relevance technique employing a square matrix:

(i) parameters are listed downwards along the y axis and from left to right along the x axis;

(ii) when a change of the 'state of art' in any parameter along the y axis offers an opportunity of deriving benefit from any parameter along the x axis a tick (✓) is inserted in the appropriate square formed by the intersection of row and column;

(iii) different forms of relevance have been recognized in some existing matrices, i.e. direct economic, direct social and direct technological outcomes have been designated with blue, green and red ticks respectively.

The need for some EDP assistance is apparent, even in sub-matrices, for example the Sand and Gravel Matrix contains forty by forty parameters!

3. *Philosophy of Proposed Matrix Technique*

To illustrate the technique we use an alphabetical nomenclature for the matrix parameters, i.e. A, B, C, etc. It is envisaged that any one parameter may be a function of all other parameters:

$$\left.\begin{aligned} A &= f^n(\not{A}, B, C, \ldots) \\ B &= f^n(A, \not{B}, C, \ldots) \\ C &= f^n(A, B, \not{C}, \ldots), \text{ etc.} \end{aligned}\right\} \qquad \ldots(1)$$

It is also apparent, if δx represents a variation in function x, that:

$$\left.\begin{aligned} 0 &= -\delta A + \frac{\partial A}{\partial B}\,\delta B + \frac{\partial A}{\partial C}\,\delta C + \ldots \\ 0 &= -\partial B + \frac{\partial B}{\partial A}\,\delta A + \frac{\partial B}{\partial C}\,\delta C + \ldots, \text{ etc.} \end{aligned}\right\} \quad \ldots(2)$$

The new relevance matrix may now be constructed as follows:

Var. / f^n	A	B	C	D	E	F	G
A	$-\delta A$	$\frac{\partial A}{\partial B}\delta B$	$\frac{\partial A}{\partial C}\delta C$	$\frac{\partial A}{\partial D}\delta D$	→		
B	$\frac{\partial B}{\partial A}\delta A$	$-\delta B$	$\frac{\partial B}{\partial C}\partial C$	$\frac{\partial B}{\partial D}\delta D$	→		
C	$\frac{\partial C}{\partial A}\delta A$	$\frac{\partial C}{\partial B}\delta B$	$-\delta C$	$\frac{\partial C}{\partial D}\delta D$	→		
D	$\frac{\partial D}{\partial A}\delta A$	$\frac{\partial D}{\partial B}\delta B$	$\frac{\partial D}{\partial C}\delta C$	$-\delta D$	→		
E	↓	↓	↓	↓			
F							
G							

Figure 1.

(i) Each row represents an equation for the total variation in the parameter listed at the extreme left along the y axis; e.g. the first row put equal to zero is the first equation of equation-set (2) above.
(ii) Each column represents the variation in the y parameters resulting from a change in the parameter, listed along the x axis, at the head of the column.
N.B. It should be noted here that the diagonal terms which were previously blank are filled in with the appropriate negative decrement to facilitate the mathematics.

(iii) If the matrix shown above was rotated through 90°, and the partial derivatives replaced by ticks, we should have the existing type of matrix.

(iv) It may help to interpret the matrix by regarding the partial derivatives as the terms which we need to quantify, and the increments as the terms which are variables. As an abstract example of this, consider the limited matrix below:

Var. / f^n	A	B	C
A	$-\delta A$	$\frac{\partial A}{\partial B}\,\delta B$	$\frac{\partial A}{\partial C}\,\delta C$
B	$\frac{\partial B}{\partial A}\,\delta A$	$-\delta B$	$\frac{\partial B}{\partial C}\,\delta C$
C	$\frac{\partial C}{\partial A}\,\delta A$	$\frac{\partial C}{\partial B}\,\delta B$	$-\delta C$

Let us assume that we have managed to evaluate all terms:

$$\left[\frac{\partial A}{\partial B}, \frac{\partial A}{\partial C}, \dots\right]$$

and we wish to evaluate the consequences of an investment in parameter A of magnitude δA.

If we fix δA the first row of the matrix is redundant and we then require the solution of the two simultaneous equations in δB and δC – represented by the determinant of the second and third rows.

Using the laws for solution of simultaneous equations by determinants we find that:

$$\left.\begin{aligned} \partial B &= \frac{\partial A\left\{\frac{\partial B}{\partial A}+\frac{\partial C\partial B}{\partial A\partial C}\right\}}{\left\{1-\frac{\partial B\partial C}{\partial C\partial B}\right\}} \\[2ex] \delta C &= \frac{\delta A\left\{\frac{\partial C}{\partial A}+\frac{\partial B\partial C}{\partial A\partial B}\right\}}{\left\{1-\frac{\partial B\partial C}{\partial C\partial B}\right\}} \end{aligned}\right\} \qquad \dots(3)$$

In general, of course, $\frac{\partial B \partial C}{\partial C \partial B} \neq 1$; δA may be made either +ve or −ve, i.e. we can increase or decrease the investment in A; and the partial derivatives may take any value including zero.

To generalize the procedure formally, we use the following theorem:

Theorem I. To derive the change in any matrix parameter, for a given perturbation (say δx), the equations in the matrix are solved with the row containing $(-)\ \delta x$ omitted.

It is useful, at this juncture, to remind ourselves that the solution of a system of linear equations in $[\delta A; \delta B; \delta C; \delta D]$ is

$$\frac{(-)^n \delta A}{\Delta_1} = \frac{\delta B}{\Delta_2} = \frac{(-)\delta C}{\Delta_3} = \ldots = \frac{1}{\Delta_0} \qquad \ldots(4)$$

where Δ_0 is the determinant formed by the coefficients (i.e. the partial derivatives) with the column of terms containing δx omitted, Δ_1 the determinant formed by the coefficients with the column of δA coefficients omitted, and so on, the columns following one another in cyclic order.

The reasons for rotating existing matrices through 90° are now immediately apparent: and the ease with which (4) may be programmed hardly needs to be stated.

4. *Quantified Matrices*

Whether the matrix be constructed for economic, social or technological benefits it will be necessary to weight the existing benefits from the parameters (A, B, C, etc.) on a normalized scale.

The next step would then be the quantification of the terms

$$\left[\frac{\partial A}{\partial B}, \frac{\partial A}{\partial C}, \ldots; \text{ etc.}\right];$$

this involves technological forecasting, 'Delphi'-type survey or simply plain intuitive approach based upon extensive reading, visits made to establishments and acknowledged experts.

Even a technique where the partial derivates are constants and not functions of the matrix parameters (i.e. a linear programmed approach) would be a good first approximation to a complex system and certainly better than innumerate techniques.

Part 3

Futures

HUGH HARVEY AND E. V. NEWLAND

Energy patterns to the year 2000

Notwithstanding the generality of our title, our discussion of energy usage patterns, how they wax and wane, will be conducted largely from the viewpoint of the petroleum industry. 'Energy is so ubiquitous that it is taken for granted', one authority said recently, and the most convenient and ubiquitous source of energy that has been developed so far is petroleum. Petroleum, in the context of this paper, is the term we will use for oil and natural gas. Ease of transportation, assurance of adequate supplies, high energy content, freedom from bulky residues like ash and the low price per unit of energy – if taxes are excluded – are some of the advantages that have won for gas and oil 50 per cent of the whole world's and 60 per cent of the free world's energy market today. However, in addition to being a source of energy, petroleum has a host of applications in the non-energy field – from road surfacing to pharmaceuticals – and any attempt to conceive the industry's future would be misleading if it did not take into consideration this rapidly expanding sector of the business.

Historic Development of Energy Sources

As Marcus Aurelius pointed out some 1,700 years ago, in postulating a design for the future, it is always advisable to consult the past. Man's original source of energy was muscle power, his own and that of his animals. Muscle power, by the way, is unique in that it is the only form of energy to have enjoyed a 100 per cent monopoly. Then at some unrecorded moment in history, man discovered how to harness fire, and he began to use wood, or if wood was unavailable he burned dung from his animals, to generate heat for cooking, to keep him warm, and eventually to fabricate crude tools from bronze and iron. The harnessing of water power dates back to at least the first century BC on the coast of the Black Sea, while power from the wind was tapped probably a thousand years later in Arabia. Both sources have contributed, and still do, to the total of man's energy needs. But theirs has been a limited role, never more so than today; and since it appears likely to diminish further we shall not take these sources into account in our discussion. The historic and future patterns of the traditional sources of energy – that is muscle power, wood, dung – are shown in

Chart 1. You will notice that wood has been, from prehistoric times up to the middle of the last century, the predominant source of energy.

Coal was the next important source to enter the picture. The earliest mention of this fossil fuel was by a pupil of Aristotle in 371 BC, and while it has been used in Britain since the days of the Romans, its consumption did not become significant until the Industrial Revolution and the introduction of the railways in the 1840's. It dominated the energy scene for almost a century, as Chart 2 shows. Besides providing fuel for steam engines of all types, it was the basis of the gas and coke industries and the source of chemicals including benzene, naphtha, creosote, and sulphate of ammonia. It is apparent from these two charts that the energy spectrum has been moving in 'waves', this is even more evident in Chart 3, which shows the rise of oil. In its early years, oil was used mainly in lamps, but Otto's development of the internal combustion engine in 1876 sparked off the steep rise in consumption illustrated here. The demand for types of products based on oil varies from country to country depending on the degree of industrialization and wealth. As would be expected, in the US gasoline is by far and away the most important product, accounting for just about 50 per cent of the crude. In the UK, only about 30 per cent of the barrel of oil is used for gasoline while nearly 40 per cent is consumed as fuel oil compared with only about 18 per cent in America. Adjusting refinery processes to meet varying market requirements – requirements which by the way vary from season to season – is one of the most complex of operations and requires careful forward planning employing mathematical models that are manipulated by computers.

As you can see, the consumption of oil began to rise steeply about 1900, and today it is supplying about 36 per cent of the total world's energy requirements.

While natural gas has been used since the early 1880's in America, outside North America it has been slow in attracting commercial interest, as compared with oil, because of the absence of known sources of gas or (where they did exist) of economically accessable markets. The post-war discoveries of natural gas in Austria, Eastern Europe, France, Germany, Italy, and the USSR started the ascent of the curve seen in Chart 4, and the recent discoveries in the Netherlands, the North Sea, Siberia, and North Africa are accelerating its climb. Techniques for transporting and storing natural gas, including shipment by tanker, are contributing to its greater availability. Today, natural gas supplies nearly a third of the total energy consumed in the United States and it is becoming significant in Europe.

We should emphasize that these curves refer to the *proportion* of the total energy supplied by the fuels we are discussing and do not represent actual quantities. Thus, because the use of energy is increasing

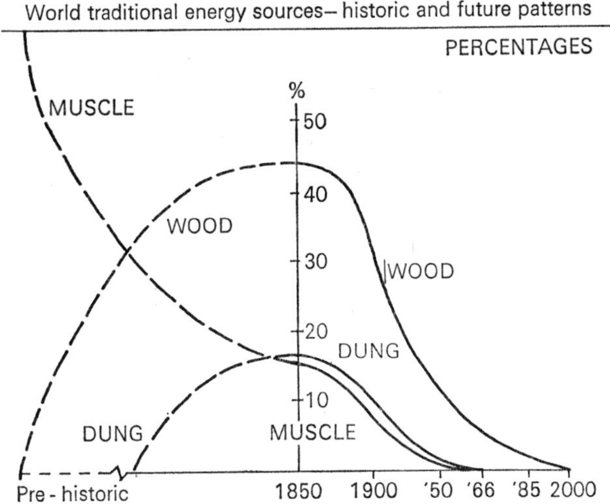

Chart 1.

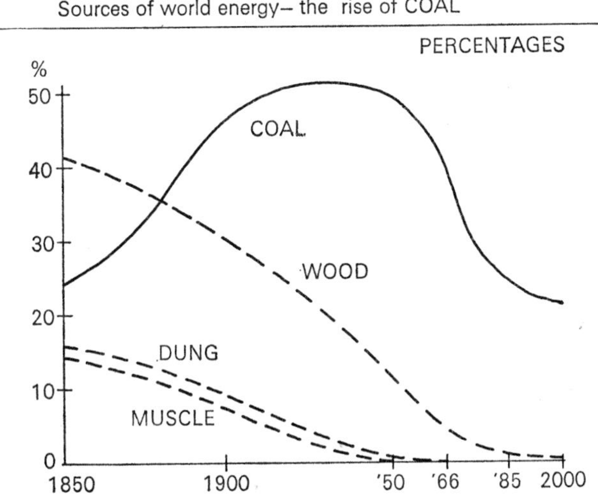

Chart 2.

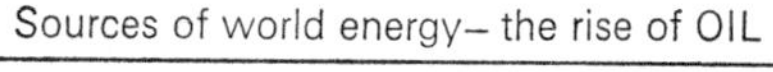

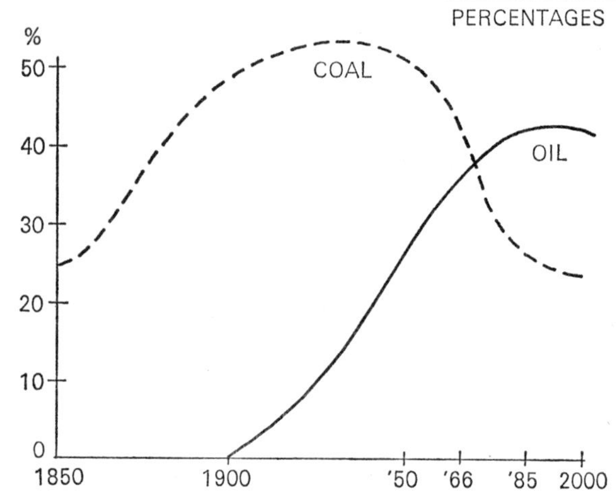

Chart 3.

Sources of world energy–the advent of NUCLEAR ENERGY

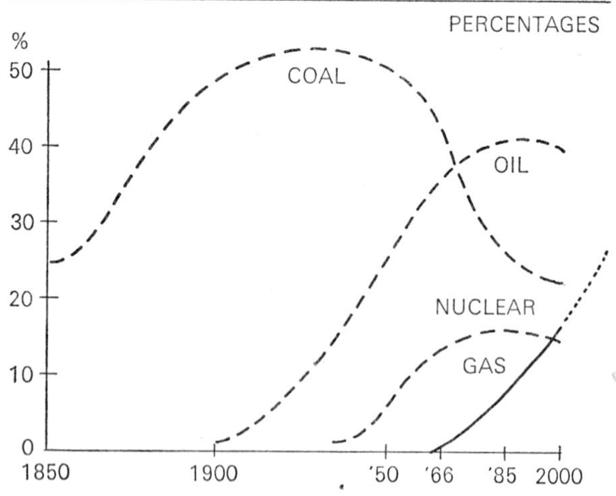

Chart 4.

every year – actually at an annual rate of about 5 per cent – the actual tonnage of coal produced has not declined.

In this same chart you will see that nuclear energy has begun that rapid rate of growth which is characteristic of all fuels in the early stages of their integration into the energy market. It is interesting that coal reached its peak about the time the curve for oil was rising most steeply; looking to the future the plateaux for oil and gas will come with the steep rise of nuclear energy.

What these charts bring out very clearly is an energy spectrum characterized by 'waves'. Each form of energy – with the exception of muscle power – enters the picture slowly, gathers momentum as seen in the steep part of the curve, levels out and then begins to decline.

There is no doubt that there is a practical lesson to be drawn from this pattern. It is that each energy resource should be utilized to its fullest at the right time – that is as it begins to rise to the crest of its wave. It is at this point, as you can see on the chart, that a competitive form of energy has historically begun its penetration of the market. Thus, if each source of energy is not developed at the right economic moment in history there is the probability that it may never be used for it may be incapable of competing with its successor. There are, for example, great reservoirs of hydro power, such as the Amazon and Passamaquoddy Bay, that will probably now never be developed. And there are coal fields in Europe that will in all probability never be mined because it is no longer economic to do so.

Britain was fortunate in being first to harness the power of coal and the rewards reaped made it the richest nation in the world. But it was the United States – a nation endowed with vast coal reserves – that was the first to recognize the special advantages that oil could offer in terms of ease of transport, storage and flexibility in use. Of course, the fact that oil was an indigenous product had an important bearing on its integration into the energy picture. But most important of all, the United States provided an economic environment that was conducive to the development of oil reserves and this resulted in the optimization of production at the right time. Similarly, when natural gas came on the scene no obstacle was permitted to prevent it from reaching its full potential. Now a similar course is being followed with nuclear power although ample supplies of fossil fuels are still available. There seems to be a tide in energy, as in the affairs of men, which taken at the flood leads on to fortune.

While oil, and more recently natural gas, have naturally and steadily assumed an important role in energy supply in the United States, their contribution in Europe was all but negligible until the end of the last war. Since then oil's share of the energy market has grown from less than 10 per cent to about 45 per cent today. And now, with the discoveries in Italy, France, the Netherlands, and last but not least the North Sea, natural gas is becoming the trend setter in Western Europe as it was in the United States two decades ago. During the coming decade, this new source of indigenous energy should treble its share of Europe's energy consumption. Well before the end of the century natural gas might contribute between 15 and 20 per cent of Europe's energy – provided, we might add, that the economic environment is conducive to its discovery and production. In fact, it is not unreasonable to believe that by 1985 three-quarters of Western Europe's energy needs will be met by oil and natural gas together.

Application of Technological Forecasting

In common with most of the large technologically based industries of the twentieth century, the petroleum industry will rely on technological innovation to provide the framework for its growth. However, the significant point to note here is that technological innovation will in the future be more and more responsive to politics, economics, sociology, and economics interacting simultaneously. *In other words, society's motivations will be important if not decisive factors in shaping the technology of the future.* Techniques for incorporating the motivation factor in the models employed by the futurists are still in their infancy, but the force it exerts will be increasingly determinative.

It is worth bearing in mind when speculating on energy and its utilization that technical ingenuity has often been more important in bringing a principle into use than pure science. As Professor Cambel has pointed out, James Watt was not held up by the lack of steam tables or diagrams of enthalpy and entropy, but he had to wait for a simple tool, James Wilkinson's boring mill that could produce round and straight cylinders. The internal combustion engine is only possible because of the internal grinder. And no scientist will quarrel if we say that we still know little about how a candle burns, let alone what goes on inside the cylinder of a car or why lead in gasoline suppresses knock. Furthermore, things that are scientifically possible may not be immediately reduced to practice. The principles of superconductivity and the advantages they offer for the generation and transmission of electric power have been known for a long time, but the stimulus to make them work in practice stemmed from the need to reduce the power requirements of particle accelerators. The first industrial application is now on the horizon – one 3,000-hp motor to drive a water coolant pump at a CEGB station, scheduled to go into operation next year. It is almost impossible to define the factors that have to be in conjunction to make it opportune to turn the scientifically possible into the technologically available.

Some major research inputs in the energy sector which might lead to technological breakthroughs have been summarized by Professor Cambel in Chart 5. This is not the time or place to study it in detail, but you will note that the subject heading at the top refers to various fields of investigation that can be brought to bear on the operations shown on the left.

Subject	*surface phenomena*	*electro chemistry*	*kinetics*	*chemistry and physics of materials*	*physics of fluids*	*cryogenics and superconductivity*	*mechanical properties of materials*	*systems analysis*	*transport phenomena*	*equipment design*	*safety and environmental effects*	*geology and geophysics*
exploration												
coal										•		•
petroleum										•		•
natural gas										•		•
shale oil										•		•
uranium	•									•		•
extraction												
coal			•	•			•		•	•	•	•
petroleum	•		•	•	•		•		•	•	•	•
natural gas				•	•		•		•	•	•	•
shale oil	•		•	•			•		•	•	•	•
uranium							•		•	•	•	•
processing and refining												
coal				•					•	•	•	
petroleum	•		•	•	•			•	•	•	•	
natural gas	•								•	•		
shale oil	•		•	•	•			•	•	•	•	
uranium						•			•	•		
transportation												
coal	•						•	•	•	•		
petroleum	•	•					•	•	•	•		
natural gas	•	•				•	•	•	•	•		
electricity				•		•		•		•	•	
storage												
coal			•									
		•					•			•		

Chart 5.

Analyses of this type are extremely useful at what has been referred to as the 'top management – laboratory' interface, for they can contribute to insight and understanding of future trends of technology that are needed at this level if the productivity of research and development is to be enhanced and capital expenditure profitably directed.

The use of technological forecasting for the petroleum industry has been extensively studied at the Battelle Memorial Institute in Columbus, Ohio, where the approach has been to consider the question *What should be forecast*? rather than *What methods should be used for forecasting*? The entangled interrelations between the forces affecting the industry – which we have mentioned previously – made an unstructured search through the labyrinth more confusing than revealing so that the question *What should be forecast*? became virtually unanswerable. To overcome this impasse, Battelle devised graphic models which proved useful in structuring the thoughts of the marketing men, the economists and scientists so that subtle, and perhaps important, factors were not overlooked. These models, which took the form of qualitative horizontal relevance trees, also helped in establishing relationships among factors that might otherwise have been overlooked.

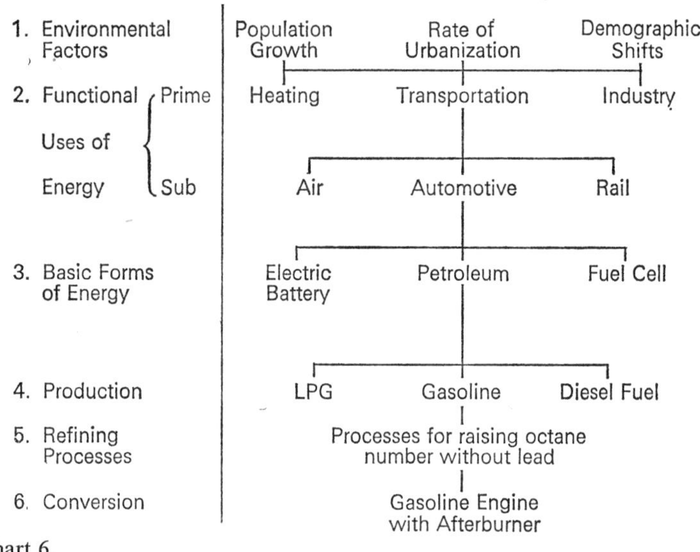

Chart 6.

An example of one of these models is shown in Chart 6. In the top line are the environment factors in a society, i.e. population growth, rate of urbanization and demographic shifts, that have an influence on the use of energy, and in this case the tree has been developed to show the relation of these factors to transportation and, specifically, automotive transport. The basic form of energy considered is petroleum though, as you can see, the approach could have been directed to the electric battery or the fuel cell.

Of the possible petroleum fuels, gasolene is the one that concerns us here, as also the matter of pollution. The path taken shows that it may be desirable to develop processes for raising the octane numbers of gasolenes so that they will be satisfactory in cars equipped with afterburners for suppressing exhaust emissions. These afterburners will not function with fuels containing lead additives for raising the octane number.

Under the basic forms of energy for automotive transportation shown in this chart you will see that in addition to petroleum the electric battery and the fuel cell are shown. For the purpose of this discussion we would like to make the normative forecast that because of such social factors as pollution, safety, noise, and congestion, which must surely play a dominant role in the selection of the vehicle of the future, there may be a requirement for an improved form of transportation. Let me hasten to add that we do not consider that the internal combustion engine cannot be adapted to meet these challenges, but we are taking cognizance of the fact that alternatives could be developed. This being the case, the approach should not be to select without question the most promising or advanced candidate of today – say the battery-powered vehicle – as being the winner. Rather one should first decide which of the contenders, say the battery or the fuel cell, would be most viable in the long term given the social constraints mentioned above. The point we want to make is that it is no use backing a particular technology in the light of a normative forecast if it is likely to be manifestly inferior and uncompetitive with existing systems or more far-out alternatives.

It was considerations of this nature that motivated Shell to invest research resources in fuel cells in spite of the fact that the technological problems with fuel cells, at this stage of the art, are more complex than those with batteries. A systems approach was also adopted so that simultaneous consideration could be given to the electrical system for controlling the power source when applied to vehicle propulsion. We should like to be able to show you a roadworthy customer-acceptable vehicle resulting from this work, but projects of this nature are not amenable to quick solutions. However, Shell has designed and built a fully integrated fuel-cell power system which can generate up to 5 kilowatts of electricity and can be mounted on a Land Rover. It does not power the Land Rover, but is a portable electric generator employing methyl alcohol and air. This power unit was built under a development contract for the Ministry of Aviation and was the first fuel-cell power system of its type to produce useful amounts of electricity from a cheap liquid fuel.

We should now like to turn to the survey of the world's energy requirements over the next thirty years which we have described in order to try to give you some idea of how each of the available sources of energy may contribute to the overall demand. The question *What should be forecast*? has, in this study, been cast in the form *What are the changes to be expected in the energy spectrum between now and the year 2000*? – the energy spectrum being simply the waxing and waning in contribution of the various energy sources over time.

The first part of this study, that is the estimation of the world's future energy requirements, was relatively simple, entailing only the extrapolation of current and projected growth rates in various areas and aggregation into a world total. We were fortunate in being able to draw on the past experience of energy requirements at different stages of the economic development of a given region or country. Furthermore, the 'lead economy', that of the United States, has now reached the stage where there is a predictable relationship between energy growth and GNP.

It is a far more complex problem to decide what proportion of the total energy requirements of the future will be contributed by each of the prime energy sources available, i.e. coal, oil, natural gas, oil shales, tar sands, wood, hydro and tidal power and fissile materials. The important thing to bear in mind at this point is that technology is advancing *on all these fronts*. Dramatic developments on the nuclear side do not preclude steady progress in the other fields. The efficiency of use of fuel oil for generating electricity, for example, has increased from 25 per cent to 33 per cent since the war and there is good reason to believe that it will reach 45 per cent by the end of this century. Perhaps the most surprising example of this technological 'progress' is that of a steel project in Brazil, which involves planting ten million trees a year to provide charcoal. The Brazilians have found that with existing agronomic techniques it is possible to harvest Australian gum trees after only seven to eight years in the sub-tropics as opposed to the thirty years required with indigenous forests.

Again the North American region provides an excellent example. Rich in fossil fuels, the strict application of financial considerations might have seemed opposed to investment in civilian nuclear power. But two motivational factors came into play: the determination to be nearly self-sufficient in energy, and the impelling desire to be the world leader in new technologies. Even so, these factors might have proved insufficient had they not come into play against a background of extreme competition between all forms of energy. Conspicuously in the electricity supply industry, this has prompted continual striving after technical improvements to reduce costs and increase sales. Another illustration from the American energy scene shows that national politics based on motivational factors can have unexpected consequences. Limitations imposed on the import of foreign oil, designed to spur domestic exploration and production for national security reasons, have tended to keep the price of oil at such a level that the use of coal, which was declining, has started to increase again. Coal hydrogenation, which was used extensively in Germany during the last war, is a strong contender for a comeback, while synthetic gas from coal could become viable within the North American energy spectrum.

Nuclear Energy

To assess the role that nuclear energy will play in the world as a whole during the next three decades it is necessary to consider the limiting factors within a framework of continued rapid growth. Certainly there is no question but that the electricity generating markets of the industrial countries will be dominated by nuclear fuels long before the end of the century. But the growth of the electricity industry itself will be constrained to a degree by overall shortages of capital. Generating facilities account for only half the capital cost, distribution networks accounting for the remainder. The cost of the latter are likely to increase as society insists on aesthetic considerations such as the burying of cables, and as grids are extended to more remote markets. The capital intensive nature of electric power is illustrated by the cost of providing the United States with the capacity it will need in the year 2000. If a moderate growth rate of 6 per cent per annum is assumed, the cumulative capital outlay will amount to some 600,000 million dollars. This demand for capital measured against comparable costs of alternative fossil fuels shows that electricity can be five times as demanding of capital. Hence, where electricity often has no inherent advantage as is often the case for steel furnaces, glass manufacture, and industrial and domestic heating, for example, its use will be manifestly uneconomic.

For the developing countries, it is difficult to detect any very pronounced growth in the use of electricity, which cannot be encouraged by such characteristic features of these economies as small markets, widespread distribution of population in rural areas, chronic shortages of capital. Hence use of nuclear power must be restricted.

Other factors that may limit the growth of nuclear power in the next twenty years include limitations in the capacity to build very large plants (1,000 MW and above), potential shortages of fuels, and problems of disposing of waste including waste heat.

All in all, we estimate that 30 per cent of the energy markets of industrial countries may be based on the atom by the year 2000 but only 5 per cent of the energy needs of underdeveloped countries will come from this source.

Increasing population and the rising aspirations of people everywhere for a better standard of living will produce an ever increasing demand for petroleum products. As we have said, up to the year 2000, nuclear energy will assume a growing proportion of the energy spectrum, and it will need to if the challenge of future demand is to be successfully met. For the petroleum industry the challenge is indeed formidable. By 1985 in the Free World outside North America the demand for petroleum fuels will have increased at least three and a half times and petroleum will be supplying over 60 per cent of the energy demand.

In the light of the tremendous demands of the future for oil you are probably wondering whether there is sufficient oil, and for that matter gas, left in the world to do the job.

The answer is a qulified yes. In looking at the future, the point that must be borne in mind is that, with the technology at our disposal, oil shales, tar sands, and coal could be sources of all the products which today are derived from petroleum. This year the first synthetic crude from the Athabasca tar sands is being fed to refineries and the use of shales and coal is more a matter of economic than technological debate. Hence the future of the oil industry would be linked to the reserves of fossil fuels, with the exception of peat. Chart 7 gives some

WORLD - estimates of economically recoverable fossil fuels in Q's (1×10^{12} kwh)

Coal and lignite	24,000 Q's
Peat	800 Q's
Oil	3,000 Q's
Natural Gas	3,000 Q's
Oil shales and tar sands	3,000 Q's
Total	33,800 Q's
World energy consumption, 1966	
- FOSSIL FUELS	40 Q's
- TOTAL	45 Q's

Chart 7.

of the most recent estimates of ultimate reserves of fossil fuels, i.e. coal, peat, oil, and natural gas, as well as oil shales and tar sands. So far as oil and natural gas are concerned, these are the estimates of all the deposits likely, in the ultimate, to be both discovered and recoverable under realistic economic conditions. If these quantities are expressed in the usual units of barrels, tons, or BTU's the numbers are so large as to be meaningless. It is for this reason that they are calculated here in an arbitrary unit Q which is one million, million kilowatt hours. This is still of a magnitude impossible to visualize, but it helps if you know that in 1966 the world used 45 Q's of energy of all kinds. Of this, about 40 Q's came from fossil fuels. Oil contributed about 14 Q's. From the chart you will see that on this basis some 33,000 Q's are available. Between now and the end of this century about 3,000 of these will have been consumed. By the year 2000 the world will be consuming energy at the rate of some 200 Q's a year, or over four times today's rate. But nuclear power can be expected to provide 20 per cent of this, leaving about 150 Q's per annum to come from fossil fuels. At this rate there would still be left a 200 years' supply of fossil resources for discovery and development.

We cannot emphasize too strongly that these resources vast as they are, will only be forthcoming if the right economic environment exists for their systematic discovery and development.

Summary

We would now like to summarize. We take first the general trends and then the future of the petroleum industry around the turn of the century.

(1) The Industrial countries are approaching the stage where the limiting factors governing energy will be less specifically natural resources but, increasingly, technology and capital – and of these capital is probably the more important.

(2) 'Quality of life' factors will play an increasingly significant part in determining the choices of technologies or raw materials made in any particular society.

(3) Regional groupings between countries or involving large continental masses portend greater emphasis on unconventional energy sources as well as the full utilization of indigenous resources within such areas.

(4) Energy technology will continue to advance on all fronts making a far greater degree of choice possible. New sources of energy will become available, existing sources will become more efficient, and some resurrection of oil technologies will take place.

(5) Natural resources which are not optimized during their 'boom' period may remain permanently unexploited.

(6) Current leading new technologies may not prove acceptable to society, it will become increasingly possible to leap-frog to better alternatives overall.

(7) Continued rapid growth of demand for oil and gas products is foreseen for the rest of this century. The penetration of nuclear power will not seriously slow the pace of growth of petroleum as a fuel during this period.

(8) The international oil businesses of today can increasingly participate in the provision of different forms of energy be they derived from conventional or synthetic sources of petroleum or indeed for sources outside the traditional sphere of the industry.

(9) World-wide, adequate potential reserves of fossil fuels exist for the

foreseeable future, but to bring these reserves into play will require the provision of enormous sums of capital and appropriate incentives. (10) The proportion of petroleum utilized for energy will diminish with time as it becomes the source of virtually all organic chemicals. By the year 2000 Western Europe should be utilizing as much petroleum for non energy purposes as it consumes today for energy purposes.

O. SMYTH

Future Trends in Automation and Process Control

I have been asked to speak about future development in process control and inevitably the word *Automation* tends to be used, and misunderstood. The process industries have to a greater or lesser extent been using automation in one form or another for some years. To appreciate the extent, let us look back to see what developments have occurred in the past ten years and discuss the position as it is today, predicting what the future holds in Process Control.

Previous Developments

The postwar process industries have witnessed a gradual increase in the use of instrumentation and many people are familiar with the modern instrument control room which is found throughout industry today. This control room is a nerve centre to which all the plant signals are sent and from which commands are normally given. In the early days these signals tended to be pneumatic but the use of electricity is becoming more widespread. Over the years the use of automatic controllers has also increased. Under normal conditions the 'plant operator' is there to monitor this automatic function (certainly as far as the simple measurements are concerned). When computers are being used, these controllers are often referred to as 'convention controllers' to distinguish them from computerized control. In the early days of process control the operator had to rely on laboratory analysis for information about the process quality. Using this analytical data from the laboratory, the operator would normally adjust the 'set-points' of the important controllers on the plant to achieve an acceptable quality of product. Often there would be fairly long delays between taking a sample of the product and receiving the laboratory analysis. These delays sometimes had the effect of forcing the operator to produce a product which was over specification and this 'give-away' normally resulted in loss of profit. Recent developments have largely removed this difficulty particularly in the field of chromatography. This technique is now widely used and has considerably reduced the time taken to obtain an analysis. As these developments progressed, chromatographs were used first of all as an indication to the plant operator and with increasing reliability and speed of response on-stream analyzers have been incorporated directly into control loops.

One of the greatest events in the process industries has been the introduction of the computer. The initial impact was in the business field, where the computer was used to do the pay roll and for stock control. These applications perhaps stand out as ones where there is a large number of repetitive calculations to be done for which the computer was and still is ideal. In the process control industries computers have been used in one form or another for about ten years. The electronic equipment needed to interface the computer to the plant has seen a similar refinement and development over the years and today there are throughout the world about 500 computer controlled processes in the oil and chemical fields alone. In the early days of computing, the majority of installations were used only for gathering data and providing a visual display for the operator and perhaps giving an alarm to the operator if any abnormality occurred. In the truly on-line computer, however, this data from the process instruments and analyzers is taken into the machine and in addition to the type of output already mentioned, signals are taken to the process control valves or to the set points of the process controllers and it is, therefore, possible to effect control of the plant without the intervention of the human operator. One of the first pre-requisites was to use the computer 'off line' to establish the mechanism of the process one desires to control, to describe it mathematically within the constraints of the plant. It has resulted in a wider appreciation of the dynamic behaviour of a plant, and the terms *mathematical model* and *optimization* are now quite common.

The experience gained so far in the process industries and in the computing industry is, of course, limited by the applications that have been completed and by those that are being worked on at the moment. Whilst the driving force that has led to the introduction of computer techniques is the pressure of increased capital and labour costs, and other economic factors, it has been quite difficult in the past to justify, on pure economic grounds, the capital cost of installing an on-line computer system. Some systems have resulted in very dramatic savings, however, but even in these cases new applications often demanded an act of faith. This act of faith was tolerated only because of the general belief that computers would prove to be economically necessary and the only way to acquire the right experience was to choose a plant which gave an indication of improvement and then to try it out. The future will, I believe, remove the faith from using a computer and substitute fact.

Present Problems

On the question of future trends, any new development will bring its own problems. These can have existed for a considerable time undetected. Suddenly they can form a barrier which must be overcome before further progress is made. One such problem is that of primary measurement. This is of fundamental importance, since whatever criterion of control one uses one is limited by the accuracy of the primary measurements. In considering accuracy it is well to remember the two aspects: (*a*) reproducibility; (*b*) absolute accuracy.

Since the normal plant control proposes employing feedback systems, one is primarily interested in the first of these since a set point is normally selected at which the system is controlled. The absolute level of the set point is of secondary importance only. If a computer is used with a mathematical model, however, when one flow has to be compared directly with another, all the measurements must refer to the same datum. This calls for high absolute accuracy as well as a high standard of reproducibility. This problem was recently highlighted in a study which Elliott's have just completed with a large chemical company. In this installation, which had over 200 analogue input signals, the instrument and analytical results were checked in two ways: first, by the accuracy or inaccuracy of the heat and mass balance achieved and, secondly, by cross checking wherever possible with existing plant instrumentation, and, in the case of liquid flows, by calibration against rates of change in tank levels. Although considerable care was taken in setting up and maintenance of the system, the overall balance on the plant could not be improved to better than 97 to 99 per cent. These errors are very important when it comes to justification of the on-line computer. An increase in the throughput of 3 per cent (real or imaginary) could well, in some plants, be worth £10 k. In the case mentioned the purchase of the computer has been easily justified.

Computer Development

Computers have undergone dramatic development both in hardware and in software terms. Not many years ago electronic valves were used throughout the industry and a big leap forward occurred with the introduction of the transistor. The early transistor computers, which were germanium machines, had to operate in closely controlled environments, but they were soon replaced by 'silicon' computers which did not have this limitation. Today it is possible to purchase a computer and all the interface equipment built entirely of integrated circuits. These developments have brought with them two important advantages: (*a*) reduction in cost; (*b*) increase in reliability.

There is a third advantage: space reduction. This does not play such an important role in the industrial as it does in the military field, but for what it is worth it is there. Another advantage, increased computer speed, has an important role to play in the future deployment of these machines. However, if we consider the other two advantages, the reduction in cost means that a whole new field of application which had previously been excluded for economic reasons can now be considered. The adoption of a hierarchy philosophy of control where a number of small computers act as a satellite to a larger machine can more easily be justified. The increase in reliability brought about by the use of integrated circuits and, for example, by replacing input relay switches by transistor switching has the effect of reducing maintenance costs and increasing the availability of an on-line system. This is obviously desirable, but I was interested to hear a speaker at a recent conference stating that when his computer failed he was prepared to shut down his plant. This view is certainly not held by many people, indeed most of the system design and the output interface equipment is in many systems associated with standby control which takes over in the event of computer failure.

Software

The development of software and programming facilities has not perhaps had the same dramatic development as hardware. The task of specifying the programme in detail is generally more difficult in an on-line system than in an off-line machine where the computer configuration is more rigid. Programming in real time increased this difficulty since the computer resources have to be allocated on an absolute time basis according to the demands of the system. It is still more difficult to use effectively the high-level languages which were developed for off-line work. Where then will progress be made in the computer itself? The hardware development will continue in an attempt to increase reliability and to reduce hardware costs. Secondly, programme development will continue, to ensure that new system programmes can be prepared with less effort while at the same time providing a more flexible system which can accommodate last-minute changes in the instrumentation or in the plant itself. It is possible today to protect on-line programmes in the event of mains failure or from corruption of another programme. This type of facility will be more widely used in the future so that changes in a programme can be carried out whilst the computer system remains on line. A particularly important development in hardware, that of the availability of reliable back-up memories, will be useful here in allowing a computer system to have access to a large memory system which is sometimes needed for this type of work. It is not hard to visualize computers holding banks of programmes which are called upon to meet changes in circumstances, for example partial plant failure. Already computers are in use with cathode ray tube and back projection displays. In the event of failure of part of the plant or indeed for any alarm point, that part of the plant affected is displayed in line diagram form together with the values of the flows, temperatures pressures, etc. It is not stretching the imagination too far to envisage the computer telling the operators what to do or what not to do in an emergency. Automatic shut down is a common feature of many plants. Usually it is an expensive but expedient thing to do. I am sure you can visualize the saving that could result if the computer could so rapidly assess the failure and issue instructions that a shut down could be avoided.

The programmes which I have so far mentioned (except perhaps the last example) all fall under the category of standard programmes, that is, aids which the control engineer will use in specifying and writing his on line programme.

Direct Digital Control

A few words on the special programmes associated with direct digital control, plant modelling and with optimization.

Direct digital control, whether as part of a larger computing function or as a small ddc machine, is now being used in the process industries. In this role the output from the computer is transmitted directly to the plant control values. The extent of its use today is not as great as was first envisaged. It does, however, have important advantages to offer. First of all there are processes which contain a small proportion of variables which are difficult to control by means of a conventional analogue system. Control loops on such variables are affected by changes in the process dynamics and the analogue instrument is incapable of adapting its mode of control at the times that these changes occur. Often the gain in the process part of the loop changes without warning and the analogue instrument is unable to counteract the change. The use of ddc permits control equations to be written in the computer which can adapt themselves to meet these changes in gain and changes in other parameters which are associated with the process dynamics. Secondly the use of ddc systems is of value in compensating for interaction between control loops. It is of course possible to speculate and perhaps reasonable to expect that the normal analogue controller will be able to abandon the three-term algorithm in favour of more complex or perhaps tailored functions. They will not be able to incorporate the same degree of flexibility that the digital computer can. It is clear then that progress will be made and is being made in this field. Here again built-in redundancy to guard against failure can be foreseen, although the quality of control will clearly fall as the faults occur. Additionally, the replacement of direct measurement of plant variables by inferential values derived from other sources or the change from a non-linear to a simple form of control in the event of partial failure is possible.

Another area where development is proceeding at a fast rate is that of plant modelling. This work can often be very time-consuming and demands access to a real plant before a theoretical model can be tuned to the plant and simplified to the extent that it allows easy and rapid operation of an optimization procedure. This type of work is still in its infancy.

The plant models I have just referred to represent one specific area of development. One sometimes hears the term *integrated system* used whenever one discusses future trends. By integrated system I mean one that is not only concerned with specific areas of a steel or chemical plant, but a system (usually embracing several computers) which cover the complete economic running of a plant. This means the integration of the process computer or computers with the top-level business machine. This type of system seems better suited to the large chemical or steel plant. We shall see more of this type of application in the future, whether done in a planned and organized manner or in a more random fashion by a control engineer or perhaps accountant deciding to link up the computers which exist on his plant. The first method is obviously clearer and probably cheaper. The development of high-speed computer-computer links has been progressing for a number of years and should not present any difficulty. Also the integration of one manufacturer's hardware being used for process control to that of another manufacturer being used for commercial purposes does not present any major problems.

Applications

Many people know of the use of computers in the steel, chemical, oil, and paper industries. But it is in other industries where the main changes will come. One such example is the management of distribution system for the public utilities. A Gas Board, for example, may obtain its gas from a number of sources, pipeline, or conventional manufacture (the cost of producing the gas depending upon the load). On the consumer side the demand for gas varies according to weather conditions, time of day, time of year and the local industrial population. The area covered by the Gas Board can be quite extensive and the computer plays an important role in monitoring gas flow and stocks at all the local stations, calculating the current demand rate, and predicting the future demand for say the next eight hours so that if need be a local gas-producing plant can be brought on line. A system such as this is currently being installed in England. It uses five satellite and one central computer and it is my belief that many more of this type of machine will be installed in the future. Other areas where computers will be used are such industries as bleaching, the food industry, inspection, and laboratory installations.

The future trends of automation in the process industries will be closely linked to the progress of the digital computer. As computers become cheaper and more reliable and as the software development continues, many more industries are going to find that using a computer is economically sound. Conventional control rooms will change to one using ddc or supervisory computers with CRT or back projection displays. These in turn will be linked to a higher-level machine to form an integrated system. More reliable and accurate transducers will appear, to overcome the problems outlined today, and the use of telemetry is going to spread right across the industry. One factor which will impede this progress is the lack of suitably trained personnel.

R. CURNOW

The Innovation Cycle in the Manufacture and Application of Computer Systems

My purpose is to fill in a grey area, that between acquiring basic data about a product or process and the structuring of the understanding of the forces behind that data. Since we are interested in forecasting not only what innovation may be expected but when and how, the paper considers a model of the innovation cycle. The actual sector chosen is a heart-industry for our near future: that of electronic digital computers.

The Innovation Cycle in the Manufacture and Application of Computer Systems

The phrase *computer system* is now in such usage that the implication of the word, system, is in danger of being overlooked. As used in this phrase it implies an organized bringing-together or assembly of various subsystems for the achievement of an overall purpose; similar definitions hold for the word, in the phrase 'subsystem', and so on down to the ultimate system elements. This concept of system underlies the technological structure of computer technology whether of production or application, and the nature of the innovation cycle in computer technology cannot be understood unless the extent and number of necessarily-present individual technologies and supporting technologies is grasped.

The following table represents, as at present, a possible plan and minimum time scale for the development of today's computer technology in the production of hardware only. A similar complex holds for software.

For the purposes of understanding the nature of the actual innovation cycle, and the necessary ingredients for the effective stream of successful innovation cycles, the breadth and depth of the supporting technologies dictates the pattern of the cycle and the interdependence of its various steps.

In summary, the innovation cycle is best regarded as three separate stages, whose end-products are successive in time. These are, respectively, *invention – innovation – diffusion/imitation*. In practice (due to

Time Scale (Years)	Technology: Fabrication	Technology: Components	Equipment	Ancillary
1	Printed Circuit Modules; Hi Resolution CRTs; Core memory modules	Resistors, Capacitors; Low Speed Transistors Diodes, Zeners	Card and tape equipment; Visual displays A/D and D/A converters	Computer quality cards, paper tapes, printer paper, magnetic tape, etc.
2	Magnetic thin films	Silicon transistors and diodes	Digital Plotters; Line printers and RS card readers; Digital tape transports, discs, drums	
3		Magnetic tapes, discs precision potentio-meters		
4	Hybrid circuits micro miniaturisation		Medium speed systems	
5		Integrated circuits	High speed systems; Very High speed systems	

Table 1.

the different time-delays, lags and buffer-stocks of resources involved in planning and forcing an innovation cycle or pattern of innovation cycles), these three stages overlap considerably from the viewpoint of decision taking. But this consideration does not affect the nature of the constraints which have to be considered at each stage.

Invention

In manufacture. Of hardware, anyone with the necessary knowledge and skill can invent a new system element, e.g. logic circuit, error correction element, printer principle, etc. But such elements require incorporation in a system in order to achieve a market. Therefore the market pattern dictates the usability in time and scope of that new element. Current commitments at the time of invention of a new element reinforce this argument. Since a new element itself will come under the competitive pressure of emerging developments in its own technology, it follows that for inclusion in a marketable system it must 'catch the train' at the right time, particularly since system advances go in long (e.g. five to seven years) cycles for major impact. This itself is a market phenomenon, elsewhere analyzed as being determined by product absorption times both for user and manufacturer, with technical development continuously building up to threshold levels to spur product announcement.

Of software, it cannot be said that anyone can invent a new system element or subsystem. The prime requirement is access to a suitable computer for concept proving, development, and demonstration. Such a computer must not be constrained by speed, size, available time, etc., and must have adequate though minimal operating system-handlers and input/output routines. Software invention, therefore, is subject to a constraint of threshold scale. Since software output is completely unpredictable, a longer purse is also appropriate.

In application. Similar arguments for inventing in application hold as for invention in software manufacture. The availability of a suitably specified computer is necessary, particularly as the recognition of an application advance is aided by familiarity with the use of an advanced system. Invention in application is also aided in contexts where there is considerable standardization in application practice (e.g. US commercial, or any large scale, standardized government application) since this enables concentration upon the frontier of application rather than detailed mopping-up in the interior. Invention in application is hindered by country-comparative delays or lags in market penetration or penetration of the educational system, since the necessary skills must then come from nearer the top of the pyramid – this general argument is particularly valid in the application field since the final key to successful computerization of a process rests with application skill and therefore money incentives exist to concentrate upon the interior rather than frontier work.

Innovation

In manufacture. The introduction and innovation of any computer system is essentially a systematized procedure of recognizing the nature of the, for example, 25 per cent increase in productivity/price ratio, and organizing and controlling the subsystem development and basically the system element development. It is not coincidental that computers are used extensively in the planning and execution of computer development, design, manufacture, and planned marketing. Here is a prime example of the use of computers to make more efficient an industrial sector; it is also a good example of how success in computers can be used to help guarantee and multiply that continued success.

The economies of scale which apply at system element, subsystem, or system production and marketing level imply that either a major attempt is made at the market, or no attempt. It is not possible to gain and hold a very small general market share, partly because of other economies of application scale and partly for credibility reasons, so that innovation in production must tend to be concentrated with those already in large production. The appreciation of innovation in manufacture of a system element requires to be understood from the viewpoint of the manufacture of the whole system.

Innovation in the manufacture of the software, a process usually requiring the continued attention of the skills of the individual inventors, usually requires gearing to the production of new hardware, and vice-versa, which again increases the importance of scale of operation to innovation. But the handling of all these considerations itself requires a large-scale planning complex, which in turn reinforces the scale argument. As a result of all this, the cost of innovation, i.e. of changing the current activities of a large activity, is high. For this reason, a large share of the market tends to be equivalent to dictating by commercial arguments the pace of innovation in that market, an argument which reinforces the loyalty and continuity arguments developed elsewhere.

In application. Innovation in application is even more risky where the innovating installation is concerned. For this reason innovation is only allowed to the manufacturer who has a depth of organization sufficient to 'insure' the risk. It follows that innovation tends to be confined to the larger and established installations or to the established manufacturer's organization. Because of the way in which an application innovation is usually tied to the configuration of the innovating installation, continuity of the perpetuation of the innovation is virtually confined to the largest and established manufacturers.

In addition, since innovation in application usually today requires supporting skills, the vacuum effect of the larger manufacturers which have a disproportionate effect on the supporting skills implies that such innovation is usually found within their ranks.

Because of the high risk involved in innovation in application, the action of the US Federal Government in giving risk-free development contracts for application innovation as well as hardware development must be noted. Numerical control, information retrieval, command-and-control leading to conversational systems, have all been developed under government contract, as well as the 10^{12} bit electron written film-money on the hardware side.

Diffusion / Imitation

In manufacture. As argued above, a major constraint is the high cost of imitation or diffusion. Particularly this is so, because lag-times in copying manufacture imply the acceptance of a technological gap equivalent to that lag-time in the advance of technology, and therefore copying means acceptance of an obsolescent technology. As a result, the very largest manufacturers have advantages in being able to isolate different types of development and manufacturer either by plant or by country, thereby aiding commercial security without incurring the penalties of too-small-scale establishments.

The major absolute constraint to imitation is the high cash flow required, still traceable to the prevalence of computer renting. The loyalty and continuity of market shares also mitigates against the newcomer, as does the non-compatibility of both hardware and software. Other major constraints afforded to the newcomer are the economies of scale available from the application market to the large market-share holder.

Certain absolute economic factors also affect would-be newcomers of different national origins. Because of the economies of scale afforded to the supporting or ancillary industries by being in large markets or in large economy, the newcomer from a large country has a built-in advantage in addition to the advantages of a larger market.

Another inbuilt advantage to the currently large manufacturer is the accumulation of experience in knowing the right degree of 'promise' in a contract. Every computer contract is in effect a promise, and the fact that most computer specialists are of high IQ and tend to confuse their idea of future performance with the present, makes such accumulated experience in marketing vital to commercial success.

Other constraints to diffusion and imitation are the inoperability and ineffectiveness of the patent-pool or licensing system since the time lags in operating this sytem are long in relation to technological advance. Another constraint is that the actual capability of a system may be tied to a critical design element often in a much older technology, e.g. the exact timing of some circuit elements, and an apparently innocuous exclusive monopoly of supply may result in a total inability to copy. This is known as 'tripwire' design.

Yet more factors operating against the new entrant are that since computer power goes up disproportionately with list price, job satisfaction is often keyed to working on the 'newest and biggest' and since each scale in this market may swing $\$10^6$ or more, there is a drain of best brains to such installations.

Apart from the obvious advantages of working in a business climate geared to the acceptance of innovation, such a climate encourages diffusion of information.

In application. Diffusion of an application innovation tends to be backward because of the commercial advantage in security, and also because computer scientists tend to regard the normal information systems used to disseminate information as being mediaeval in technology. In any case, the best user co-operatives are those which directly or indirectly are subsidized by individual manufacturers, again a costly element.

In considering all the various points raised in the above analysis of the innovation cycle, a three-stage process which occurs in manufacture/application and hardware/software, it is noteworthy how many of the constraints described are such that they feed back positively upon the current market shares. Under these circumstances it would seem that unless some of the constraints are removed, further intensification of the present market imbalances will ensue. In so far as the present market differences reflect disparities in the economic multiplier effect upon the rest of the economy, it follows that the tendency to produce different levels of overall economic efficiency will be enhanced.

What, then, are the ingredients of success? The short answer, be like IBM, is unfortunately an unavailable remedy, although it is clear from previous analysis that IBM (plus its resource endowments in the punched card market) created a market, and whether by design or accident, most of the factors are now in its favour. The alternative, say for a European computer industry, is to form larger more homogeneous markets, supporting industries, supporting standardization, and to exchange public money for relief from all the adverse factors nominated above, to the extent that disparities in the aggregate performance between countries' economies is removed or is in balance with social and political aspirations. The history of merged companies in the computer field is not such as to give confidence in the feasibility of this approach as an evolution from the present state but no immediate alternative presents itself at present.

As a first step, having decided upon the normative goal of a viable computer industry, whether at national or cross-national level, an assessment of the ranking of the constraints operating on the innovation cycle as appropriate to that goal should be made, and economic strategies devised to divert their impact into constructive channels.

V. R. GRAY

Future Developments in the Construction Industry

The Construction Industry comprises all building and civil engineering, repairs and maintenance, building materials and component manufacture. Civil engineering is to some extent distinct from building when it concerns construction of roads, bridges, power stations, or railways, and it has distinct professional bodies. In many construction jobs the distinction is less clear since site works, roads, foundations, and structure may be regarded as civil engineering and provision of walls, floors, roofs, fixtures and fittings, the installation of heating and ventilating services, repairs and maintenance as building. Despite these distinctions, the construction industry has many unifying features and it is convenient to consider it as a single industry.

The output of this industry in the UK is now (1967) £4,271M, which amounts to 12½ per cent of the GNP. It provides about half the annual investment by society in fixed capital, and since replacement of buildings and structures is much slower than other forms of capital investment (for example the houses built each year are about 2 per cent of the total stock), construction represents the major fixed capital of our society. About half of this stock is financed from public funds (central and local Government and Nationalized Industry) and about 25 per cent of the cost is on repairs and maintenance.

The construction and maintenance part of the industry employs about 1·7 million workers. Seventy per cent of all building firms (less than 9 per cent of output) employ less than seven workers whereas less than 0·1 per cent of the total number of firms 22½ per cent of the output employ more than 1,200 workers.

Rapid changes in an industry with traditions which extend from the dawn of civilization is not to be expected. Trends in value of construction output, or in number of houses built over the past twenty years are remarkably constant when one considers the economic ups and downs and the fluctuating fortunes of other industries over the same period. The long life of buildings means that any new developments cannot have a widespread impact on the building stock as a whole until they have operated for decades. This makes some types of forecasting much easier than with other industries.

There are unknown factors. Changes in social attitudes could change the pattern of urban development. Regional development, new methods of transport, greater mobility of employment (which may lead to the concept of a 'pool' of empty housing) could all change our trend lines.

International comparisons also raise questions. We spend only 8 per cent of our gross national product on fixed capital for construction (i.e. excluding maintenance) whereas the Netherlands spend 12 per cent and France 11 per cent. We could change. Our lower usage of flats is even more puzzling. Switzerland has 76 per cent of its dwellings in multi-dwelling buildings, France 58 per cent, Netherlands (a similar country to ours in many ways) 46 per cent, yet in Britain this figure has increased from 7 per cent to 14 per cent from 1951 to 1960. Will this trend continue, and if so, where will it stop?

The Role of Government

Government is concerned not merely with forecasting but, increasingly, with planning, or to use a jargon word, with normative forecasting. Responsibility of Ministries for sectors of industry developed from the necessities of two world wars. Today aspects of forecasting and planning of future developments over the whole of British industry are divided amongst the Production Departments of the Government. The construction industry is the concern of the Ministry of Public Building and Works. It is the largest single client of the industry, with a building expenditure of £250M per annum. It is responsible (through the present Construction Economics Division) for the collection of industry statistics, including production statistics of building materials.

The Report of Sir Harold Emerson (a former Permanent Secretary of the Ministry of Works) on the Problems of the Construction Industry, published in 1962, called for 'a new form of relationship between the Government and the construction industries' and led to the setting up in a reconstituted Ministry of Public Building and Works of a Directorate General of Research and Development which was made responsible for Development Groups within the Ministry and for co-ordinating their work with other similar Groups elsewhere. It also had the job of encouraging the use of new and rapid methods of construction and other modern practices with particular emphasis on standardization of building components.

There are at present five Directorates in the Directorate General, charged with improving the performance of the Ministry's own work and with various sections of the Ministry's general task of modernizing the construction industry. The Building Research Station, the main centre for scientific work on building, was transferred to the Ministry in July 1967.

Although the Ministry of Public Building and Works has main

responsibility for modernization of the Construction Industry, several other Ministries have related responsibilities. The Ministry of Housing and Local Government is responsible for town and country planning, local authority housing, and revision of building regulations, one of the most important Government instruments for enforcing new standards of construction. They have responsibility for the National Building Agency, the body which assesses low rise industrialized housing systems.

School building is controlled by the Department of Education and Science and hospital building by the Ministry of Health. Roads and the Road Research Laboratory are the responsibility of the Ministry of Transport. Although Ministry of Public Building and Works is concerned with most building materials, timber is under the Board of Trade. Conditions of employment, industrial relations, and training are the concern of the Department of Employment and Productivity.

The Ministry of Technology runs research stations such as those on Fire Research, Forest Products, Water Pollution and Hydraulics and it contributes research grants to Research Associations which include the Construction Industry Research and Information Association (also supported in part by the MPBW) the Heating and Ventilating Research Association and several others which deal with building materials.

The National Economic Development Council sponsors Economic Development Councils for Building and for Civil Engineering.

This section has briefly summarized Government involvement together with industry in the future of the Construction Industry. The fragmentation of the industry between designer, client and contractor and amongst the multifarious sections of the industry make co-ordinated action difficult to achieve even when it is widely desired and it is the aim of Government to seek to stimulate this co-ordinated action.

Topics for the Future

In this section I propose to discuss the more significant future developments in the construction industry which are already well advanced, at least in plan, and which can be confidently said to be here to stay.

Industrialized building. The general aim behind industrialized building is to convert the construction industry from a bespoke, craft based, fragmented industry to one more closely allied to industrial manufacture. It is important not to oversimplify or to argue too much from analogy. Some parts of the industry have been industrialized for some time – the manufacture of doors, windows, rainwater goods, bricks, paint. The production of complete large buildings in a factory will probably never become widespread because of the difficulty of meeting varying planning needs and because of the difficulty of transport of either factories or buildings to building sites. Industrialization of component production and site assembly have made tremendous strides in the past few years, but preparation of sites, excavations for services and sewers and foundations are still pre-industrial. Finishing and maintenance are slow and labour consuming.

All the problems cannot be tackled at once. Emphasis in the past few years has been on the rationalization of traditional building techniques using a wider range of factory made components including not only the well-established windows, doors, and roof trusses but also wall units, framing members, partitions, cladding panels, services and bathroom units, and on the development of building systems based on wall-sized precast concrete units. The systems have already firmly established themselves in local authority housing where in five years they now have some 40 per cent of the market. For flats over five storeys they are 3·6 per cent cheaper than traditional building but for low rise housing they are still slightly dearer, though giving advantages of speed of erection, labour saving and economy of tendering.

Future development of systems depends on greater standardization and interchangeability of components. The move to metric dimensions is providing an exceptional opportunity to standardize and coordinate dimensions.

More complex building components will incorporate those services which used to be optional extras but which are now essential.

To those who deplore this evident progress towards standardization I would point to the car industry. It is still possible to buy a custom built Rolls Royce or even a specially modified Mini – at a price, and bespoke buildings will certainly not disappear. Their importance is bound to decline, however, if there is a great reduction in costs by the use of industrialized techniques.

Component building. At present most building components are made in a wide range of shapes and sizes, apart from a few like the brick, the 2-inch nail or the standard 13-amp plug. Even components used in systems are only standardized for that system and for no other. The benefits from really large-scale manufacture can only be obtained if there is a much greater standardization of the more complex components such as doors, windows, partitions, wall units, roof trusses. These new components must fit any building system, and the whole process of factory manufacture must be integrated in a systematic way with planning, design, transport, labour supply, material deliveries with careful timing of each stage, rather like car manufacture.

Besides the problems of financing, organization, and management there are a number of technical problems that need to be solved, notably the design and production of reliable jointing procedures for interchangeable components and the establishing and enforcement of tolerances and accuracy to ensure success.

Metrication. The programme for the change to the metric system is a textbook example of normative forecasting. The programme for the construction industry published in February 1967 shows that the construction industry is likely to be ahead of several other industries in this essential reform. British industry, which has committed itself to the introduction of the metric system, is responsible for initiating the change. The Ministry of Technology through its Standing Joint Committee on Metrication is supervizing the change and the British Standards Institution has the job of publishing new metric standards.

The programme for Construction envisages a change from 1st January 1969 in design offices and 1st January 1970 on sites. The Ministry of Public Building and Works, represented on the main committees, has announced that it will adhere to the programme in its own work. It is also promoting through its Directorate of Building Development the simultaneous introduction of dimensional co-ordination and the use of performance specifications for building components.

It has recently appointed a Metrication Officer in the Directorate of Central Services of the Directorate General of Production charged with the implementation of the recommendations of the Ministry's Metrication Internal Policy Committee and its Sub-Committees. A programme of training in the new techniques will be an important part of his work.

Because of the long life of buildings and the need to maintain them, components using old dimensions will be required for maintenance work for some time to come. It is not expected that the changeover will be free from snags and pitfalls.

Performance specifications. The wealthy man who commissions an architect to build him a house usually makes sure he gets what he wants. The rest of us live in houses, or work in factories and offices which have been designed without our being directly consulted. Systematic industrial building producers will have to find ways of ensuring that standards of these buildings are to the liking of the various users before they set the production line going, for by then it will be too late to change. Minimum standards of structural stability, safety, moisture protection, thermal and sound insulation that are consistent with modern scientific knowledge and likely economics are set by the Building Regulations, and by the other Ministry controls such as those by the Ministry of Housing and Local Government for houses (Parker Morris), the Department of Education and Science for schools and the Ministry of Health for hospitals, usually related to a cost yardstick.

With the development of industrialized building components of increasing complexity, manufactured on a large scale, it is essential that their fitness for purpose, consistent with cost and ease of manufacture, is established before the assembly line is set running. This implies a thorough examination of functional and user requirements combined with comprehensive development of testing procedures. British Standard Specifications and Codes of Practice, various Ministry and industry specifications and requirements of Building Regulations and other statutory obligations vary in scope from extended manufacturers' guarantees through various methods of quality control, but usually stopping short of a comprehensive definition of performance required and testing methods and criteria adopted for determining compliance with this performance.

The setting up of the Agreement Board by the MPBW, based on a pattern established for some years in several continental countries, has provided the building industry with the means of certification of new building products as to their suitability for purpose and their ability to comply with statutory requirements including building regulations. The issuing of performance specifications by my Ministry and others combined with bulk Government orders for components which best meet the requirements will help to establish a market for good components.

Computers in the Construction Industry. The uneven development of industry means that a traditional industry like construction expects to call on advanced techniques from the technologically progressive industries. Computers are finding their way into so many aspects of our life and they are already transforming parts of the construction industries where unusually complex problems are common. The Ministry of Public Building and Works Committee on Computer Applications in the Construction Industry has done a great deal to identify and stimulate uses for computers and they will be making an increasing contribution to the following fields of activity.

(a) *Structural design.* The computation of stresses, movements, and other quantities from complex design is already widely practised. The most important present need is for proper co-ordination and interchangeability of programmes, which is being provided for by a current Ministry study called GENESYS.

(b) *Coding and data co-ordination.* One of the most meticulous and difficult jobs in building is the communication of information from design to building contractor involving the quantity surveyor in the preparation of bills and quantities, for materials and building operations, to provide cost and tender information. Coding and pricing on a computer can very considerably reduce this work and the preparation of bills of quantities by computer is already practised by several firms. System Building Consortia are also operating a number of computer based ordering and pricing systems. In the future the use of computers, backed by data banks will enable all participants in the building process to communicate readily.

(c) *Computer-aided design.* Computers have the potentiality of enabling much more rapid alterations of designs so that architects are free to experiment more widely between the limits of their brief. The techniques for doing this, including the 'light pen', provide a means of conversation with the store of design information which gives the designer scope to exercise his proper function to the full.

(d) *Management.* The use of computers in management, notably in critical path methods of programming in payroll, stock control, resource allocation cost control, linear programming and estimating, can be very widespread, and we have only scratched the surface so far.

The new British computer company ICL has a special Building and Civil Engineering team to cater for the industry's needs, which now account for a total investment in computer and associated equipment of £6M.

Building materials. We are at present passing through a materials revolution. New metals and organic plastics have transformed many familiar articles and several well-established industries, as well as making new industries possible.

The construction industry is coming under their influence, as well as expanding the use of recently developed materials such as reinforced and pre-stressed concrete. The fundamental knowledge on the strength properties of materials which has shown the importance of fibre reinforcement will cause further changes. Most traditional building materials (with the exception of timber) are heavy, with poor insulating properties, and these characteristics have been shown by our buildings. The newer materials and the methods by which steel, timber, and concrete are being employed as frames are tending to reduce the weight of buildings and increase their thermal insulation. The trend towards lighter buildings seems a firm one, but it will be necessary to overcome the problems arising from low thermal capacity, the poor sound insulation, and the lower structural stability. Prefabricated building components made from composites including cheap fibrous materials bonded with plastics, weatherproof skins of certain plastics and ready decorated linings are already being made by several firms and it seems probable that whole rooms, including windows, doors, and service ducts can be extruded in a continuous form, or moulded in a large press like a car body. The inorganic building materials also have a part to play. The Building Research Station has recently shown that it is possible to improve the properties of concrete and plaster by glass fibre reinforcement.

Maintenance and cleaning. In 1966 maintenance of buildings cost more than £1,130M a year and occupied 40 per cent of the building labour force. Most of the present technical changes are in economizing on erection costs, so that the prospects are that an even higher proportion of building labour will be on maintenance in years to come, with costs correspondingly high, since labour content of maintenance work is high.

My Ministry, in recognizing the importance of this problem, has a committee under the Parliamentary Secretary trying to see what can be done to avoid the prospect which faces us under one possible extrapolation of present trends, that the entire population will be doing nothing but maintaining buildings in fifty years' time.

The unco-ordinated structure of the existing maintenance demand favours the small builder. But the legislation envisaged by the recent White Paper *Old Houses into New Homes* would open the door to a restructuring of the maintenance and rehabilitation market into much larger units likely to be of interest to major contracting organizations. This may be expected to produce important contractual and technical developments in the maintenance field.

One of the main economic virtues of owner-occupation is the incentive on owners to do it themselves. Landlords (both private and public) have to pay heavily for maintenance. The large amount of do-it-yourself maintenance means that our figures are a gross underestimate.

The related and interpenetrating activity, cleaning, is traditionally the unpaid and unrecorded work of the housewife. Limiting the entry of dust and dirt into buildings is the best way of reducing this work. Greater efficiency in maintenance and cleaning is also of crucial mportance if we really are going to achieve the age of leisure that is spoken of by so many soothsayers.

It is a field of great technical difficulty. Greater efficiency means training and technical aids. Training requires a multitude of skills and mechanical aids are difficult to design. The vacuum cleaner and the floor polishers have taken decades to evolve. Mechanical painting is still beyond most of us and the robot housemaid even more remote.

Designing and costing for maintenance give us better scope. More durable materials and components and costing techniques which reveal savings in running costs will save a great deal. In the present component revolution comparatively little progress is being made in providing prefinished components, partly because of the difficulty of imposing greater care in handling and cleanliness on building sites. Pre-glazed windows, decorated wall panels and pre-polished floors require an approach to building which can possibly only be solved by a greater feminine influence on building sites, combined with greater attention to cleaning and maintenance at the design stage.

Unless we pursue the problems of maintenance and cleaning vigorously they will be our leisure occupations even more in years to come than they are today.

Information services, training, and education. The information explosion is one of the characteristic features of our age, affecting all industry, and of particular importance to this conference. It is characterized by an enormous increase in printed material on every subject produced in a chaotic and unplanned fashion, containing a decreasing proportion of valuable or original information. The problem is not to classify the information (though probably you have to start there), it is to transmit the small part of it that is useful to those who can use it. One way this could be done is by a network of qualified advisory officers operating over the whole country. A Working Party reporting in 1964 recommended the setting up of such a nationwide building advisory service, similar to that existing for agriculture. This recommendation as such was not accepted because of financial and organizational difficulties, but a start has been made with the setting up of the Construction Industry Research and Information Association in 1967 financed jointly by the Industry and the Government which has just appointed its first regional advisory officer. With training, finance has been easier to find since the 1964 Industrial Training Act and the setting up of the Construction Industry Training Board. The task here is formidable since a high proportion of building workers are poorly educated and unskilled. Even the skilled are too highly specialized and lacking in experience of modern techniques.

The problems are even greater on the technical and management sides. University training in building is relatively neglected and the various professional bodies are all facing problems of rapid change.

Management training is particularly important. Not only does it lack the support of an established professional institution, but some of them debar members from management functions. The RIBA, for example, do not allow architects to accept directorships in firms connected with building.

Research and development. The future of every industry is tied up with the amount, quality, and significance of scientific and technical research and development deployed on its problems. National figures are misleading since the greatest effort in every country tends to be on projects of military or prestige value. In Britain about £10M were spent on construction research in 1966, about 0·5 per cent of the industry's output. Although this is higher than most comparable countries it is still well below our overall average of 2·6 per cent of the GNP. The significance of effective research and development at much higher levels of expenditure has been demonstrated for the technologically advanced industries. It has yet to be proved as an effective means of transforming a traditional industry such as construction but the chances are that a modest doubling of expenditure could transform the industry to an extent that this paper is unable to predict.

The fragmented structure of the industry with its high proportion of small firms, both of builders and professionals, has meant that whole sectors of the industry are unable to concentrate the resources necessary for effective research and development.

Of the £10M 1966 figure, about half was spent by manufacturers of building materials, nearly £6M by national and local government and other public bodies, most of the rest by contractors. The high public contribution is a reflection of the difficulty the industry has in helping itself (though this characteristic is also shared by advanced, concentrated industries such as aircraft). The Building Research Station is the most important public centre of research and development for the industry. The first of its kind in the work (it celebrates its 50th Anniversary in 1971) it has been imitated by many other countries.

The Construction Research Advisory Council, recently set up by the Government, is expected to recommend significant increases of effort in research and development in construction at universities, research associations and Government establishments.

Forward Planning and Management

Building as an activity takes time. A large housing scheme may take two to three years to complete and perhaps five or six between conception and occupation. Some construction schemes – Channel tunnel, motorways, Whitehall development, new towns, take even longer. The Government has to give a lead on much more forward budgetary planning in public investment in which construction on jobs are assured finance by a rolling programme several years ahead. Road building is now planned four years ahead, schools two to three years, local authority housing four years.

New building techniques require relatively large orders and continuity of demand for success. The setting up of consortia of local authorities has helped to establish system-built schools and houses and it is probable that the coming reform of local government will confirm this increased size of public clients. For individual firms the contracting side is found to crystallize into large units which will employ serial tendering and other techniques for ensuring continuity of work.

The planning of large building programmes needs skilled management over the whole spectrum of planning design, tendering, pricing, materials supply, site organization, and sub-contracting.

Another aspect of forward planning is the prediction of demand and supply of materials and labour, nationally and regionally. Recently we have experienced an unbalanced supply of plasterboard and bricks. Sand and gravel threaten to be short in the south-east in the near future. Timber, in excellent supply, is a burden on our balance of payments. Forecasting techniques based on improved statistics are being used to provide better anticipation of these fluctuations, so that shortages can be anticipated.

A study of large construction jobs within a region can be used to anticipate the consequences of local demand on labour and materials. The formation of multi-disciplinary design teams is an essential part of the planning and execution of large construction projects and it is becoming widespread. A recent exercise in our Ministry showed that it could produce very considerable savings.

Some Unpredictables

This paper has dealt with the foreseeable future of the Construction Industry. Much of the changes are obvious and have been expected for some time; in some cases they are changes that are long overdue. Prediction of time scale is difficult in most cases, but for the reasons given at the beginning change is inevitably slow in this industry, though correspondingly inexorable.

Perhaps a few words might be devoted to the changes which, though widely expected, are not so likely to be important. One is rapidly replaceable houses. We are a long way from a society which can lightly replace its capital assets frequently. High interest rates admittedly improve the economics of replacement, but we are a long way from producing temporary houses that are so significantly cheaper than permanent houses as to make them economic. Of course, there will be an expansion of special purpose temporary buildings. Caravans will flourish. Light-weight or plastic air-inflated buildings will increase in use for erection on inaccessible sites, for temporary storage, exhibitions, covering swimming-pools, and holidays chalets. Replaceable components are likely to come before replaceable houses, which would merely add to our growing and unsolved problem of how to dispose economically of the waste products and materials of our society.

Construction provides the framework for living. Better living implies a high priority for improvements in the quality of the environment, in a conscious attempt to plan the future ecology of mankind. The responsibilities of architects, planners, and engineers is not just for individual buildings and structures, or to individual clients, it is for the background of community life for generations to come. There must be much greater consideration to fitting of individual buildings and structures into an organic community, an attempt to consider not merely the users of individual buildings but the entire community, now and in years to come. This presents a great challenge to architects in particular, since they are the custodians of community aesthetics. Planning controls must obviously be more complex and comprehensive, and they must include control over pollution of the atmosphere and the waterways as well as control of noise, traffic. Community services will expand to include heating and perhaps cleaning by communal suction. At a time when community standards appear to be declining in advanced urban centres, it is appropriate to insist that improvement in these standards is our most urgent necessity.

LLOYD P. SMITH

Technological Forecasting Applied to Urban Development *

Urban Symptoms

One of the main objects of this study is to identify and understand the principal set of driving forces that have brought our urban centres to their present lamentable state, and to delineate possibilities for the future. By an urban centre I mean the system composed not only of the physical facilities and services but the behaviour of city dwellers, the in and out people, the city management and the interactions of all these elements. If anything has become clear, it is that the urban centre must be viewed as a system to be understood. Much has been written about urban planning, but this for the most part has dealt more with the structure of physical facilities than with human behaviour and desires. In this sense urban planning has depended more heavily on technology than on behavioural science. But urban planning cannot be properly done based on technology alone. Inasmuch as the human element has been poorly understood and the forces which operate in an urban system have not been identified, the answer to the problem of cities does not lie in traditional planning. Until we understand the forces at work and the social functions which must be performed in order that people in high-density areas may live together in a productive and contented manner, it is hard to see how traditional urban planning can arrive at anything but incremental modifications of cities that already exist. As we shall see later, it will take a whole team of disciplines intelligently to plan an urban centre.

To identify the forces which operate in an urban centre and to understand the actions produced by them, it is necessary to determine and relate the symptoms associated with degenerative and regenerative processes to the causes which produce them. Many people are unable to distinguish clearly between the real driving forces which form the foundation of present-day urban problems and the symptoms generated by these forces. For example, I consider such things as joblessness, poor housing, high rate of delinquency and crime, traffic congestion, and degenerating commercial centres, which are always discussed in connection with the urban problem, to be symptoms of the problem. They are effects – not causes.

* This is a shortened version of the paper as delivered.

We can make very little progress in the solution or forecast the future by treating symptoms as if they constituted the problem. We must use them to determine the causes which produce them. Cause must be distinguished from effect. Our ability to separate cause from effect is of paramount importance in the determination of the forces involved. Concern with this matter comes naturally to a physicist because of the assessment of cause and effect which led to Newton's laws of motion, and the effect these had on the future development of physics. Suitably paraphrased, they seem useful as a guide in our thinking. A statement of relevant portions of these laws would be that *for every action there is a reaction* and *to change the state of motion of a body it must be acted upon by a force*. It seems natural to try to apply extensions of these laws of nature to individuals or social systems. For this purpose the extensions might be phrased as follows: *For every action taken against an individual, bio- or social system, there will be a reaction* and *to change the state of an individual, bio- or social system, it must be acted upon by a force* (*in a generalized sense*). I have found these statements helpful in separating cause from effect, and indeed even understanding some of the actions of the members of society.

Let us first review and classify the symptoms (the reactions) as we now see them. It will be useful in connecting the symptoms with the possible causes to classify relevant symptoms according to whether they are associated primarily with technology, politics and finance, or social behaviour. As might be expected, some symptoms result from a combination of these. We shall begin with those related to technology.

Technological Symptoms

Symptoms in this class are the easiest to notice and to identify, and are set forth as follows:

(1) *Limited public transportation*. The city exists because it has a role to play. It provided the centre of interaction for a highly interdependent society and consequently is characterized by high population density, not uniform, but characterized by localized peaks (the ghettos, for instance). Inadequate public transport is a *result* of the rapid increase in size of the city and the concomitant increase in population density, together with the increased necessity of daily interaction of people of various specialties. It is also the *result* of inadequate application of technology, economics and management.

(2) *Traffic congestion*. This is the *result* of high structural density in the cities and the desire and ability of individuals to own automobiles as a status symbol and to have an independent mode of transportation.

(3) *Substandard dwelling facilities*. This is the *result* of several causes. Technology failed to anticipate the need for continual upgrading of dwellings and economical modification of them. It was, and still is,

highly profitable to rent substandard, wholly inadequate, dirty and unsafe housing to poor and uneducated people. City tax laws and property ownership laws prevent concerted action on the part of government and city management to bring about improvement. However, the existence of such substandard living-quarters is a direct *result* of the concentration of poor, unemployed, and uneducated people. Thus, a primary cause is the existence of poverty and unemployment.

(4) *Inadequate waste removal.* A region of population density is a generator of large amounts of waste. Technology has not yet provided economic waste removal and processing systems. Inadequate waste removal is a direct result of high population density and the lack of technical development of an economical waste removal and conversion system. A contributing cause, even now, is the lax enforcement of housing codes. Methods available for enforcement are too cumbersome and time-consuming. Technical enforcement puts the poor at a definite disadvantage. Further, the reasons for the lack of certain services to the poor is that many of them do not feel they have a stake in the community.

(5) *Air and water pollution.* Pollution primarily *results* from desires and requirements of a large affluent population. It is only secondarily related to population density. It results directly from the large amount of energy generated or converted for the use of a large population and from the millions of products produced or manufactured, wherein vast amounts of materials, not yet economical to save, are disposed of in streams, lakes, or the air, thus creating an unclean environment for plants, animals, and people over a wide area.

Sociological Symptoms

The sociological symptoms will be the most important in providing the clues which can open the doors to the discovery of the principles and forces which have produced the reactions now so evident and upon which the solution of the urban problem depends. The list is long.

(1) *The increase in concentration of the poor and unemployed in cities.* Cities attract and propagate poverty and unemployment. The city appears to offer greater opportunity for all kinds of jobs, but when jobs are not available the poor and unemployed are stuck there and find it impossible to move out. They congregate in areas occupied by people with similar problems and this is likely to amplify the problems because of the principle of negative feedback. The more the unemployment and poverty, the more there will be unless there is a positive feedback introduced. The consequence of this is that the gap between have and have-not people in the city must increase. Thus, ghettos are

formed. The concentration of the poor and the unemployed increases because the employed and financially successful move out to the 'anti-city', i.e. the suburbs [1]. It is reported that, after 1960, American families had a median-income jump of $900. Suburban dwellers received $150 more and city dwellers received $150 less.

(2) *The feeling of hopelessness and frustration of the city dweller.* The existence of this feeling is graphically brought out by the words of Iva Mothner when she says [1], 'We hate the grit and sooty air, the din and the feeling that there's nothing we can do about any of it; no one we can blame or curse or ask to make it right'. This feeling results from the fact that the causes are so many and diffuse that the average person cannot come to grips with them and chart a course for improvement.

(3) *The feeling of worthlessness.* Such a feeling often results from an individual's knowledge that he is not making a constructive contribution to society or doing something useful for which someone will show appreciation. The reasons are again many, but include inability to obtain a meaningful job, submission to welfare support, or the receipt of other subsidies.

(4) *The dwindling of individual pride and the accompanying decrease in quality of workmanship or accomplishment.* This has reduced the quality of products over the country and minimized the extent of achievements an individual was capable of making. This in all probability is one of the diseases of an affluent society. It is closely associated with the tendency of individuals or groups to get the most reward for the least effort.

(5) *The deterioration of self-respect, family relations and moral fibre.* The weakness and deterioration of family life results in part from compaction of the family. Overcrowding leads to irritations, intrafamily fighting and the urge of individuals to spend less time in the serried conditions of the home. In fact, this often leads to breakup of the family. Such deterioration is not confined to the poor. We find its presence in those city dwellers embedded in a life of easy affluence. Symptomatic of this situation, we find the acceleration of alcoholism, drug addiction sex perversion and a general increase in the crime rate.

(6) *Aggressiveness and militancy.* There seem to be two main routes for the overcrowded, the poor, or the jobless to take. One is the route of despair and degeneration, the other the route of aggressiveness and militancy. The driving cause here may be related to an inherently evolutionary trait of man to fight for survival or, perhaps, more likely it is associated with a defect in our educational system. Our educational system has hardly prepared children, teenagers, or adults to cope with a highly interdependent society which on an evolutionary scale has developed so quickly.

(7) *The lack of respect for law and order.* This is the result of many of the causes already discussed, but it has arisen in no small measure from the permissiveness and indecisiveness of government and law enforcement agencies. It is easy to understand why people, especially the young, feel that those responsible for national and world conditions have made rather a mess of things.

(8) *Creative and productive interaction.* With all the abrasion, and at times violent interactions among individuals squeezed for space in the inner city, the city has been and is now, a fertile generator and birth-place of original ideas, new art, neoteric music, advances in science and medicine, innovations in the practice of law and discoveries in many walks of life. When looking at our cities now or debating whether there should be urban centres, this creative and productive aspect of close interaction is of paramount importance and should not for one moment be overlooked or minimized.

Thus we see that cities are in the ambivalent situation where high population density is associated with a breeding place for poverty, lawlessness, human degeneration, and at the same time essential for the close interaction that makes them the birthplace of a creative and productive society. Our present cities are simultaneously subject to degenerative forces and forces which drive the system toward constructive creativity. There are then two ways to improve conditions in the city, one being to decrease the resultant degenerative force and the other to increase the resultant constructive force. Success in either or both ways will lead to substantial improvement.

Obstacles which inhibit Urban Improvement

It is now possible to recognize many of the obstacles to urban improvement. The list of obstacles is undoubtedly long, but some of importance may be noted.

(1) Support of the physical sciences and technology has traditionally been at the expense of a concurrent programme of research in the behavioural and social sciences, which seemed to have less direct effect on economic growth and the standard of living. However, without this, people were not in a position to understand themselves and the laws of interaction which were necessary to prevent the build-up of social stresses.

(2) An absence of knowledge about phenomena is usually a cause for people to abrogate their responsibility toward them.

(3) Konrad Lorenz [2] has decided that there are three important obstacles which have prevented man from acquiring the self-knowledge necessary to understand his own behaviour. He asserts that these obstacles are: (*a*) the reluctance of man to believe in our evolution from animals so he ignores the behavioural characteristics of animals

as having anything to do with his own; (*b*) man's antipathy toward the causal determination of animal or human behaviour; (*c*) man's deeply rooted belief that what can be explained in terms of natural science has no value – he simply does not see himself as a part of the universe wherein his own behaviour obeys the laws of nature. All three of these obstacles are bound up with one of man's most inhibiting qualities – his transcendant spiritual pride.

(4) Scientific research into the basic causes of human behaviour suffered from dogmatic boundaries set up between what was explorable and determinative and what was considered to be beyond exploration.

(5) A general antipathy existed on the part of the affluent section of the population and government at all levels toward the examination of the nature of human behaviour and practical social principles. Hesitancy or disinterest on the part of the affluent population came from the fear that a reliable insight into behavioural or urban problems might decrease profits or reduce the individual's pseudo-independence or his personal freedom. Politicians were more interested in their own image and their dependence on the upper class to hold their offices to risk disturbing the status quo. There was always the feeling that certain elements of the social strata did not count and could therefore be ignored.

(6) Even today, the existing knowledge of biological and human behaviour is only sluggishly being applied.

(7) In the past, educational institutions were complacent about the human reactions and social needs of the less gifted or the underprivileged. The research in the fields of human behaviour and human relations has been entirely inadequate to cope with today's social problems. The resulting state of affairs was graphically brought out when the US Government wanted to recruit a team of behavioural and social scientists to determine what makes certain peoples think, react and enact violence the way they do. It was impossible to field an adequate team of truly experienced professional people.

(8) The United States has really never cherished its cities. As Iva Mothner [1] says, 'Jefferson chose to stick the capital in a swamp, rather than in New York, and thought yellow fever wasn't too terrible if it discouraged the growth of great cities. We rejected cities first because they weren't woodsy enough, then turned on them because they weren't quite civilized. They were filled with noisy immigrants sweating their hopes out over machines that made America rich.'

(9) Existing but out of date laws, institutional practices, and building codes make it difficult to change our present cities by the application of new technology or the use of new material. The United States

Federal Government is trying to get around some of these difficulties by assuring a degree of financial responsibility when experimental housing developments do not comply with antiquated local building codes and legal impediments.

Every human has powerful built-in forces which resist change. Man seems to be unusually rigid when it comes to matters involving social practices, political philosophy, law, education or human behaviour. Unfortunately, this characteristic becomes more predominant the older an individual becomes.

Though it is difficult to see the present urban crisis in perspective or view it with objectivity, being an integral part of it as we are, we may be witnessing another upheaval from which could come a new and significant social advance. If so, we will undoubtedly eventually note stimulation, acceleration, and a branching out of science, in this case hopefully social science, since this has normally been the pattern when conditions called for large-scale order and organization.

The Drive to Concentrate

The present situation of many American cities is only partially depicted by the symptoms already discussed, but for the purpose of identifying the principle causes or forces which bring them about, the list is perhaps sufficient. Before attempting to identify the forces which produce the symptoms, it will be useful to review certain historical developments, changes, and attitudes which I believe are germane to the problem.

Urban problems apparently began with the Industrial Revolution in the eighteenth century. Though the period until the mid-nineteenth century is referred to as a period of industrial revolution, it marked the beginning of a social revolution which has had many ramifications. The rate of change in manufacturing, agriculture, the productivity of people and the resulting social changes has kept on increasing to the present time, stimulated by rapid increases in scientific research and technology and the availability of more and more energy at cheaper rates. There is no sign that we are reaching a plateau in the magnitude of the change in technological development. What we must and will see is a major increase in research in the behavioural and social sciences to cope with the increase in the resulting complexity of man's relationship to man and his physical and social environment which in a sense was a compelling result of the great changes in technology. The rapidity of these changes was so great compared to society's ability to adjust to the new conditions that stresses inevitably built up within the social structure which by now have become so great that they are relieved only by explosions.

Let us return to the nature of the social changes that began with the

Industrial Revolution. I believe that these changes – still going on – provide us with the key to the urban problem. As an hypothesis, the principle might be stated as follows: To achieve maximum production with greater efficiency and economy, the population density in a given region increases in proportion to the degree of interdependence required. For reference purposes we will designate this as the interdependency principle. There is surely a critical density for humans no matter what ethnic or economic group they belong to.

We arrive at the conclusion that the principle of increasing population density will apply until the critical density for humans has been reached. From then on, a definite conflict arises between the advantages derived from the interdependency relation and an individual's loss of personal freedom. Above the critical density the interaction with others becomes so abrasive that great discontent, frustration and actual fighting takes place.

We noted before that the population density in cities was not uniform but within the cities there were areas of peak density, in particular the ghettos. These peaks can be accounted for on the basis of the proposed theory if it is assumed that different ethnic or economic groups have different critical densities. For example, the poor may have a high critical density acquired by living through a long, long conditioning period. Perhaps they have been trained to tolerate a higher than normal critical density. Whatever the magnitude of the critical density may be, there will exist one.

On the basis of the foregoing phenomenological theory of city formation, most people will always live in cities. In the United States two-thirds of the people already do. For stability there exists a maximum density. So far as I can see there is nothing to limit the area of cities except geography or the resources to support the population, or the ability of the system to remove and convert wastes, etc. However, it seems clear that for the population of the city to function with optimum efficiency there must be a lower limit to the population. We could call this lower limit the critical population or critical mass. Since the critical density is not known accurately, nor have the best ways been found of distributing power, converting wastes, recycling products used in the city, and transporting people, it has not been possible to make a reliable systems study for determining the critical population of a city. However, as a rough guess, it might lie between 250,000 and 500,000 people.

The principle conclusions to be drawn here are that most of the population of the world will always live in cities from a population between 250,000 and 500,000 on up, with an upper limit of total population not necessarily in sight, and the population density in various sections of the city cannot exceed a critical density depending on the ethnic or economic group. If this is exceeded, internal stresses will be built up which will result in explosive instability.

Goals to be achieved in Urban Development

What are the specific goals we should try to achieve for the future by whatever means?

In this discussion I will be referring to urban development in its broadest sense. People and their functions are the elements of the urban system of paramount importance. Thus, urban development must perforce start with people and include their needs, their reaction to each other, their interactions with other people, and their interactions with the physical and material elements of the city to form a stable, productive, and emotionally rewarding system.

The characteristics, desires, and potential of people are the action-determining elements in urban systems and consequently these become the independent variables in the problem and the physical and structural facilities become the dependent variables. Thus we essentially invert the concept of urban development, and why not, since the material aspects of the city must serve its workers and its residents. Thus, it is logically appropriate because once the human aspects of the problem are properly planned, the ability to lay out, design, and build the subsystem of physical facilities to do anything that is required is for all practical purposes assured at this stage of technological development. Therefore, much more emphasis needs to be placed on the human aspects of urban development.

Therefore, I wish to broaden the definition of urban development to include the development and improvement of those aspects of human behaviour which will be required if the future urban system as a whole is to be highly stable and productive in all respects. The goals which we will set forth cannot be reached by physical, architectural and organizational considerations alone. Much more understanding of human behaviour is required and significant changes must be induced in human attitudes and reactions before we can have a stable system.

In setting forth what I believe the goals should be, I have tried to place them in order of priority, those at the head of the list I assume will have the most important effect on the proper functioning of the future urban system.

(1) The abolition of class distinction and acts of favouritism, whether the class be ethnic or economic, from the thoughts or memory of members of any urban society.

(2) Do away with the need for welfare for all except the sick and disabled and work out a system which will permit every able-bodied person to be *usefully* and *gainfully* employed.

(3) Find a way (and contrary to some I do not think this is at all impossible with intensive effort) to purge the minds of individuals of hostility and hate to the point where they will automatically make allowances for inconsiderate acts, or acts with which they strongly disagree and react to them with understanding firmness, kindness and patience.
(4) Replace destructive aggression (sometimes called militant enthusiasm) [2] with an enthusiasm and drive for constructive action.
(5) Arrive at a clear and definite understanding of what the basic and essential mental and material needs of human beings are.
(6) Restore respect for law and order.
(7) Increase as rapidly as possible the number of mentally mature individuals.
(8) Bring about a stabilization of the population by birth control, preferably voluntary but by inducement if this is required.
(9) Learn how to manage a city intelligently, objectively and justly, and provide adequate service and a stimulating environment.

There are other human goals, but the successful accomplishment of these would produce a vastly improved society – one much more fitting to envelop the potential intelligence and dignity of human beings.

What should the technological goals be? These I believe are quite obvious and most of them can be achieved by the application of presently known technology. My list in order of priority is:
(1) Create a housing and building industry with the resources and fabrication means to provide houses, apartments and buildings of pleasing but flexible design, capable of being continually updated, modified or moved to other sites at costs which provide comfortable living for families with low to high incomes. Associated with this should be new land and housing financing, development, and management.
(2) Provide adequate waste removal and conversion systems that will provide useful products instead of pollutants so that no reason will exist for a filthy and unhealthy environment.
(3) Provide new rapid, convenient, and quiet transportation systems for intracity and interurban service, and direct routes to the ocean or open country.
(4) Eliminate unhealthy air and water pollution. This includes control of all toxic emissions into the air or injection into streams, lakes and even the ocean. Also included is the determination of the role of vegetation in producing or converting air and water pollutants.
(5) Develop better sources of food and systems for its storage and distribution. The objective here is to reduce the cost of food to city residents but increase the quality.

(6) Develop practical systems for requalifying used water and recirculating it.

The Starting Point

Before we can outline what needs to be accomplished to attain our goals, we need to know the conditions and situation that prevail at the start. It is necessary to know in concise and clearly etched terms what the present characteristics of the spectrum of human beings are which make up our present society, as well as the present state of technology. We need also to know at least short-term trends. It seems to me that the major factors and the likely trends of an immediate nature with respect to the state of individuals, technology, society, and government that we must recognize to start with are: that the individual is the key to all group action; that society can be no better than the sum of the attributes of the individuals who make up its membership; that the reaction of an individual to any action or stimulus is conditioned either from information and action patterns learned from time of birth or from instincts, however modified, from our prehuman ancestors (I think at present we do not know definitely which); that as presently visible over the world an adult with a truly mature mind is very rare indeed; that an important school of psychology [3] holds that all humans are born ignorant, inarticulate, irresponsible, selfish, and egocentric; that it has become sadly obvious that all humans, on the average, harbour unconscious but powerful traits of hostility; that there is much evidence that an individual is more likely to secretly hate others than like, respect, or love them, and those in lower levels of social structure, such as the underprivileged, are more likely to be driven to acts of violence against his fellow-man than to exhibit fondness and respect for him; that present and former events show that fear of God, or fear of the law is no longer much of a deterrent to individual acts of violence or participation in crime; that to the thoughtful observer, human behaviour gives little evidence of being dictated by intelligence or moral responsibility; that the signs are that poverty and joblessness may become relatively worse before progress is made toward eliminating it because at present the relative gap between the society of affluence and the society of poverty is becoming wider; that about one-half of the world's population is continuously on the verge of starvation [4] and the prospect that this situation will soon improve very much, especially in the developing countries, appears to be dim indeed; that the critical population density has been exceeded in peak density areas in many cities; that there are doubts in the minds of people with respect to the adequacy and quality of our social and political system; that however much we claim that all men are created equal with respect to ability, they are not – class distinctions and favouritism exist – severe stresses exist within and between ethnic groups, and the groups of widely different economic status; that mass violence and rioting are the order of the day, exhibiting the militant hostility and the ingrained hate of man to attain his purposes rather than the use of intelligent persuasion and mature statesmanship; that there are busy people who seem to live a middle course between the culture of poverty and the culture of affluence and these and the affluent may live in the suburbs if they wish and try to obtain the advantages of both the city and the suburbs; that the average person in the United States, Western Europe, and Japan is getting richer, while the average person in the developing countries is getting relatively poorer; that an important nucleus of creative and productive people exist who have been most influenced by education in science and technology; that research in the social and behavioural sciences is meagre and social education to improve the attitudes and behaviour of the masses has been nearly non-existent, evidence indicates we don't know how to conduct such education; that the population is interspersed with highly talented artists, musicians, writers, and intellectuals generally, but many suffer from behavioural defects which indicate that as a society we are far from being mature, in fact who of us really is?

On the technological side we know: that through machines and devices man labours less to produce his needs; that the current growth rate of world population is fantastically great; that people now operate in an interdependent society, needing the work and services of a host of others to survive and be efficiently productive; that housing is poor and in some areas despicable, in others it is comfortable and pleasant and in still others it is luxurious; that urban and interurban transportation leave much to be desired and with the wide use of the automobile a large percentage of the population is independently mobile except for the limitation imposed by traffic congestion; that if the world population can be stabilized most of the required resources to support a healthy and productive middle-class society over a large part of the world are and will be available, and production of basic materials is increasing rapidly, e.g. the doubling time for steel production over the world is about twelve years; that new materials with exceptionally useful and beneficial properties are available, and more are being constantly developed for use in housing and better machines and devices; that superior medical knowledge and science is available, and continually increasing, to decrease human suffering and cure men's ills and prolong human life expectancy; that means are available to transmit data, voice, and video information all over the entire world, and useful knowledge available in one part of the world can quickly be made available in another part which tends to increase the interdependency of people everywhere; that the environment is fast becoming flooded with gaseous, liquid, and solid garbage, endangering the physical and mental health of people living in peak density areas; that scientific and technological education is adequate in many countries but entirely inadequate in the developing countries, and it is far ahead of education in the behavioural and social sciences.

The Means available to achieve the Goals

Having set forth some important goals to achieve, and the present state of things, it is logical to explore and suggest what means are available to attain them, together with some estimate of the probability of success. I believe we are in a position to say with great confidence that the technological goals can be attained within a decade through the application of the physical sciences and engineering. I believe that the experts in science and engineering, and those leaders in business and government who have had faith in the ability of science and engineering to solve important and complex problems would be in agreement. For example, David Sarnoff, long the successful Chairman of the Board of the Radio Corporation of America which, under his direct leadership, pioneered in the solution of many difficult problems recently said: [5] 'I have always felt, and still feel today, that almost every material problem can be solved by science and technology'. The same confidence in the power of science and technology to solve all major problems of world economy and the material needs of society has been expressed by Dr Bernal [6]. He says that for the first time it is evident to all that science consciously directed, rather than left to grow by blind chance, can transform almost without limit the material basis of life.

I think it safe to assume that science and technology intensely applied can make available all the material and technological requirements needed to provide renewable housing, waste removal and conversion, rapid, safe and quiet transportation, a pollution-free environment, and all other material needs. These goals will not be met automatically, however. It will require intensive effort and the will, leadership and financial support in sufficient measure to meet the challenge. So, in a realistic sense, the basic problems of the urban centre are not technological in nature – they are human problems, behavioural, sociological and political.

At this stage, social science is just not the same as physical science and to pretend that it can be used with the same degree of confidence is premature. However, progress is being made. Looking over the historical development and success of the physical sciences there is good reason to believe that with efforts properly focused and scientific disciplines properly combined, that firm foundations can be laid which will permit the science to be reliably applied. To reach this stage will require a greatly enhanced effort. Progress can be accelerated appreciably by forming a coalition of physical scientists, bioscientists, and social scientists. Properly financed and supported, such a team would constitute a powerful interdisciplinary force to attack the complex problem of human behaviour of individuals and groups. I am really saying that total science should be focused on the problem. It would take a great deal of money but vast amounts of money used for less important and ill-conceived enterprises could be directed to it, thereby filling a research gap too long permitted to widen. Viewed as a long-term investment such research would ultimately pay for itself from the reduction in public moneys spent on welfare, mental and physical health, law enforcement, and the like. It is already very late. Economy exercised in connection with the effort to develop a definitive and reliable foundation for the behavioural, political, and social sciences is waste, and waste that the world can no longer afford until problems initiated by conditions in the cities, the social instability in nations, and warfare and destructive aggression are solved. A measure of the economy in this area exercised in the United States is the fact that as high as 60 per cent of the budget has been spent each year for military purposes, and something like 6 per cent for the things that would improve education and human behaviour – the crux of the urban problem. If these percentages were only in part inverted, one might expect that the good that could come from a greater understanding of human behaviour would make it unnecessary to spend so much on machines of war or defence in the future.

Education is the single most potent means of employing the results of research in the social sciences to attain the human goals. We must know how people learn most effectively. We have to understand the unlearning process – how to permanently brainwash, i.e. purge the brain of incorrect information, untrue beliefs and hostile and hateful mental attitudes. If, as Overstreet [3] maintains, the human being is in fact born ignorant and if this means that no information, attitudes or preconceived beliefs are stored in the brain before birth, then the possibilities of attaining the stated human goals is indeed enormous. A newborn child would not then be burdened with built-in traits of hostility and hate, or conditioned reactions leading to destructive aggression. The possibility then exists to educate a human being who would be devoid of hostility and hate. On the other hand, these traits now exist so universally in humans that they are considered *a priori* to be instinctual traits handed down from our prehuman ancestors. If they are not, our traditional educational system is permeated with grave faults and misconceptions.

I suggest that a non-governmental interdisciplinary institute be designated which would be capable of making an impersonal, objective application of physical, social, and behavioural sciences to provide answers in depth to the questions raised. The type of institute I have in mind should be able to marshal and combine a wide group of productive disciplines as Stanford Research Institute can. The important disciplines would be biological and life sciences, behavioural science, economics, management sciences, physical sciences, and engineering. Experience in creative research and development for government, industry, and the public good would be essential. Knowledge gained by working in a variety of fields at any given time, such as disease, artificial organs, toxicology, air and water pollution, new foods and food distribution systems, self-organizing machines, man-computer relationships, management systems, education and educational policy, crime prevention and law enforcement, new materials, housing and public works, new fibres and textiles, electronic and communication systems and transportation would be invaluable. Such an institute in co-ordination with universities and all other relevant agencies should be obligated to devise the best means of successfully breaking into the feedback loop and to supervise the resulting operation to be carried on at the national, state, and urban levels.

Without anticipating the results of the study, one could imagine that an intensive and bold training programme would have to be devised to train people to feel and manifest in every way the kind of behaviour a mature people should exhibit with a reliability akin to reflex action. The people so trained should probably be young people because they would be the easiest to train and the bright and restless young people are looking for a worthwhile cause to embrace. This new corps of 'social teachers', reinforced with all of the rightly designed visual and audio aids, would have to interact closely with the children of the household from the very youngest ages, because it is at this stage that the greatest force for change can be exerted. Whatever would 'wear off' on the parents would be a plus but the full energy of the 'social teachers' should be devoted to the young since the chance of producing meaningful changes in the older parents will be small. At this early stage we are not in any position to fill in the details of this operation. It would be a huge and expensive task, but the means are available if we have the will to act. I can imagine that it would take at least one 'social teacher' to every fifteen families to make the impact that would be needed in a reasonable time. This would be a bold and daring programme but one with great chances for success. An encouraging thing about it is that as behaviour is improved and success becomes evident the normal social feedback will then accelerate the change until the whole set of social changes become incorporated and locked into the new society.

A Look at the Urban Centre of the Future

In technological forecasting it is usually the custom to analyze the data, determine what is possible, extrapolate trends, and examine the various combinations of possibilities and present various alternatives. If one tried to analyze the problem one would become smothered in the complexity of detail and the victim of the vagueness and desperate opinions of the behavioural sciences and the uncertainties of the political climate. Consequently, in this situation I believe it is best to take note of the present symptoms of urban conditions, realize certain past obstacles to urban development, accept the phenomenological theory of city formation and growth, and assume with some conviction that the goals set forth are achievable and that reasonable means are extant to attain them and use this information as the basis to take a look at what future urban centres could look like if the problem is attacked with boldness and vigour.

Let us then take a look at what future cities could be like. Most people think of the city of the future in terms of the technological improvements. There will be fairly spectacular technological and structural changes, but let us look first at the human side of the picture. Important aspects would appear to have the following characteristics:

(1) An urban society where traditional class distinctions have disappeared. The membership would be made up of a large and complex mosaic of disciplines containing all the elements that are needed to perform the functions of a highly creative and productive urban society.

(2) Each individual will be a member of a highly interdependent team each effectively working with others without rancour to play his role and use all the city's services and facilities to make his efforts more productive.

(3) Though it will be hard to imagine, we would see a society in action free from hostility, hate and destructive aggression.

(4) One would not find a segregated society in the traditional sense and every able-bodied person would be performing a useful job, a job that he could take some measure of satisfaction in. Except for the sick and the very old there would be no degrading doles or welfare handouts. Thus there would be no densely packed areas occupied by the jobless and the poor.

(5) One would witness a society that had time for cultural pursuits and educated to appreciate and make their own contributions to culture. Because of the high productivity of such an urban centre its residents would have shorter work periods which they would use in taking part in cultural activities and healthful recreation.

(6) One could have the unique experience of seeing a vital society devoid of the irritations and aggressiveness of a too highly compacted

population. It would have been educated this way so that one would experience cheerfulness and friendly helpfulness from one's colleagues or those who provided service. A lighter-hearted population with a minimum of frustrations would be a more dynamic population.
(7) One would be likely to find educational television in most homes to supplement the new social and technological educational facilities and for the inquiring mind, families could have access to a televideo-phone where they would obtain information by voice or demonstration.
(8) The population density would be below the critical density and because of the changed attitudes the social stresses would not build up. There would be no need to riot.
(9) Individuals in the city will not really be consumers. They will be users of property, materials, and services.
(10) It is likely that in the future, people in urban centres will not own anything except personal things (many in California do not own much now). They will select and own the services that serviceable items provide. This will include housing, property, household goods, automobiles and the like.
(11) As education is essential to all and would be required and provided up to some point, everyone at some point needs medical care. People living in the future city would have access to the best doctors and medical facilities. The people through their agent–the government – and through private means would support on an equitable basis medical schools, medical research and modern medical facilities so that adequate medical care for everybody would be available.
(12) The task of managing the future city should not be as difficult as it is now because the control of people would be simpler. More of the management should be devoted to the services and facilities supplied, such as education and schools, medical care and hospitals, maintenance of transportation and waste removal systems, etc.
The city of the future could benefit from a tremendous storehouse of science and technology which exists now and will develop further in the future. As I said earlier, it is possible to solve almost any material or technological problem. As far as cities go, tremendous changes are still possible but technological changes should not be made just for the sake of change. The whole power of science and technology should be used to provide those structures, serviceable facilities, and material environment that will provide the mature society that we have in mind with the necessities and conveniences that it requires.

The components of the structural and technological subsystem of the future urban centre that would impress one would be:
(1) A clean and comparatively quiet city whose residential and business sections will be composed of a variety of building units which can be

flexibly arranged in many convenient and desirable ways. Any structural unit or household service unit (cooking facilities, heaters, air-conditioners, bathrooms, etc.) can be exchanged or upgraded. People can trade in rooms or increase or decrease the living space, or replace a refrigerator with a new model. The kitchen or cooking centres may be completely adapted to already prepared convenience foods so that the cooking centre might be equipped with ovens and refrigerated drawers, etc. There are almost an infinite set of possibilities. This will all be possible with the establishment of whole housing industries which designs, manufactures, delivers, installs, and perhaps leases and maintains all components. The deterioration of housing and housing areas can be prevented because of the possibility of continuous upgrading of the housing units. It will not be necessary to raze or destroy old housing to avoid a slum. Housing units turned in will be reconditioned and released, or when no longer serviceable dismantled and the materials reclaimed and recycled. Such flexible and adaptable housing equipped with the facilities modern technology can supply would provide living quarters befitting the intelligence and dignity of human beings.

(2) To avoid the aspect of looking like a big blob of buildings, and to have open areas for air and sunshine, business areas and housing areas will be separated by scenic, well-kept and safe parks for daily or local contact with nature. Facilities for physical exercise and sports would be found here, or a quiet and pleasant glen to be alone.

(3) There would be a rapid and quiet intracity transportation grid connecting points in the whole urban area from any one of which people could get to their destination by walking a comfortable distance. This would reduce the noisy automobile traffic to a minimum. A secondary transportation system which would fan out from various stations of the intracity system to the surrounding country so that city dwellers could have quick and direct contact with scenic country within perhaps 200 or 300 miles of the city. This would also give people in the surrounding country quick access to the city. There is no necessity to go into the details of how this could be done. We simply know it can be.

As an adjunct to the transportation system to transport people there would be an integrated system to deliver mail, parcels, foods (especially convenience foods), to collection points close to the person or business for whom the items are addressed. The delivery system would be coupled to these collection points to deliver the items to the person's door. There could even be refrigerated delivery service.

(4) The city would have the capability to requalify and recycle used water. There is no need to dump all the water used once in the city into rivers or the ocean. This is pure misuse of water resources.

(5) There would be a complete system for the handling and reconversion of waste. No garbage or other 'wastes' need appear on the street, be disposed of in dumps or landfills or the ocean. One should not think of 'waste' disposal but rather waste reconversion. Wastes can be handled or transported much like sewage to waste processing centres where materials are separated and converted into useful products, or into re-usable materials. It is wasteful and unnecessary to dump these wastes. The city could then be rid of rats and rodents and other disease-carrying animals or insects. The city need not be limited in size because of inability to get rid of waste.

Since all wastes and emissions would be controlled and reconverted, there would be no air or water pollution.

(6) There will be improved intracity communication systems. Service will be relatively cheaper and be available to almost all the population. Televideophones will be available with direct access to sources or centres of information. The greatest improvement will be the availability of educational information by television from sources not only in the city but all over the world. Residents of one city can establish an empathy with citizens of a city in another part of the world and thus learn about and even absorb that citizen's culture. This could be an important influence in reducing international tensions. Television will play a role in the new educational system. There will be improvements in entertainment and cultural programmes because there will be an audience that has been educated to appreciate them.

(7) One may visualize a large proportion of the food coming into the city being delivered to a number of preparation centres where convenience foods and a variety of meals to order would be prepared, as well as standard meals, which could be ordered by telephone and delivered to residents by means of the transportation and delivery system already referred to.

By now it should be evident that while the urban problem is complex, mostly because it is a people problem, it is, in its entirety, one of the most worthwhile if not *the* most worthwhile problem that society should solve. The more I think about it, the more convinced I become that clear lines of approach to its solution can be laid out. It is possible to use the symptoms to get at the fundamental causes and understand them. I am also convinced that the causes can be corrected and definite programmes to achieve this can be outlined. This I have attempted to do. At best, it is only a start. Nevertheless, seeing a possible road map ahead to improve urban society and provide it with the physical facilities and services it deserves, one can dare to glimpse into the urban future as I have done.

I shall conclude on the note that the urban problem, far from being hopeless, can be solved even as one is hastening the building of a mature society. The means are available. It is only a question of whether we the people want to solve it. I believe we do, and to what better cause could we bend our efforts, use our money, and apply the knowledge and power of science and technology, especially when we know we can succeed? In the final analysis the people will have to declare their firm intentions, as they are now beginning to do, and government support and allocation of public funds in realistic amounts must follow.

References

1 'Our Cities, The Upright Life'. *Look Magazine*, Vol. **32**, 1968, pp. 27.
2 Konrad Lorenz, *On Aggression*. Harcourt ,Bruce & World, Inc. pp. 221.
3 H. A. Overstreet, *The Mature Mind*. W. W. Norton & Company, Inc. 1959.
4 *The Next Ninety Years*. California Institute of Technology, pp. 21.
5 Remarks by David Sarnoff at the 25th Anniversary of the David Sarnoff Research Center and dedication of the David Sarnoff Library, Princeton, New Jersey, 28th September 1967.
6 J. S. D. Bernal, *Science in History*, 3rd Edition. C. A. Watts and Company, London.

H. L. BOS

Forecasting Developments in Transportation

Metra Consulting Group has been concerned over a number of years with transport problems. With regard to the technological forecasting aspects of the studies we have made, two conditions usually applied:

(1) Greatest understanding and most useful forecasting guidance came once we had developed a model to describe the interactions of all the factors relevant to complex transport systems.

(2) Progress in transportation does not come mainly from technically sophisticated improvements but rather from a change in the way things are organized or executed, using only well known technology. The container is a classic illustration.

Since it is impossible to cover the whole field of transportation, this paper will be restricted to ocean freight and distribution of goods, which are both fields in which we have made studies, and in each case we will show the extent to which the two conditions mentioned above are met.

The paper will conclude with some observations about a field of transportation in which we have not developed a model of the full system, and in which we believe that it is highly desirable that greater effort should be devoted to building such a model. The field we refer to is passenger transport by air – both private and public.

Ocean Freight

Transport by sea involves five distinct phases, each of which can come under a separate administration. The complete journey covers: (1) land transport to a port; (2) unloading, storage and loading at a port; (3) sea transport; (4) unloading, sorting, storage and delivery from a port; (5) land transport to destination.

Not only are these phases separate but the owners of the equipment used can have conflicting objectives and have therefore to strike a balance in the co-operation they offer to each other.

The final customer is interested in three main factors, whose balance is influenced by the goods he transports. The predominant factors are:

(1) Cost.

(2) Speed of arrival.

(3) Frequency of service.

Clearly there are others, such as reliability of timing, damage and risk of loss but for simplicity we will concentrate on the conflicts which factors 1–3 present.

We will consider the future for bulk, low value commodities and for higher value mixed cargoes.

Bulk, low-value cargoes. There has been a trend towards larger ships as a means to reduce the proportion of fixed ship costs per ton of cargo and also to reduce propulsion cost per ton. However, there are physical limits to this process set by the size and depth of terminal installations. Recently it has also become apparent that long tankers can undergo severe structural strains on launching – a factor which was evidently not forecast or not calculated correctly in the scaling-up process.

The current largest vessels operating or under construction are classified by type of cargo they will carry:

Oil	380,000	deadweight tons (120–250,000 is the more common range)
Iron ore	90,000	deadweight tons (which has special problems owing to the very high density of cargo)
Salt	140,000	deadweight tons.

With oil the law of diminishing returns to larger size has set in and it is already necessary to transfer the cargo some way away from the shore in order to get deep enough water. However, as the size of cargo increases, so the frequency of calls must drop for a given traffic volume, and so also must the available storage at the ports rise. Where the large ship is taking a significant proportion of the output of an installation so errors in timing can either overfill shore storage capacity, or they can reduce the amount of cargo available for loading when the ship arrives. A ship must load at a rate far in excess of an installation's output rate and cannot wait for stockpiles to build up.

With solid bulk cargoes it is more costly to have an off-shore loading facility in deep water, hence ship sizes for bulk cargo will be more constrained by the availability of deep water harbours – at both ends of their routes.

One solution being considered for this problem is the artificial off-shore island set in deep water which provides transport of cargo to the shore either by smaller vessels or by conveyor. Such an island represents an extra investment which must be off-set against the lower freight cost of large ships.

A further solution to the problem of inadequate shore facilities but only for short routes, is the self-unloading ship. This system increases ship charges by about 30 per cent but gives a better turn round in port than would otherwise be available with inadequate equipment and also reduces port charges for cranes. These gains off-set the freight rate differential. As more ports modernize so the need for such ships will reduce – except for ports having insufficient general demand for high capacity handling facilities.

Speed could be increased with current technology. However, current propulsions and fuel prices and the structures of freight rates and routes is such that extra speed is uneconomic. Bulk carriers do 15–16 knots cruising and only container ships have an advantage from travelling at 21–25 knots. The Yarrow Admiralty Research Department has developed a computer programme which accepts all parameters relevant to the design and duty of a ship – including the cost of alternative propulsion units. Potential operators or designers of ships can find the design best suited to their needs. With such a programme the effect of any proposed technical or technological change can be tested in a short while and such a programme is essential for predicting the economic consequences of major design changes in such a complex and competitive business as ocean transport.

Higher value general cargoes. The major development has been the unit load concept which enables ship turn round in port to be reduced by a factor of 20 and more. In addition, the quantity of stevedore labour is reduced and this item was often in excess of £2 a ton. Such a change in port time means that speed at sea is now worth more since the sea journey is now a major part of round trip time. Prior to containers, a ship on short routes could spend less than 20 per cent of its time at sea and now it can spend 60 per cent on the same type of route.

The development of containerization is limited by two main factors:

(1) Suitability of cargo for containerization – and estimates are that 80 per cent of general cargo may ultimately be containerized.

(2) Availability of sufficient cargo on a route to justify the capital investment in containers, heavy duty cranes, and specialized ships.

The latter factor has been one that caused Metra and the Port of London Authority jointly to develop a computer programme to evaluate the complete economic consequences of a given pattern of trade on a route. Only by evaluating every one of the many interacting factors can the viability of container traffic on a given route be tested. A major difficulty is the imbalance in world trade. Countries tend to have bulk cargoes in one direction and manufactured items in another. This is a technological and technical challenge and future developments may be in the form of ships able to carry bulk in one direction and containers in the other. However, such ships would require some stability in the pattern of trade and would tend to be tailored to particular routes.

The container principle is an extremely interesting example of an integrated approach to transportation, made in response to the lag of port development behind ship and industrialized materials handling developments. We will draw the analogy between container through systems and passengers air traffic later in the paper.

The future in unit load systems lies in alternative approaches to unitization for routes not able to present an adequate volume of conventional containers. Once a ship operator sets his rates and bases his schedule on large drops and fast port turnround, it becomes increasingly uneconomic to make small drops or to use ports without rapid handling facilities. This is an example of the general trend in industry towards standardization and concentration on the profitable in contrast to the small or special item.

One approach to the problem of less suitable ports and routes is in floating barges out of larger ships and unloading them later using slower methods. Such a solution will be restricted to ports leading to a canal system, and will require considerable organization if barges are not to be left behind or underutilized. The cost of such a system is about 30 per cent in excess of the container cost on routes which are suited to containers.

Another solution is the articulated ship, which drops the hold unit for unloading at a slower rate and quickly takes away another full or empty hold unit which is coupled on to the expensive engine and crew holding part of the ship. Such a solution if it is viable will be restricted to very special circumstances. Most conditions under which such a ship would be justified could be equally well met by putting the extra cost of the hold unit into rapid handling equipment on shore.

A consequence of faster transportation on the sea route and faster unloading in the port is that it may now be worth while for the port to destination leg to be speeded up through rapid transfer systems and computerized storage, indexing, and advising. The time of delivery from a port depends on a combination of sequencing from the ship and priority claimed by the consignee. The marginal improvements possible in this final leg of the journey have only become appreciable now that previous legs are shorter. It is also essential that computers be used for this operation since to keep track of more than 3,000 containers and their contents in the time scale required is a mammoth undertaking. Thus the computer is an essential component of the container system.

Computer control and data transmission systems will also assist port operators in solving the problem of the arrival rate of cargo for particular voyages. In the past much cargo has arrived on the last possible date for acceptance, making loading plans difficult to organize. The development of hinterland depots at which consignments are assembled gives an opportunity for advanced planning of loading. Such arrangements lead to marginal improvements in overall journey time by preventing departure delays, and also contribute to lower handling cost, by arranging that the slower procedures for handling small consignments are completed before the expensive ship and ship loading system has to be tied up. As mentioned previously, there is also a significant differential in the cost of a stevedore operation and an on-shore materials handling operation.

Planning of any schemes can only be undertaken using a complete cost model of the system. Piecemeal approaches designed to speed up particular handling operations may have their effectiveness dissipated by slackness in another part of the system.

One development which is now being studied is the land link to cut out canals. The canal journey has now become sufficiently important to warrant examination for three reasons:

(1) Cost, because draft and other constraints prevent the use of cheaper large ships.

(2) Cost of the dues themselves in comparison with relatively reduced land and ocean transport cost structures.

(3) Ship cost and time involved in the journey through the canal.

Two land links are actively under discussion. The first is the trans-Canada container link to by-pass Panama and the second an oil link to by-pass the Suez Canal.

Future developments in ocean freight will be based on successive improvements to each leg of the journey from source to destination. We have seen that the process is primarily constrained by the patterns of trade and the availability of shore-based equipment, rather than by lack of sophisticated technical developments in ships. However, some technical developments in special ships may solve particular problems of the smaller port (floating barges in ships, articulated ships and self unloaders).

Having made these observations it is worth mentioning the current status of hovercraft and the technological forecasting of their future role.

The hovercraft and the hydrofoil have been under development for some years now. The current situation is one in which several parties have their own ideas about particular developments which meet the technical requirements of a variety of applications. The approach is concentrated on technical problems and indeed there are several to be overcome. A major one is the skirt life on hovercraft.

However, due perhaps to the obvious nature of the technical problems there seems to be a lack of cost effectiveness appraisal or total system approach in order to show just how far the parameters of the craft must change in order to produce a viable transport system in each application. Perhaps if cost and performance models similar to those used on containers and distribution systems are developed, then the critical design parameters can be appraised in an economic as well as a technical sense. It is well known, however, that a major cost item i that of the hull per passenger mile. The hull is subject to heavy corrosion and must therefore be assumed to have a life less than that of the conventional ship; however, it is also a higher initial capital cost per passenger accommodated and is likely to remain high.

Competitive performance with other transport systems will come first for the larger size hovercraft over 250 tons, where speed is appreciated by users. Present cost structure limits the hovercraft to the routes with the highest tariff per passenger mile. On cross-channel routes the hovercraft could provide for expansion over the next three to five years, but it could not be economic to keep in service for winter operation and would have to be laid up – giving very poor utilization of capital.

Below 250 tons the hydrofoil will be more competitive as a fast passenger transport. Limitations arising from the basic hydrofoil principle prevent there being any advantage in exceeding 250 tons.

Distribution of Finished Goods

This is another field where the availability of a model of an entire distribution system helps to put the benefits of changes in particular components into perspective.

Distribution in this context covers the transfer of products from the point of manufacture to the consumer. In most cases we have worked for the manufacturer who was concerned with getting his goods to the retailer or wholesaler; thus we were not considering the system for distributing to the ultimate consumer from retail outlets. Below we discuss the possibility that this part of the retailing system itself could (in some cases) be eliminated as a stage in distribution. However, the communication facilities necessary for such a radical change will not be available for several years. Thus we will assume that distribution in the present context covers a trunking system from factories to warehouses or depots, and detail delivery from there to retail or other outlets.

The following discussion is based on our experience and is divided into the headings: (1) development of component parts of the system; (2) trends in demand by customers; (3) foreseen changes as a result of customer demand and technical changes in the system.

(1) *Development of component parts of the system.* The trend towards standardizing the dimensions of the units for distribution will continue over the next few years. Thus, possibly based on the overall dimensions of a few different container sizes, pallets and cartons will be designed to fit exactly into these containers. These standards will have to be based on international agreement.

There will be a trend towards the use of larger vehicles with standard attachments, in a form of containers, articulated vehicles and further 'warehouse-extension' type of vehicles. They will probably be powered by electric motors, because rationalization of distribution at the retailer/consumer level will lead to shorter trips being made in terms of mileage, therefore leading to greater loads per day and less need for rapid acceleration and long trips, both of which militate against the use of electric power. Freightliners and allied long-distance transport systems will continue to develop at a rapid rate leading to more groupage systems throughout the country, where goods can be reassembled from containers for onward shipping to different destinations. A problem still to overcome on trunking by rail is the possibility of total disruption due to long strikes. (The Unions may strike at regular or irregular intervals for short durations, which will probably lead to less disruption to the general user, while still being critical to British Rail.)

The development of warehousing will take the form of greater space utilization by using height. Under favourable conditions the extra capital cost of raising the height of a 15-foot single-storey building to 30 feet would be only an extra 5 per cent. Therefore better and more capable equipment in the form of fork-lift trucks and similar devices will be required. There will be a number of automatic warehouses introduced, probably not always justified by costs, and companies manufacturing warehouse handling and storage equipment will develop equipment for these automatic and semi-automatic warehouses. These systems will be more refined with built-in flexibility to deal with changing requirements. Goods will then be transferred and stored under the control of either an on-line computer or by a centralized control room, operated manually.

There will be further trends in safety requirements in storage warehouses, therefore probably leading to the use of automatic equipment in place of fork-lift trucks, where a great height of storage is justified.

(2) *Trends in demand by customers*. There will be greater and greater demand from customers for a high 'service level'. This means that goods will have to be delivered within a short time of ordering. At the same time, the suppliers will be able to dictate either minimum order quantities or a series of discounts according to size of order, and they will also develop systems of timed deliveries so that sections of a town are served on one day.

The delivery at the customer's premises will have to be co-ordinated, both because of the possible congestion at the premises and because of specialized equipment which the customer may have installed. This approach will lead to faster turn-round times at delivery points, therefore leading to the use of larger vehicles for delivery. In a sense, these two factors are in conflict as larger vehicles lead to more difficult manœuvring at points of delivery. These will be reconciled over time by the introduction of special approaches for unloading, particularly at retail shops (see the Buchanan report).

(3) *Foreseen future changes.* Two trends can lead to completely different patterns of distribution in the future. These are the pressure on deliveries within congested areas and the pressures brought about by the freightliner operation. The first may well lead to the use of more grouped (multiple product) delivery systems, even to the extent of the introduction of town depots. The latter will lead to fewer and fewer supplying facilities being required.

Therefore, the trend may well be towards, say, a manufacturing multiple enterprise producing goods at a few major factories, to be trunked by freightliner to town depots. Thus, orders for a number of the manufacturer's products will be labelled and placed on a freightliner for trans-shipment through a town depot for detailed delivery thereafter. Alternatively, some large outlets may be able to use the freightliner itself as a delivery vehicle, but, at present, the road facilities are not capable to any great extent of taking the large containers.

A further trend, as a result of the cost and difficulty of detail deliveries, will be the multi-product warehouse. The warehouse is operated by a factor who holds several companies' products. He is not a wholesaler because he does not own the goods; he merely delivers on instructions. However, by dropping more than one type of product at each outlet the cost per unit of this expensive stage of the transport process can be reduced.

There will also be a tendency for manufacturers to move towards freightliner terminals. This means that those few ports with container facilities and those inland towns with liner train terminals will attract more and more industries to their outskirts. A problem thus arises – which comes first, the liner train terminal or the demand for the service? Thus, if liner train terminals were placed at strategic points in, say, development areas, this in itself will attract industry to that area.

There may be a trend towards the introduction of automatic freightliner trains. This will eliminate, to some extent, the problem of strikes, and, of course, will reduce the manning. A further factor in general distribution will be the building of the Channel Tunnel. This could lead to a new pattern of export distribution subject to the European network being built-up on some form of international standard. For example, it has been found that a feeder service can be justified for bringing containers to one port in order to obtain a full load shipment and therefore it may be possible that a western port in the British Isles could act as a central through-container port for all European exports to, say, the Americas. But faster ships would reduce the value of such a system.

In the really long term, the introduction of real-time information within the home would lead to the more rapid elimination of the wholesaler and possibly some retailers. This may mean that orders from the home can be relayed direct to the factory, which would then aggregate them rapidly, i.e. within twenty-four to forty-eight hours, for shipment to the town depot from which they will be delivered with the milk round the following morning. With the grouping of the consumer deliveries to the home, a large lorry would deliver during the morning the milk and other goods that have been ordered and can be delivered at that time, and a second round could possibly be introduced in the afternoon for delivery of bread and other goods which were ordered and arrived from a distant source.

It is apparent from the last paragraph that the information system associated with distribution could be the factor which leads to a major change from the current pattern of retailers and wholesalers for certain types of product. However, as previously mentioned, the communications requirements associated with direct consumer ordering will not be available for several years.

Air Transport

This will be covered in three parts: (1) freight transport; (2) private and business passenger transport (general aviation); (3) civil passenger transport.

Freight. The growth in freight carryings by air has intensified as a result of companies taking a broader look at the overall distribution problem. In the past the criterion most commonly applied was minimum freight cost per ton. Now management realizes that different products have different delivery criteria. Time, reliability of delivery date and damage free arrival are important factors in modern marketing methods. In addition, two other factors have contributed to make air freight attractive:

(1) The general trend in goods towards high value per unit weight – both as a result of complexity of products and of miniaturization in all fields, especially electronics.

(2) Realization that packaging is part of the distribution cost and that if a cargo can be guaranteed a safe journey, it needs less of the expensive protective packaging which adds nothing to a product's value to the customer.

The second factor is also working in favour of containerized traffic on sea routes, but the first factor combined with an appreciation of the value of rapid delivery makes air freight the best solution for some products – especially to impatient customers for whom hold-ups may cost much more than the value of the item they purchase (computer hardware, or electronic capital goods for example).

Even if per ton, the freight cost is appreciably higher when the differential is expressed as a percentage of the profit margin, on high value goods it becomes small.

With the continuing trend towards miniaturization and sophistication of goods of all types, forecasts of growth in air cargo are that by 1978 receipts from this source will exceed those for passenger traffic. As yet, however, no detailed forecasts exist for the growth of this traffic by route or by type.

General aviation passenger traffic. Similar arguments about the value of time and of merchandize apply also to the businessman. More and more companies are looking at total cost functions in taking decisions. Total cost with regard to executive travel includes the opportunity cost of having a man incommunicado in a transport system, or incapacitated by the rigours it imposes upon him.

For this reason there will be increasing pressure for private aircraft to give door to door travel times which are impossible if the scheduled carriers' flight times are inconvenient or the major airport is too far away from origin or destinations.

However, there will eventually be a countering force which reduces the need for executives to travel. Television links for the participants in conferences and facsimile transmission for the documents they need will make some personal visits unnecessary. These facilities are now in their experimental stages and their introduction to general use is mainly dependent upon the supply of transmission facilities.

In addition to business flights, pleasure flying will grow as standards of living rise. Trends in the USA indicate that major conurbations need one general aviation airport for every 300,000 population. Even small townships of 100,000 people may have their own facility. Recent estimates show that there are in the USA 117,000 privately owned aircraft and only 2,270 commercial airline aircraft. However, the present situation, due to lack of airport facilities, is chaotic. The lead time for extending airports is much greater than that for purchasing aircraft. In the USA due to increased size of civil aircraft their numbers will increase by only 1,200 in the next five years while general aviation planes will increase by 40,000. Each type of aircraft needs the same time to 'take-off' or land and congestion leads to an increasing waiting period for the expensive 100+ passenger aircraft.

The future in the United Kingdom with regard to general aviation could be serious if the development of airports is not planned with some eye to the growth of general aviation traffic and the overall effect on the community. We have carried out studies on the effect an airport has on a community, considering the noise, the road traffic, the attracted industry, the expansion of the community and many other factors. Just as in the past a sea port has influenced the town and the hinterland it serves, so an airport can have such a profound effect on the future that the full system must be studied in order to prevent mistakes caused by neglect of non-technical factors.

A valid parallel is the use of an integrated approach to road transport in urban conditions. This has now started in some areas, but previous mistakes made by allowing one set of considerations to predominate have produced congestion, chaos or have consumed capital without solving problems.

The approach to air transport so far has been dominated by the technical problems associated with the aircraft and the landing system. This paper concludes with a forecast that future plans will be much more integrated and will tailor the services to fit the users' needs both when he travels and when he stays at home.

Civil aviation. Both jumbo jets and SST are the logical extensions of trends foreseen by aircraft designers. They are purely technical developments. To make a technological forecast of the future in passenger air transport requires a model of the full system, including the land journey, the environment near the air routes and passenger attitudes to the cost, comfort and safety. Such a model does not exist for the United Kingdom and therefore we have to limit our forecasts.

The forecast that can be made with certainty is that the phase of unco-ordinated planning by aircraft manufacturers, airports, and airline companies is now ending. A second forecast is that developments to improve journey time and comfort will now take place on the ground rather than in the air. The following discussion outlines some of the issues contained in these two forecasts. In particular there are two issues which cannot be foreseen clearly until the SST and the jumbo jets are introduced into service. These are: (1) passenger safety versus cost; (2) aircraft noise versus cost and speed.

Passenger safety versus cost. Each passenger will use the SST, the conventional jet or the jumbo jet according to his individual objective. However, since the SST will be subject to a greater risk per aircraft mile (owing to the greater stress on its components) and the jumbo jet will involve a greater loss per accident, the question of the overall weighting of speed, cost, and safety may be influenced by public pressure. Safety is known to cost money and perfect safety is known to be unobtainable, but the compromises of safety versus cost incorporated in the SST and the jumbo jet may come up for review once the emotional impact of their first accident is assessed. This statement does not imply criticism of current safety measures, rather it implies the possibility of a willingness by all parties to tolerate a different level of expenditure on safety devices in the interests of greater absolute safety.

Noise versus cost and speed. It is now necessary to consider two aircraft noises; first that of the engines and second the sonic boom.

For the first time the aircraft has the possibility of affecting the population along its entire route. Already some limitation is placed on engine power in the vicinity of airports. The third London aircraft investigation may, if it is conducted properly, produce a rational weighing of the social costs of noise round airports against the extra journey time caused either by a longer land journey to an isolated airport or by a slower airspeed near the airport.

The impact of sonic booms remains to be assessed in practice, but they are likely to offend pressure groups along their routes as well as the captive groups who are unable to move away from airports. Thus the man who is interested in speed in the air can find himself questioning its advantage if he is affected by its consequences when he is on the ground. Routes over the sea present less problems but land routes must either involve a reduction to subsonic speed or a specially devious route to minimize objections.

It is interesting to note that one hundred miles travelled at 600 mph is equivalent to a loss in time of 0·1 hour in comparison with travelling at 1,500 mph. On a journey providing 2,250 miles at maximum speed (plus acceleration and deceleration distance) such a loss can be made up only by an extra 100 mph on the maximum speed. Put another way, any further attempts to reduce door-to-door journey time by six minutes can be made either by adding 100 mph to the aircraft speed of 1,500 mph or by attempting to reduce one of the journey's waiting periods.

Before discussing the problem of air speed and the ground journey any further, it is worth considering the reasons why conflicts exist among the parties involved in air transport. Each has, up to now, planned in a relatively independent manner. Since each has considered mainly its own interests it is more understandable why the present service shows the incongruity of fast air travel and slow ground travel.

The objectives of the aircraft manufacturers are: (1) to make a profit from civil aircraft by selling a sufficient quantity; (2) in addition, or sometimes alternatively, to produce a superior type of aircraft.

The objectives of the airlines are: (1) to make a profit from a scheduled route; (2) to have all passengers arrive fully documented on time; (3) to have immediate access to airport facilities.

The objectives of the airports are: (1) to have a uniform demand and high utilization for all services they provide; (2) to cover costs to the extent required by their commercial policy.

Some of the conflicting objectives of the passengers are: (1) to arrive safely at the scheduled time and scheduled place; (2) to arrive as soon as possible; (3) to pass the total journey time in as profitable manner as possible (working, reading, relaxing, or sleeping for example); (4) to suffer minimum physical and mental discomfort; (5) to travel as cheaply as possible; (6) to have unlimited luggage transported without trouble.

Finally, because of the noise problems and safety there is another interested party concerned with the planning of integrated air transport services. The objectives of the community when not flying are: (1) to live in peaceful surroundings; (2) to be free of grief from loss of life; (3) to be able to travel anywhere according to one's personal objectives; (4) to continue to live under the conditions that existed when one chose one's residence.

Like all service situations, the interests of the server who wishes to have maximum utilization of his facilities, conflicts with those of the user who wishes to have freedom to time his arrival for service, have immediate attention, fastest service, and pay a minimum price. So far no authority has been able to calculate what the optimum balance of each interest ought to be. This is not only because the calculation will be difficult but also because the calculating resources and the authority have not yet been made available. The consequences can be illustrated in two areas. The first is the rush to introduce an SST service because it is thought technically possible to produce the aircraft. The second is the unsatisfactory performance of the present land-based feeder services to the aircraft. We will conclude by discussing these two issues. The first is an example of a technical innovation spurred by the manufacturers with little thought about market needs. The second is an example of concentration on the prime mover in a transport system, with less regard to the need to advance the ancilliary services in parallel.

The value of the SST. The SST will come into service, but premium fares will have to be charged. The value of making the air journey faster must be greater than the premium in the air fare or the passenger will go by subsonic jet. What are the values of a faster journey?

(1) If the journey is regarded as uncomfortable – it will be over quicker. However, there is the alternative of making the journey really more comfortable (more space per passenger) or seem more comfortable (in-flight movies or sleeping pills).

(2) If time is worth money, then the time saved by making the SST journey must have a value in excess of the cost premium.

With regard to the second point there arises the problem of time zones. To get work done immediately at the end of a journey of 3,000 miles distance, representing a five-hour time differential, requires a certain amount of synchronization or willingness by one party to work odd hours or go without sleep. Thus, for example, only a restricted number of departure times on each side of the Atlantic have any value with regard to doing normal business in the immediate time saved by the SST. The time can most often be used only if one of the participants works abnormal hours. Tests conducted by the RAF and others show that mental performance after the disorienting effect of a journey through time zones can be such to make people unfit for exacting work. This is especially true of the day after the journey, hence all travellers suffer equally in this respect – regardless of whether they came by SST or subsonic means.

The nature of work done by people who are worth sending by SST is clearly exacting and thus unless they can do a few hours work immediately after arriving they must lose all advantage on the second day. The total cost function for an executive's journey must now include his actual efficiency as well as his normal value to the Company.

Here is a technological forecasting factor which the man who sets out to design an SST does not consider and one which severely limits the value of paying a premium price to travel by SST as a means of gaining time. The demand for SST travel can be expected to be constrained by this phenomenon in much the same way as first-class air travel is limited to a few individuals for whom the premium is inconsequential in comparison with other factors. It is also apparent that the advantage of increasing speed of aircraft still further is very limited in terms of useful time gained or even of comfort during the journey.

The land journey to and from the aircraft. The gap in performance between the landward journey and the aircraft journey is similar to the disparity that developed between ship performance and port cargo handling facilities. Overall journey time must be reduced by cutting the landward part. After that, advances in long-distance journey times are constrained by the factors outlined in the previous paragraphs.

The following stages are familiar to all travellers and each is labelled as a journey, wait or documentation:

Travel from house/office to town terminal	T1
Check documentation for air journey	D1
Deposit luggage into system	
Wait to leave terminal	W1
Travel to airport	T2
Check passport	D2
Wait to travel to aircraft	W2
Walk/Ride to aircraft	T3
Wait to leave runway	W3
Fly	T4
Wait to land on runway	W4
Walk/Ride from aircraft	T5
Check passport	D3
Wait for luggage	W5
Present luggage to customs	D4
Wait to leave airport	W6
Travel to town terminal	T6
Travel from terminal to destination	T7

This journey involves seven modes of transport, six waits and four actions requiring documents or interaction with officials. To conduct one of these stages at mach 2·2 will heighten the irony of the situation in which already the air journey is often a minor part of the total journey time and will heighten the sense of frustration by passengers when they feel delayed. For this reason we forecast that the emphasis will be put on three things. (1) actually reducing delays and the time taken in the land journey; (2) reducing the discomfort associated with waits caused by the variability in the scheduled arrival time of any transport system, or of the passenger himself; (3) reducing the number of changes of mode of transport.

Proposals exist for raising the speed of the link between airport and city centre. However, the passenger is not interested in speed *per se* but in arriving at his destination as comfortably and as soon as possible after he arrives at the starting point. Buses or trains currently provide this service for the passenger who does not use his private or hired car. However, the passenger wishes to get to the aeroplane and not the airport, hence the emphasis must be on the aeroplane to town terminal service rather than the airport to town terminal link.

Unfortunately the aeroplane may not yet be at the airport when the passenger arrives from a terminal, so a wait may be inevitable. However, a wait is objectionable only if it seems a waste of time, or is passed in uncongenial activity, like walking round a hot lounge, loaded with hand luggage, forever needing to remain alert for an unclear summons in a foreign language to a far-distant exit. Airports are beginning to tackle the problem of distance between lounge and aircraft by thinking of conveyor systems, but the basic problem remains for the passenger arriving from the town terminal in that he is obliged to wait and to give up the mode of transport used from the terminal. Los Angeles is already investigating one solution to this problem in the 'sky lounge'. This is a box which may be driven from town terminals to heliports and from heliports may be lifted to airports or even driven right up to the aircraft.

The 'sky lounge' eliminates one of the most objectional aspects of all travelling, which is the change of mode and the risk of missing connections. One development which will assist the functioning of such a system, especially on international routes, will be a documentation system relying on remote communications by magnetic cards or key punches. Each airline ticket can be capable of signalling its content or alternatively details will be keyed in before the passenger enters the ground transport. The passport formality, since it must be centralized, must rely on the owner being able to communicate his identity by magnetic card to a clearing computer or, until this is possible, any ground transport would have to pass by a passport control office

This would not violate the principle of a single transport mode if the passenger were able to remain in the same vehicle.

It has been suggested that the lounge may even be loaded into the aircraft. This implies that a very high value is placed on aircraft turn round time and high aircraft utilization. However, there are alternative ways of ensuring rapid passenger transfer to and from the aircraft which will not carry the weight penalty associated with using 'sky lounges' as containers for loading the aircraft.

This limited forecast of developments in aviation has been made largely in the hope that it will be a spur to greater effort in this field.

J. CHRISTOPHER JONES

A Credible Future for City Traffic

Part 1 – Summary

A credible future for city traffic was written in 1959 as a plan for solving the problems of traffic congestion in London. It was rejected at the time by leading urban planners, but the early stages of the prediction have recently materialized in some cities. There is, however, little sign of the very large-scale planning upon which the prediction depended.

The prediction began with functional and economic specifications for an ideal system of city travel and showed that the conventional system of urban motorways plus off-street car parks was inherently unsatisfactory. A credible future for a system that would eventually satisfy the specifications was proposed, in the form of a four-stage evolution over a period of about twenty years ending in 1980 or thereabouts.

Stage 1. A largely improvised man-machine system for rapidly measuring and simulating the behaviour and cost of city traffic.

Stage 2. Immediate relief of congestion, and of parking difficulties, by using the data handling system of Stage 1 to control traffic lights and to broadcast information to vehicles trying to avoid congestion or to find parking places.

Stage 3. Existing vehicles phased out and new vehicles (compatible with both manual and automatic control) phased in. Existing vehicles can hire radio links to receive individual routing instructions and parking guidance from a traffic control centre. The phased-in vehicles provide an on-call hire service from any parking meter or telephone and gradually replace private cars, buses, and taxis. They are manually controlled in Stage 3 but are compatible with automatic control in Stage 4.

Stage 4. All vehicles are now of the new type and most roads are equipped for automatic control by cable of fast single lane traffic. Full automation permits continuous intersection of traffic streams and the high utilization of vehicles that are automatically moved to kerbs where demand is greatest. The final system permits fast travel at little delay, with predictable journey times and in comparative safety.

Each stage generates the know-how and hardware to begin the next and alters the economic balance to make it feasible to begin.

The method of prediction. The prediction was arrived at by a search strategy that appears to be applicable to other problems:

(*a*) Identify inherent weaknesses of existing system, e.g. delays, accidents.

(*b*) Identify the functions of system components contributing to these weaknesses.

(*c*) Search for new kinds of system components capable of removing these weaknesses.

(*d*) Find a sequence of changes that would enable existing system components to evolve into the new ones.

Discussion. The structural changes brought about by a planned evolution of this kind are difficult to implement because of the vested interests of many people, including urban planners, in system components rather than in system performance. There is an urgent need to release people from professional, economic and educational practices which tie them to components that have to be transformed in the course of technological change.

Part 2 – The Forecast, as written in 1959

The forecast took the form of an entry for the competition 'New Roads for London' organized by the Roads Campaign Council. It will be seen that it is not an urban motorway layout but a long-term plan for the automation of traffic. The leading urban planners who judged the competition awarded the prizes to motorway layouts and did not accept the argument given here that without traffic automation no motorway layout can solve what was described in the advertisement of the competition as 'the problems of movement in London'. The entry is reprinted here without alteration. It is a fairly difficult document to read, being full of precisely worded specifications that are not intended for rapid reading.

NEW WAYS FOR LONDON – a new solution to the traffic problem.

Introduction

This entry is an analysis of the requirements of road travel in terms of: (*a*) the service available to road users and the demands and costs of road using; (*b*) the means by which services may be provided and these demands and costs may be minimized.

By starting from these elementary beginnings, rather than from the idea of urban motorways which is suggested in the competition rules, a different solution, not involving the building of new roads, has been arrived at. This solution comes of finding that nearly all the disadvantages at present attributed to inadequate roads can in fact be overcome by the provision of information concerning traffic and routes which is not available to road travellers at the moment. From this finding we are led, inevitably so it seems, to the conclusion that the problem may be solved by the provision of various kinds of electronic devices which can make available this information when and where it is required.

Section 1

The service available to road users and the demands and costs of road using. The value of a road system can only be rightly expressed in terms of its usefulness to those whom it serves. In the absence of generally accepted criteria by which the requirements of road users may be stated, we can only begin by postulating some requirements which we hope are generally acceptable. These are given below.

(1) *Facilities available to Road Users*

(a) *Travel between points very close to origins and destinations*. To move people or goods from points *very close* to their origins to points *very close* to their final destinations. This closeness is one of the chief advantages of road travel. To obtain maximum appreciable advantage it should be of the order of ten yards. Origins and destinations can be at *any point* within the urban area.

(b) *Very short delays at beginning and end of journey*. To permit the beginning of a journey *very soon* after the decision to make it has been made and to permit the people or goods to reach their final destinations *very soon* after the journey is finished. This short time delay is another of the chief advantages of road travel. To obtain maximum appreciable advantage it should be of the order of one minute. Time delays are to be equally short at any time during the day or night.

(c) *Service not affected by weather, visibility, etc*. The facilities noted here should be available regardless of weather conditions, visibility, and the like.

(d) *Total journey times not exceeding durations of visits or times between deliveries*. The total journey time should be of the same order as, or less than, the duration of the activity which the traveller has come to his destination to carry out. In the case of goods the total journey time should be of the same order as, or less than, the time between deliveries at the destination concerned. (It is suggested that these two criteria would be verified by an operational analysis of transport costs.)

(e) *Total journey times not exceeding road users' expectations*. The total journey time should never exceed travellers' expectations, i.e it should always be possible to obtain an accurate estimate of arrival time.

(2) *Demands made upon Road Users*
(a) *No bodily or mental stress remaining after a journey.* No traveller should endure stresses that cannot be recovered from during the journey, i.e. there should be no residual stresses of mind or body. (It is suggested that this criterion would be verified by psychological and physiological studies of fatigue during road travel in relation to the expressed discomforts of drivers and passengers and to such long term effects as nervous breakdowns and stress disorders.)
(b) *No learning required of road users.* Actions expected of drivers and passengers should involve no new learning on their part and should therefore be compatible with the behaviour learnt in early life and should be well within the capabilities of the less capable members of the population.
(c) *Low accident risk.* There should be a very low probability of accidents.

(3) *The Cost of Road Using*
(a) *High utilization of resources.* Resources that are tied up in the system should have a high utilization so as to get maximum benefit from the capital cost of the system. Utilizations to be aimed at should be near to 100 per cent.
(b) *Adaptable to changing conditions without obsolescence.* The system should be adaptable to changes in traffic volume and vehicle performance without putting existing parts of the system out of date before they wear away.
(c) *No rebuilding necessary.* Improvements to the present system should not entail great changes to existing buildings and structures.
(d) *No planning limitations.* The system should not impose any limitations on the planning of places between which road travel is provided.

Section 2
The extent to which existing roads and proposed motorways do not meet the requirements of road using. It can be noted at this point that the present system of roads in London does not meet the above requirements very fully. It may also be noted that the addition of urban motorways and large car parks to the existing roads does not correct very many of these defects and introduces additional problems. The extent to which the present road system plus motorways and car parks meets, and does not meet, these requirements is noted in the following table.

Services available and the demands of road using	*Existing road system*	*Existing road system plus motorways and large car parks*
1. *Facilities available to road users*		
a. Travel between points very close to origins and destinations.	Fairly well provided except when parking places and bus stops are far from origins and destinations.	No better than at present – possibly worse if traffic densities are increased and kerbs parking becomes even more difficult.
b. Very short delays at beginning and end of journey.	Fairly well provided except when there are delays in walking to car parks and bus stops, in waiting for buses and cabs to arrive, in searching for car parks, and so on.	No better than at present – possibly worse if local roads become even more congested.
c. Service not affected by weather, visibility, etc.	Service is greatly reduced in fog, ice, and snow.	No better than at present.
d. Total journey times not exceeding durations of visits or times between deliveries.	No objective evidence that journey times are longer than road users can afford.	Probably considerable reduction of total journey times but no evidence that time saved will be gainfully used.
e. Total journey times not exceeding road users' expectations.	Failure to meet this requirement is a major defect of present system and may well be one of the chief ill-effects of congestion, unexpected delays being much more frustrating than expected delays. Also inability to predict delays may be the cause of traffic entering routes which are already full to capacity.	Portions of journeys on motorways will become more predictable but no evidence that total journey will be any more predictable. No evidence that motorways will not attract far more traffic than can be accommodated on the other roads. No provision for discouraging saturation by predicting journey times.

Services available and the demands of road using	*Existing road system*	*Existing road system plus motorways and large car parks*
2. *Demands made upon road users*		
a. No bodily or mental stress remaining after a journey.	Failure to meet this requirement is a major defect of the present system and may well be one of the chief ill-effects of congestion.	Some reduction of present stresses for portions of journeys on motorways but possibly the introduction of new stressses when driving under these more monotonous conditions that give so little outlet for human variability.
b. No learning required of road users.	Learning to drive in traffic calls for the acquisition of skills of vigilance which nobody can maintain continuously and are beyond the less capable members of the population Route finding makes further demands beyond the capability and existing knowledge of many road users.	Some reduction of skill necessary for route finding but extra learning necessary to drive on motorways.
c. Low accident risk.	Accident risks are much too high.	Road users are protected from ordinary traffic risks while on motorways but are exposed to the new risk of multi-car pile-ups. Probability of greater risks in other roads due to new traffic attracted by motorways.

Services available and the demands of road using	Existing road system	Existing road system plus motorways and large car parks
3. *The cost of road using*		
a. High utilization of resources.	Present roads are of inherently low utilization (see analysis in Section 3) but as initial costs have been paid in the past this is no great disadvantage to us. All day parking implies a very low utilization of vehicles.	Motorways are also of inherently low utilization (see analysis in Section 3) and are therefore a poor investment for which it will be difficult to raise money. No increase in vehicle utilization.
b. Adaptable to changing conditions without obsolescence.	Cannot be changed at all without rebuilding the city.	Can be widened at considerable cost but could be made obsolescent long before they wear out by changes such as an increase in vehicle manœuvreability, acceleration, or braking. Once obsolescent, motorways are very costly to remove.
c. No rebuilding necessary.	Does not arise with a system that already exists.	The cost of rebuilding, or of siting motorways to avoid rebuilding, is a major difficulty.
d. No planning limitations.	Does not arise with a system that already exists.	The motorway approach completely dominates town planning to the detriment of all the requirements for which a town exists.

This expression of the defects of the present system in terms of actual disadvantages to the people using it rather than in terms of road congestion hold-ups, bottlenecks, traffic jams and the like is the basis of any attempt to alter the system so that the real disadvantages are removed. To seek a solution to the problem by trying to avoid 'congestion' itself without discovering what exactly it is that makes congestion so unpleasant is to treat the symptoms instead of the disease. The way in which urban mtoorways can speed up traffic in one place while making worse the congestion and parking difficulties in the smaller roads near to the road users' destinations is an example of this partial and incorrect approach.

Section 3
The means by which the services available to road users may be provided and the demands and costs of road using may be minimized. Having seen how far a system of urban motorways falls short of fulfilling the requirements of road using, we can now list the characteristics of a hypothetical system which would fulfil all these requirements. Once such a system has been described it can become a standard towards which the present system can be adapted as and when the means and resources become available.

(1) *Facilities available to Road Users*
(a) *Travel between points very close to origins and destinations.* This requirement can only be met if there is always sufficient kerbside parking space available for the number of arrivals and departures that are being made at any street at any time. This implies that no vehicles shall wait longer than is necessary for people or goods to enter or leave their vehicles. It also implies that the traffic arriving at or leaving any street at any time shall not be more than can be parked within a very short distance of the origins and destinations of the people or goods concerned. A further implication of this requirement is that all pasenger vehicles shall be in continuous use and that there shall be no long duration parking.
(b) *Very short delays at beginning and end of journey.* In addition to the above this requirement implies that a vehicle going to any destination is available at a point very close to any origin within a very short time.
(c) *Service not affected by weather, visibility, etc.* Being unaffected by ice and snow implies that vehicles are propelled by a system that does not depend on there being a high coefficient of friction over the whole road surface. Being unaffected by fog implies that the guidance of vehicles shall not depend on human vision.
(d) *Total journey times not exceeding durations of visits or times between deliveries.* This requirement does not imply very fast travel but it does imply that traffic is always kept moving at a reasonable speed and never exceeds the capacity of the system at any point. The means by which the number of journeys is kept within the capacity of the system is by the prediction of arrival times that is described in (e). The need to prevent traffic that is already within the system causing local delays and stoppages implies that there is a means of diverting approaching vehicles before a limiting traffic density is reached.
(e) *Total journey times not exceeding road users' expectations.* The requirement that it should always be possible to obtain an accurate estimate of arrival time implies that the position and destination of

each vehicle shall be known at all times (at least to statistical accuracy) and that there shall be a means of computing arrival times and communicating these to travellers and intending travellers. As the predicted journey times exceed the road user's available journey time (as defined in (d)) to a greater and greater degree the user will have an increasing incentive to cancel his journey or postpone it until traffic is less dense. This is the self-regulating method of limiting traffic to the capacity of the system that is required to meet requirements (d).

(2) *Demands made upon Road Users*

(a) *No bodily or mental stress remaining after a journey.* This requirement probably implies that the present need for continuous vigilance and the present occurrence of unexpected delays be avoided. The system as so far described would do this by providing guidance that did not depend on human vision and by providing predictions of arrival times. Other stresses, such as those involved in finding parking spaces, waiting for buses, route finding and enduring traffic hold-ups would also be avoided by the system as here described.

(b) *No learning required of road users.* This requirement implies that the guidance system here described shall operate automatically so that road users need not be capable of finding their way to their destinations or of controlling the vehicle on the way.

(c) *Low accident risk.* This requirement implies that there is no dependence upon actions susceptible to human error that cannot be checked before they take effect. An automatic vehicle control system does this by making it possible to confine human errors to occasions such as planning and maintenance which occur sufficiently long before they take effect to be checked. To complete this requirement it is necessary to prevent pedestrians moving into the traffic when not expected to do so. This implies that all footpaths be fenced or at a different level from the roadways.

(3) *The Cost of Road Using*

(a) *High utilization of resources.* Analysis of the functions of existing roads shows that they provide vertical support, friction for propulsion, braking, and turning, and visual guidance along the route. As any particular piece of road surface provides these facilities only for that very small part of the time when there is a wheel on it, or when it is being glanced at by a driver, the overall utilization of roads is extremely low. This is no doubt why it is so difficult to raise money for road making. Motorways differ from roads in being straighter and in segregating crossing streams. By these very costly and elaborate means they make up for the inadequacy of frictional forces in braking and turning and for the lack of communication channels that would allow anticipation of motions of vehicles far ahead and would allow streams to cross each other without collision. A system with high utilization would minimize the provision of functions through the inherently inefficient medium of roads and make maximum use of media which are in much more continuous use. This implies the use of existing roads (which have been paid for already) and using these to provide vertical support only. Propulsive, braking, and turning forces should be provided by means that are within the vehicle rather than outside it and are therefore in much more continuous use. Guidance devices to permit anticipation of vehicles far ahead and to permit streams to cross without collision should also be within vehicles and used continuously.

The utilization of private cars in the present system is as low as that of roads. Not only are cars parked for a large part of the time (to obtain chief facilities 1 (a) and 1 (b) but they entail the relegation of large areas and buildings as parking places. High utilization implies the continuous use of all vehicles and no long term parking. The factor that makes this impossible at the moment is the lack of information channels which would permit the moving of vehicles without drivers and the optimization of vehicle journeys in relation to road user's requirements.

(b) *Adaptable to changing conditions without obsolescence.* This requirement implies that the system involves only devices that are not closely tied to any particular kinds of vehicles or traffic conditions. This is the case when all the guidance and power functions are separate and not dependent on each other or on the type of road. The automatic traffic guidance system so far outlined, and a means of propelling, braking and turning independently of the road friction, would be sufficiently adaptable.

(c) *No rebuilding necessary.* The only way to avoid unnecessary rebuilding is to use existing roads very largely. This implies using existing roads only for vertical support and providing all other functions by means that are independent of the shape of the road as described in 3 (a), i.e. automatic guidance and the increasing of vehicle manœuvreability by devices that are independent of road friction.

(d) *No planning limitations.* This implies that future improvements are obtained by making changes to vehicles and control systems only. As such changes will probably take place in any case it is unwise to base our present plans on elaborate roads, which impose many planning limitations, in making up for the temporary inadequacies of vehicles and the lack of automatic guidance.

Section 4

Proposals for the introduction of an automatic traffic system by stages. It is proposed that a complete system of automatic guidance and high vehicle utilization be developed and installed by stages over a period of about twenty years. Each stage would introduce some of the facilities not available at the moment and would provide the experience and information by which the next stage could be designed. The stages are summarized as follows:

(*Stage 1*) An operational research study of traffic behaviour using traffic measurements available at the moment and an electronic simulator of the present system.

(*Stage 2*) Rapid traffic diversions (to reduce congestion) and available parking information obtained from observers and counting devices and transmitted from a central computing centre through traffic signals and through radio receivers in an increasing proportion of vehicles.

(*Stage 3*) Two-way radios in each street and in most vehicles, parking recorders in most streets and car parks, providing estimates of arrival times and detailed route and parking guidance for each vehicle. Traffic routed to avoid congestion and to obtain minimum journey times. During this stage buses, cabs, and a proportion of private cars are replaced by small passenger-hire vehicles that can be called to any point by phone and provide immediate transport to any destination at varying costs and journey times. Such vehicles would incorporate all available advances in powered steering, braking, and when possible a means of turning without slowing down or skidding.

(*Stage 4*) All the present vehicles would have worn out and been replaced by vehicles having powered steering and braking and a means of turning without slowing down or skidding. All vehicles controlled directly by signals from cables laid in the road and kept in continuous use. Long-duration parking discouraged by parking charges at the true cost of putting both kerb space and vehicle out of action. Private vehicles and car parks made uneconomic by the provision of a sufficient number of small passenger-hire vehicles (of the kind introduced in Stage 3) to meet all road travel requirements in the urban area.

Stage 1. A quantitative study of traffic movements using measurements by statistical samples of the traffic by such readily available methods as putting counters on the pads of vehicle-operated traffic lights, questioning road users about their destinations, cinematographic recording from helicopters, etc. It might also be necessary and possible to make an electronic analogue to simulate traffic behaviour. This study would make use of the techniques of operational research to devise computing methods by which the proposed system could be economically developed and controlled. Studies of this kind would be continued at all stages and would use the increasingly complete and accurate information that is made available by the guidance system itself.

Stage 2. The first attempts at relieving congestion would be by the setting up of a computing centre, at which people and computers would make predictions of traffic movements and provide instructions for diverting traffic before congestion develops. The information on traffic movement on which these calculations would be based would come from the most readily available sources. These might be persons employed to observe traffic and parking, or counting devices connected to traffic-signal actuating pads, or similar pads installed for traffic counting at other places. Parking information could be obtained from counting devices attached to parking meters. Traffic lights would be controllable from the computing centre and this would permit the use of an improved form of block control at linked intersections which would make full use of feed-back information from traffic counters. Verbal warnings of impending congestion and alternative routes would be broadcast to radio receivers in vehicles. Such receivers would be available at hiring rates that were directly related to the economic value of this information to vehicle owners. A separate wavelength would continuously inform road users of the places where parking spaces are available. All broadcast information could also be obtained on the telephone by intending travellers. The radio receivers available on hire to vehicle owners would be designed to be adaptable to two-way radios during Stage 3.

Stage 3. The following additions are made to the facilities provided in Stage 1.

Vehicle radios adapted to transmit as well as receive and used in a greatly increased proportion of vehicles. Separate transmitters capable of sending only to traffic close by are installed in each street that carries substantial traffic. All parking meters connected to central control and installed in most streets. Some parking meters linked with telephones for obtaining journey duration estimates and costs and for calling up passenger-hire vehicles.

Passenger-hire vehicles available in increasing numbers to replace buses, cabs, and private cars. These vehicles, of varying size and hire costs, and available with drivers or for self-driving, and usable for journeys outside as well as inside the London area. Payment made through a credit card system with costing done automatically at the computing centre. These vehicles to be specially designed for use in traffic and fitted with all available advances in power, steering, braking, and when possible a means of turning without slowing down or skidding. (These facilities will only be fully usable in Stage 4 when there will be no vehicles without them and traffic will be able to keep up a constant speed regardless of corners and intersections.)

The two-way radio communication would provide information of the movements of each vehicle so fitted and allow computing and transmission of individual guidance to each vehicle with consequently greater possibility of averting congestion and keeping up on constant traffic speed on all roads. Some degree of speed as well as directional guidance would be possible. Each driver could indicate his destination and get an immediate estimate or arrival time which would be corrected during the journey if traffic conditions changed meanwhile. He would also get instructions at each turning so that he need not know the way. These instructions would also be the means of diverting traffic to avoid congestion. Each intending traveller by passenger hire vehicle would be able to indicate his destination by phone and obtain a list of arrival times at increasing costs for vehicles of decreasing capacities. He could then indicate which, if any, he required to pick him up close to his present position without appreciable delay.

Stage 4. The following additions are made to the facilities provided in Stage 3.

All vehicles fitted with a means of picking up continuous steering, acceleration, and braking control information from cables laid in the road surface providing automatic control without any need for a driver. Manual controls still provided for journeys on roads not fitted with guidance cables. All remaining buses, cabs, and private vehicles replaced by private-hire vehicles capable of turning without slowing down or skidding. (This replacement is done only when the remaining vehicles have worn out.) Parking grounds released for other uses, and kerbside parking for long periods made uneconomic, by setting parking charges to the true cost of putting both vehicle and parking space out of use. All footpaths fenced or at a different level from roadways.

The system would now be capable of all the requirements described in previous sections of this report and would operate as follows.

Traffic would be kept to an even speed within single streams with no overtaking thus releasing much space for kerbside stopping. Stops at intersections would be avoided by controlling speeds so that each vehicle passed through the spaces between others. Slowing down at corners would be avoided by the improvements in vehicle manœuvreability. Estimates of journey times could be much more accurate than before and traffic would never reach congestion level at any point.

Final note. These proposals can only be tentative at this stage because the detailed knowledge of traffic behaviour upon which definite and detailed plans could be based is not available until at least the preliminary stage is put into effect. The cost of doing even a part of the preliminary calculations is much greater than can be spent in preparing an entry for the first stage of the competition.

Part 3 – The Forecasting Method

Examination of rough notes for the competition entry suggests that there is an underlying method that is applicable to other problems of the same kind. This method appears to consist of the following actions.

(a) *Identify inherent weaknesses of the existing system.* The inherent weaknesses of existing city traffic were found to include: traffic congestion (some of it induced by the presence of urban motorways); low utilization of vehicles; low utilization of road surface; high cost and rigidity of urban motorway building; high accident rate; shortage of parking places adding to journey times despite urban motorways; no quick way of diverting traffic from a road before it becomes congested.

(b) *Identify the functions of system components contributing to these weaknesses.* A detailed analysis of the function of motorways (not appearing in the competition entry) showed that their higher traffic speed comes of the guarantee that sharp corners, intersecting traffic and other hazards that cannot be negotiated at high speed, have been eliminated. This implies that a major function of the slow and costly process of road straightening is to *permanently* remove hazards that are themselves *transient*. It follows that there may be dynamic methods of achieving the same effects with much higher utilization of equipment.

A similar analysis of the effects of traffic congestion showed that it is not the traffic jam itself that is at fault but the irritation that it induces. Further analysis of the irritation suggests that this comes of chiefly from the fact that the people in the traffic jam did not expect to be held up and now have to change their plans. It follows that devices that would foresee congestion could predict journey times and redirect traffic to other routes. It also follows that warning of journey times before journeys begin, or during a journey, could be expected to keep the number of vehicles on any route to a density that travellers would experience as acceptable.

Each of the inherent weaknesses was analyzed in this way to form a network of functions in which to search for better solutions.

(c) *Search for new kinds of system components capable of removing these weaknesses.* The new components emerging from this search included: rented vehicles capable of both manual and automatic control and decreasingly dependent of road friction; manual and automatic means of observing and predicting traffic behaviour; two-way car radios to monitor, control, and divert traffic; two-way radios and telephones to call vehicles to kerbs and to provide journey time predictions.

Investing in dynamic components of this kind appears to unravel the problem, whereas investment in static components, such as urban motorways, appears to make it more acute.

(d) *Find a sequence of changes that would allow the existing components to evolve into the new ones.* It will be seen that elementary versions of many of the devices essential to traffic automation existed in 1959. The evolutionary sequence that was proposed made the maximum use of these crude devices from the start so as to bring substantial, rather than marginal, benefits to road travellers right away. Matching all the devices at each stage (crude at first and sophisticated later) to give, throughout, major benefits of interconnection, is the criterion for deciding the evolutionary sequence. This, it will be seen, is in marked contrast to the present policy of attaching sophisticated computers to crude devices like traffic lights. The latter policy does not initially produce substantial benefits and buys know-how for the next step at the cost of very slow evolution.

Part 4 – An Outline of Urban Traffic Developments since 1959

This is a list of some of the significant developments in urban roads, vehicles, control systems, and political/economic controls in recent years. Some of the developments in the list existed, at least as plans or prototypes, in 1959. All of them have been the subject of planning or investment since that date, either in the UK or elsewhere. The developments are classified as being compatible, or incompatible, with the credible future outlined in Part 2.

Most of the investment in the last nine years has been in such developments as one-way traffic, urban motorways, off-street parking and pedestrian segregation schemes that embody pre-electronic thinking. To this extent the 1959 forecast has not come about. There are, however, a large number of piecemeal attempts at introducing such essential ingredients of traffic automation as computer control, self-drive hire, the use of radio for traffic diversion and recent plans for road pricing. The result of these efforts is disappointing. Area control of intersections in Toronto and elsewhere reduces delays and journey times by only 10 per cent to 30 per cent (Wehner, 1966) despite the vast increase in information handling capacity when computer control is applied. It seems that this failure to get big benefits at the start of traffic automation comes of overlooking the need to increase the capacity of the information channels between traffic and computer *before* and not *after* the addition of a more flexible control device. In Tel Aviv, where channel capacity has slightly increased, the mean speed of traffic has increased by 75 per cent to 120 per cent in some cases (Wehner, 1966).

Despite the poor performance of the first generation of traffic automation schemes and devices that has appeared in the last nine years, it can be said that the 1959 forecast has been partially borne out. The vital missing element is large-scale planning and investment ahead of,

Developments since 1959	*Compatible with traffic automation forecast*	*Incompatible with traffic automation forecast*
Urban roads.	More fencing of pave-ments. Pedestrian controlled crossings.	More urban motorways planned or built. More roundabouts. More 2-level intersec-tions.
Car parking.	Automatic entry and exit for car parks. More parking meters. Mini-radio-transmitters for automatic access to restricted areas.	More multi-storey and other off-street car parks. Widespread prohibition or restriction of kerbside parking.
Vehicles.	More vehicles with powered steering and braking and with automatic gear change and dimming. Mini-cabs (inhibited by conventional cab operator opposition). Mechanizing of fare-collecting in buses. More self-drive hire cars. Prototype electric city cars.	More privately owned vehicles.

Developments since 1959	*Compatible with traffic automation forecast*	*Incompatible with traffic automation forecast*
Traffic controls.	Warnings of congestion on pop radio channels. Area control of computer-linked intersections. Closed-circuit TV for bottle-neck control. Helicopters and radio for rush-hour control. Vehicle detecting devices. Audible and visual variable-message signs for advance indication of hazards ahead, parking space availability, etc. Computer tracing of vehicle journeys from air photos. Remote control of motorway access to forestall overloading.	More one-way traffic schemes with banned turns, etc.
Political/Economic controls	Legislations to control traffic noise, exhaust fumes, drunken driving, and for fitting safety belts. Plans for road pricing.	Buchanan Plan for traffic segregation (which increases delays at each end of journey.
Alternatives to road traffic.	Evolutionary plans for an automated electric guideway to take all vehicle types off congested streets (MIT Project Transport)	Plans for urban monorails, etc.

rather than after, the evolution of specific devices and subsystems. It still seems conceivable that planned evolution of the whole, as well as of the parts, such as is outlined in the 1959 forecast, could, by 1968, have produced both, a big drop in journey times, and the economic basis and the know-how to evolve full traffic automation by 1980. As it is we have made large investments in road alterations, and so-called control experiments, that have had only marginal effects on journey times and provide an insufficient basis for the rapid evolution of full-scale traffic automation. It seems now that the opportunity of avoiding five to ten years of largely unregulated traffic congestion has been lost.

A major exception to this sad conclusion is the evolutionary plan for off-street traffic automation put forward in 1966 at MIT as 'Project Transport' (Breuning, 1968). This includes many features of the 1959 forecast, particularly that of investment (initially by General Motors) in evolutionary planning, on a sufficiently large scale, before, rather than after, detailed feasibility studies.

The essential feature of 'Project Transport' is the realization that we must plan from the start at three levels of generality:

(1) Prototype Experimentation for Feasibility.

(2) Design for System Integration.

(3) Long Range Plan for an Ultimate Goal with Effective System Evolution.

Important differences between 'Project Transport' and the 1959 forecast are listed below.

In retrospect it seems that the two schemes are complimentary, rather than competitive. The 1959 forecast is predominantly for moderate cost automation of moderate speed traffic, at moderate density, on existing streets whereas the 'Project Transport' is predominantly for high cost automation of fast, high density traffic, on off-street links. The arguments advanced against urban motorways in the 1959 forecast seem to lose much of their validity if motorways are seen as prototypes of automated guideways of the 'Project Transport' type.

Part 5 – Obstacles to the Evolution of Large-scale Systems

Both the rejection of the forecast in 1959, and the failure of subsequent attempts to solve the problem of traffic congestion in cities, point to the existence of major obstacles to the evolution of emerging large-scale systems. It is easy to see that the immediate obstacle is the lack of a sufficiently large authority to co-ordinate the activities of the many existing organizations whose actions must be in step if an efficient large-scale system is to appear without a great deal of trial-and-error. A credible future, such as that described here, cannot become a viable plan until a large enough authority exists to put into effect.

This, however, is not the ultimate obstacle. If we ask why an authority

1959 forecast	*MIT 'Project Transport'*
Automation of existing roads with evolution of control system, and of vehicles (to inhibit congestion and to permit turning and intersecting at near constant but moderate speeds).	Construction of a fast, automated guideway linked to existing roads.
Assumes evolution of private cars, buses and taxis into automatic rented vehicles.	Compatible with existing and future types of private cars, rented cars and public transit vehicles, and includes some 'captive' vehicles.
Solves parking problem by increasing utilization of vehicles and of kerb space, i.e. reducing demand for storage.	Solves parking problem by moving empty vehicles to low cost parking areas, i e. increasing storage capacity.
Inhibits congestion by traffic diversion and journey time prediction.	Alleviates congestion by removing traffic from streets.

large enough to plan traffic automation does not yet exist we can see that the ultimate obstacles are conceptual, educational, economic, and political. Nobody wants such an authority until the feasibility and attractiveness of traffic automation has been demonstrated but one cannot demonstrate these things while the experience, education and political beliefs of most people (including urban planners and traffic engineers) are firmly tied to the existing subsystems that traffic automation would replace and transform. As we saw in Part 4, the methodology of evolutionary planning is based on identifying *components* of existing subsystems that have to be transformed if the new large scale system is to evolve. In the case of traffic automation the subsystems that have to be transformed include:

public transport
vehicle manufacture and distribution
private ownership of cars
urban planning policies
traffic engineering practices
traffic legislation and law enforcement.

In each case there are well-embedded beliefs, attitudes and professional practices, as well as large capital investments, that have themselves evolved in response to the appearance of the automobile at the beginning of the century. What we now seek are ways of inducing change in all these things before, instead of after, the appearance of physical developments which depend upon co-ordinated transformation in all areas. It seems unlikely this will be achieved until the leaders of both professional and public opinion have re-educated themselves to the idea that planning depends, not on what is feasible at present, but on what is likely to be feasible when plans are put into effect. Re-education in evolutionary planning methods seems to be the essential first step.

References

S. M. Breuning, 'Evolution Potential for Automated Transportation'. Condensed version of paper given at IEEE meeting 18–21 March 1968.

B. Wehner, 'Area Control of Traffic'. *Traffic Engineering and Control*, **8** (Dec. 1966), 8.

S. A. GREGORY

Steel Industry Futures: Approaches and Techniques

The projection of futures is an act of the imagination founded upon existing knowledge. Whether this act is to be seen as art or as engineering depends upon the extent to which the various decisions involved in the projection may be exposed and related to existing knowledge in an objective manner.

In this paper it is taken that the projection of futures may be treated as having some resemblance to engineering design; attempts will be made to discuss the basis of projection exploiting this the design analogy.

Within design there is a sequential decision process involving the repetition of a pattern of steps: (i) specification, (ii) generation of possibilities, (iii) evaluation, (iv) decision. This repetition, which may include recycle, with modification, is illustrated in Figure 1.

Specification of Needs

Since no clear utterance has been detected regarding the kind of futures which are needed, it is going to be assumed that the futures are in the period ten to forty years ahead, that the iron and steel industry concerned is that of the world as a whole and not that of the United Kingdom, and that our interest lies more in uncovering the possible technological compositions of the industry rather than in guessing its magnitude.

It is possible to make forecasts of the magnitude of the industry, but such as emerge from time to time almost invariably assume that the technology of the industry will remain largely unchanged and that the price of steel can only become greater in relation to polymers and other materials.

A feature of the present contribution is the questioning of these assumptions. As a result it may be argued that forecasts of future magnitude of the industry should come only after exploration of possible technological changes. Questioning is an essential part of technological forecasting.

Generation of Possibilities

Overall it will be assumed that the driving force most significant in

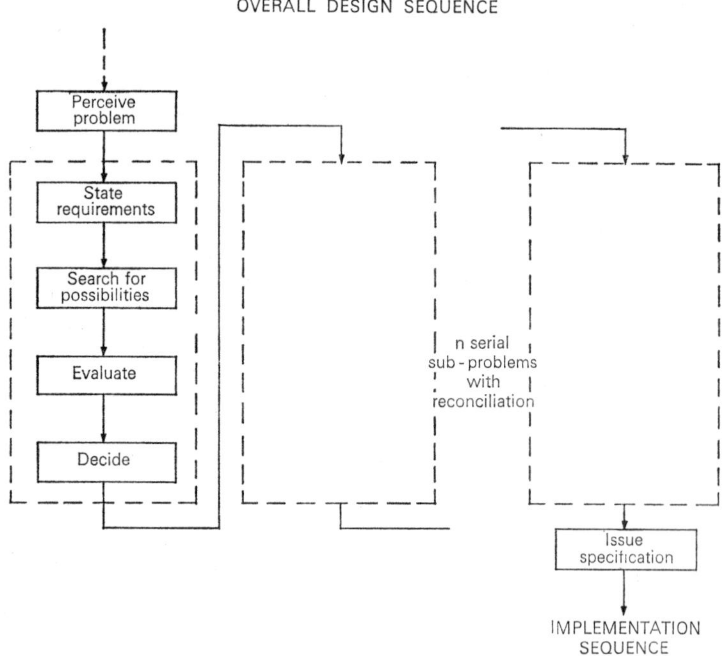

SYSTEMS APPROACH IN PROCESS DEVELOPMENT
Major evaluation stage *only*

Entry may be made at any point; recycle may be at same information level or continue with improved information and more relevant techniques.

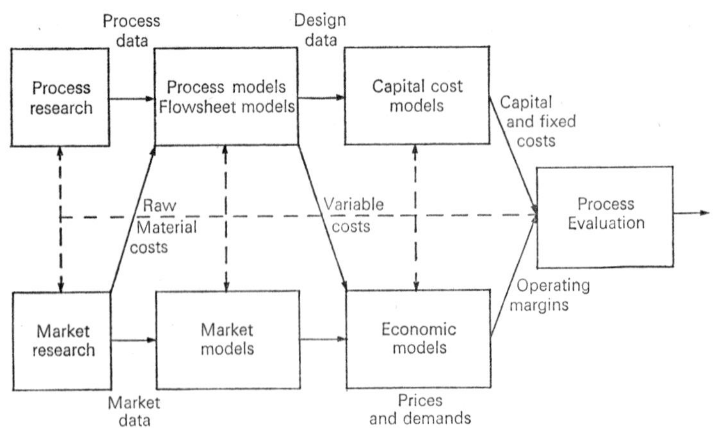

Figure 1. Patterns of Design.

bringing any future for the industry is its ability to provide certain mechanical properties at as low a price as possible. This is in keeping with the normal experience of the progress of metals, as shown in the sequence suggested by V. Gordon Childe (Table 1), who, it should be noted, saw the emergence of iron as the democratic metal – a metal with supplies of raw material almost everywhere.

TABLE 1 Materials utilization sequence (derived from V. Gordon Childe)

Stage 1: Discovery or introduction
Stage 2: Ornamentation or military use
Stage 3: Technical exploitation
Stage 4: Everyday practical application
Stage 5: Throwaway outlets

This empirically observed sequence is parallelled in the later correlations between price and quantity which have been numerically expressed.

The fact that iron and steel have long histories provides us with rich sources of information about possible futures. That this should be so depends upon the fact that the industry has undergone a number of evolutionary changes and has thereby revealed the basic patterns necessary for such an industry, indeed for any industry concerned with the provision of metals, and, by some obvious modifications, for any industry concerned with the provision of materials. We may summarize the needs of any iron and steel industry in the following steps:

(1) Provision of feedstock containing iron.
(2) Purification.
(3) Reduction.
(4) Shaping.
(5) Provision of energy and other supplies for these steps.

It is instructive to review the way in which these steps have been accomplished in the past. This is done briefly in Table 2.

This historical summary emphasizes the evolutionary character of the iron and steel industry.

In looking to the time ahead, possible futures have to be seen as variations on the basic pattern of steps. It is convenient to employ here the language of biology. One of the mechanisms of evolution is the continual 'shuffling' of genes whereby variations occur around a basic species pattern. This shuffling we can produce for an industry by means of the generation of alternative combinations of ways of carrying out individual process steps. This is what morphological analysis is concerned with. It is a paper study of the generation of possible new

TABLE 2 Metal forming: morphological introduction

1. *General Forming Possibilities*

---

a. Deposition: vapour (volumetric or superficial)
solution (volumetric or superficial)
electrodeposition (volumetric or superficial: ex-solution, melt or suspension)

b. Assembly: mechanical fastening, interlock,
self-adhesion (solid phase)
adhesion by additive
fusion adhesion (liquid phase)

c. Moulding: melt
hot solid (homogeneous or preform)
cold solid (homogeneous or preform)

d. Subdivision: melt (mechanical, 1-fluid, 2-fluid)
solid (vaporization, melting, solution, cutting, shattering, bulk shear)

2. *Necessary Elements of Assembly* (example of one forming approach, assuming powder material available):

entry of components, including auxiliaries
distribution of components
orientation of components
application of pressure
application of heat
removal of assembled shape
removal of residues

3. *Application of Pressure* (example of one element from (2)):

manual
gravity
artificial gravity
mechanical
hydraulic external
hydraulic internal
electrostatic
magnetic
explosion

4. *Economic Operation Parameters*:

capital cost (number of separate element embodiments)
rate
power
power efficiency
material efficiency
accuracy
continuity
difference from alternatives

---

processes or other systems and is, effectively, the equivalent of genetic variation, but with the important difference that real plants do not have to be built and then tested for ability to withstand competition in evolutionary struggle. Just as the shuffling is only done in model form on paper so it is possible to carry through the evolutionary struggle in model form. The equivalent of mutation is the discovery of revolutionary new facts.

Provision of feedstock. Among the elements existing on the earth's surface able to form potentially useful solid structures, iron is third in abundance, silicon being about six times more abundant, followed by aluminium which is rather less than twice as abundant. Iron itself comprises more than 4 per cent of the earth's surface. It is not scarce: it is, in the form of ore, a cheap material needing only digging.

Recent surveys of iron ores have indicated the availability of large reserves of iron-bearing materials containing a high percentage of iron. The particular interest in ores of the last decade has been in the exploitation of such rich ores which have advantages in the existing technology of iron manufacture which employs the blast furnace.

More and more industrially advanced countries employ iron and steel in 'throwaway' form. This is the last stage in the development of a material as indicated by the Childe sequence. In addition to the scrap becoming available in this way, there is also the heavier scrap arising from the salvage of values from industrial decay and the supply of scrap from current manufacturing operations with iron and steel. Scrap is a richer feedstock than ore and needs less done to it.

When a country is expanding fast, or when it lives by exporting, the percentage of iron-bearing feedstock as scrap which it can use overall is likely to be less than a country which is well developed, not expanding, and without a large export trade.

For the newcomer a scrap-based industry is attractive in that production of steel can be thus obtained at a lower capital cost than by going through the initial manufacture of iron. For the well-developed country the same attraction holds. But for the well-developed country much of the throwaway kind of scrap is contaminated by other metals which make its re-use unattractive by the conventional steelmaking processes.

Purification. The kind of purification needed depends upon the feedstock and the eventual product. With ore, purification involves the separation of metal value from gangue, i.e. the main mass of siliceous, clayey, or limey material in which the iron is dispersed, and its purification from phosphorus and sulphur. Normally this is done in two stages and involves the blast furnace and then the steel furnace. There is no intrinsic reason for any more than one step.

With minerals the cheapest method to attempt purification is by what may be termed 'mechanical' methods. In these, lumps of metal value are separated from lumps of impurity. Ores which permit this kind of purification alone to give a suitable product are extremely scarce and can only be seen as providing for special cases. Most likely practical feedstocks, whether ore or scrap, need purification which is able to separate the wanted material from the unwanted at the molecular level.

The range of ways to bring about separation at the molecular level is very large indeed. Any method whatsoever for this kind of separation needs heat to carry out the operation, as may be deduced from thermodynamics. Up to the present, practice has tended to rely upon high-temperature heat. In the blast furnace individual molecules of iron oxide are reduced and the resultant iron is melted and runs together into a pool which is separate from the pool of slag which arises from the melting of the gangue in association with certain added materials. Some sulphur is removed by chemical reaction with lime. The high temperature, the reducing gases for the iron, and the support of the whole mass in the blast furnace, depend upon the provision of coke of special quality. This coke is an expensive source of heat and, in some countries, an expensive reducing agent. At the blast furnace stage some of the carbon from the coke combines with the iron produced. This has to be taken out in the steel furnace at the same time as attempts are made to remove silicon, phosphorus, and remaining sulphur.

When metallurgists discuss advance in iron and steel manufacture or their future (see e.g. *Ironmaking Tomorrow*) they take for granted that they are discussing possible variations on the pyrometallurgical operations carried through in the blast furnace and the steel furnace. Up to the present they have not appreciated the tremendous number of possibilities outside pyrometallurgy, although such are recognized in non-ferrous metallurgy, nor have they studied in any detail the rather fewer outside possibilities which have potential as competitors in the evolutionary struggle. They tend to 'phenotype' rather than 'genotype' studies.

Some of the possible alternative ways of carrying out the separation are discussed by Bridgewater in his contribution on morphological analysis and he gives a skeleton diagram. It is this kind of questioning the underlying assumptions in present-day discussion, discovering the general pattern requirements, and then generating alternatives in a methodical manner, which are essential in any attempt to make objective studies of possible futures.

Reduction. In reduction, oxygen (but it might be sulphur from ore, or chlorine if this material is used in a purification process) has to be removed from combination with the iron. Although complex compounds may be used for the reduction, practical requirements almost inevitably diminish the possible reducing agents to elemental carbon, carbon monoxide, or hydrogen, or their precursors.

If pure reducing agent is to be used, and this becomes necessary if reduction is carried out after purification has been carried through, then only gases may be employed.

The reducing agents commonly available are coal, with coke as a derivative from some kinds of coal; petroleum fractions; natural gas. One important factor in choosing between these is relative cost, either as precursor or as resultant derived reducing agent.

If scrap is used as feedstock, the question must arise whether reduction is still necessary. This depends upon the purity of the scrap in the first consideration. With low-grade scrap, of the type unsuitable for normal steelmaking, it is possible to convert the contained iron into a chemical compound for purification at the same time as producing hydrogen which may then be used for subsequent reduction. No reducing agent is necessary in principle although reduction has to be carried out. This reduction process may be accompanied by some purification.

The reducing agent which is to be supplied in any process has to be seen in its other capacity as energy source.

Shaping. We have grown up accustomed to the notion of the shaping of iron and steel by casting, or by cutting or deformation of homogeneous solid material. A more reflective approach shows that we should be able to shape the metal in a number of other ways. In Table 2 is provided an introduction to some of the alternative possibilities.

The table is only intended to suggest possibilities in an initial way. The full exploration of possibilities is a study in itself and probably only justified in connection with specific proposals or suggested requirements.

Thus, let us suppose that interesting products for the future might be: (*a*) rod; (*b*) tube; (*c*) whisker crystals.

For rod we may consider the alternative ways of forming. Beginning with deposition there are the possibilities of commencing from vapour, etc. A check on absolute deposition rates suggests that this is a slow process when used for the formation of a single body by superficial deposition. Volumetric working is likely to be faster but does not lend itself directly to building up rod. This can only be done indirectly by forming powder volumetrically through deposition and then using the powder to form rod. This has led us to assembly. An alternative entry to assembly is through the use of many fine fibres formed continuously by some kind of deposition.

The moulding method includes casting (batch as well as continuous), extrusion and drawing, whether hot or cold. These are areas which have been well explored.

The subdivision method most directly includes slitting. This would normally be followed by rolling and drawing, i.e. moulding methods.

For tube we have to follow a similar line of exploration as for rod. At the subdivision method there are more possibilities worth considering than is the case with rod, such as versions of cutting, including boring, etc.

For whisker crystals in the form of separate pieces, only deposition or subdivision seem possibilities, with deposition as the most likely area.

The importance of the shaping analysis lies in the fact that here is the opportunity to relate the ultimate consumer requirements with the method of metal preparation. We have to find out what shapes give the best value to the consumer in the materials likely to be available. In this thinking we have to be prepared to see the ultimate shape as consisting of some composite e.g. rod or wire (continuous or 'needle') in concrete, or as whisker crystals in polymer.

Steps: Provision of Energy

We are passing through a period of substantial change in the economic sources of energy, on the world scale and, particularly, in the United Kingdom.

In some countries cheap coal is still available in very large reserves, but the development of bulk transport of petroleum materials has made cheap energy and reducing agent more widely available, particularly in the case of those areas which have good marine access or lie on the axis of pipelines. In more restricted situations the increased availability of natural gas has had similar consequences. In terms of something like conventional pyrometallurgy 'direct reduction' by liquid or gaseous hydrocarbon is competitive when available at 1·5 cents per therm.

Nuclear power, according to the trends, promises to be the cheapest general source of electricity within the next decade. This gives the potential of almost universal, i.e. not tied to particular locations, availability of energy for the relevant kind of pyrometallurgical steelmaking. In North America (both Canada and USA) considerable effort is being devoted to the exploration of processes based upon direct reduction of enriched ore, either by uncoked coal or hydrocarbon fuel depending upon relative cost, and the subsequent execution of steelmaking using electrical heat.

What has been omitted by the conventional steelmakers is consideration of the possibility of cheap thermal energy direct from the nuclear boiler without the cost of going through electricity. I have discussed this elsewhere and so has Wenzel. A large steel works is, perhaps, the only kind of plant able to soak up the thermal output of a modern nuclear reactor. The grade of heat needed by a chemical process is likely to be in the temperature range available in the next decade.

The changes taking place in relative availability and cost of energy and reducing agent are such as to demand attention in all future steel-making projects. This is done at present only for minor projects in special locations. The day of unique reliance on coke is past. One important teaching from the study of evolution is the danger of loss of flexibility in development.

Evaluation

A methodical generation of alternative processes leads to extremely large numbers of possibilities. This kind of generation can be set up for execution on a computer and the application of morphological analysis in such a manner has been done for the OSCAT Project.

Such a programme by itself only leads to the print out of possibilities. Provided we know the requirements of the system problem, it is possible to inject some suitably simplified and relevant criteria into the computer programme and cause the computer to lose the unwanted possibilities. This markedly reduces the print-out.

For the iron and steel industries some attention has to be paid to the requirements of the problem situation. Our initial project brief was very broad: to find radical new ways to make steel. But later these have to be evaluated in terms of likely locations. These locations are analogous to niches in biological evolution. Do the processes we might have in mind possess the ability to occupy a niche and maintain it against competitors. This niche has a geographical location (this may be a country or a town); it has access to certain kinds of feedstocks at identifiable prices; it has an existing market of a certain size and growth pattern; the related community is at some characteristic state of industrial development; competitors are known.

As a first approach it is appropriate to use the more obvious forms of benefit/cost or satisfaction/resources analysis as the method of attack and then to investigate the specific situation parameters and constraints. In addition, however, account must be taken of psychological and comparable constraints. These all add together to provide a situation 'profile'.

The effect of evaluation criteria on design is so great that we are obliged to arrange the design procedure to fit the situation. This is the basis of what I have termed the 'outside/in' approach. From the situation profile we work inwards to successively greater depths and in more detail. At each stage we deploy the available useful methodical procedures and evaluate in terms relevant to the level of work but

TABLE 3 Some approaches to evaluation

1. Establish major objective
2. Develop essential profile of general situation requirements
3. Assign weighting or ranking of individual aspects
4. Develop subsidiary criteria, consistent with total profile requirements, but suitable for deployment in detail at successive levels, including the necessary aspects of:
   - *a.* technical performance:
     - i. technical feasibility in principle
     - ii. technical information status
     - iii. technical resources availability
     - iv. relationship to other technical problems, including balance, parallelism, compatibility, reinforcement
   - *b.* individual and social interactions:
     - i. ergonomic
     - ii. in-plant safety
     - iii. worker aspirations and need fulfilment
     - iv. social-legal
     - v. amenity
     - vi. social need fulfilment
     - vii. aesthetic
   - *c.* economic performance:
     - i. resource needs, particularly minimum capital cost, operating cost
     - ii. minimum scale of successful operation
     - iii. cost/benefit or satisfaction/resources ratio, including discounting to allow for time value of money, and uncertainty analysis
     - iv. economy of investment with scale
     - v. further development possibilities
     - vi. implications with respect to other developments
     - vii. status of competing alternatives
5. Relate to specific location classes:
   - *a.* market size (small; medium; large)
   - *b.* product sophistication (primitive; average; highly-worked)
   - *c.* market change rate (static; fair expansion; rapid expansion)
   - *d.* prior industry (nil; fair; highly-developed)
   - *e.* feedstock and energy availability and price
   - *f.* entry problems (size; approach; strategy)

compatible with the overall profile requirements. In Table 3 are given some of the aspects of evaluation.

In biological evolution one solution is not tried in isolation in a niche. Rather, multitudes of one variety of organism compete with multitudes of other varieties. Is there any analogy in evaluation for this kind of selection procedure?

One such is coming in with Monte Carlo methods of venture analysis. Here, instead of trying a multitude of individuals of one variety against the situation, one candidate is tested against a substantial number (e.g. 1,000) of combination of randomly selected values of significant parameters with specified variability patterns. This may be repeated for other candidates and enable alternative candidates to be compared for expected economic viability.

In general, apart from feedstock iron cost, which tends to be rather stable, the principal items which influence product cost are energy and the factors associated with capital cost. Energy costs are the subject of almost continuous inspection. Furthermore, the changes in energy cost relationships tend to be easily seen from the trend curves provided by the competing suppliers of energy.

Capital costs have been rather difficult to obtain, certainly for the assessment of alternative configurations. This is now changing. For conventional pyrometallurgy Leckie has made available valuable correlations. For chemical processes we have developed new methods of capital cost forecasting. With these quick methods it is possible now to provide many alternative configurations for venture analysis.

It is important to stress the contribution which adequate capital investment forecasting can make to technological forecasting which deals with products for human consumption, which come from process systems capable of substantial change. At the lower levels of output capital cost factors can dominate all other items of cost. By capital cost factors are understood maintenance charges (usually estimated as a function of investment), depreciation, and necessary cash flow to earn a satisfactory return on investment.

Pioneering processes have usually to enter into competition for niches under conditions in which capital cost factors dominate. For this reason every effort has to be made to provide systems with low investment/output ratios. This is, therefore, a primary criterion in evaluation and becomes an important sub-objective in design itself. We must not use a Cadillac where a Ford will do.

In addition the ability to obtain economy of investment with increased scale of operation provides further competitive advantage, given the possibility of establishing a toehold in the new niche. This provides a further important criterion which becomes built in as a sub-objective.

Finally, attention must be drawn to the correlation between price and quantity, and its connection with economy of investment with scale.

Problems of Implementation

In evaluation the usual concern is with fitness for purpose, and with the incentives to make a particular choice, associated with the satisfactions arising, usually those of the investor or provider of resources.

But decision-making, in the sense of going from apparently rational economic recommendations to actual performance, is beset with difficulties. These may mostly be seen as resistances.

Before considering these resistances the 'point of entry' problem needs attention, in terms of economic location, approach route, and overall strategy.

The entry problem occurs with known technology or new technology. For known technology, a typical situation is that of a developing country. Initially the products of interest are imported. At what stage will it become possible for a small local producer to be able to compete effectively with imports from a large producer? The large producer will have economies of scale and low incremental costs. The small local producer has distinct problems of scale and, possibly, feedstock and other supply problems. His advantages lie in proximity to and knowledge of, the local market, and in distance from the big producers. Techniques for dealing with this kind of situation are well developed.

If new technology has to be introduced, the situation may become much more complex. Let us take the example of the United Kingdom and its need to find ways of effectively competing by manufacture on the small scale with products made elsewhere on the larger scale. The satisfactory technoeconomic solution appears to be radically new technology. Here, in addition to finding the entry level of scale, it is necessary to find the best way to build up the technology with minimum expenditure of resources and with least risk at the final jump. Finally, the psychological problems have to be overcome.

The new technology entry approach route problem requires the location of possible alternative commercial markets at different price levels. If we look at powder iron production in the UK the size of the present market is hardly adequate to encourage major investment in a new production facility. This is for making powder of the low quality commonly acceptable for making engineering components. But if it is required to make high-quality powder suitable for steel products, the kind of powder production plant, now almost ready for exploitation, is too expensive, because the market for its powder is too small. We are faced with a 'chicken-and-egg' or 'bootstrap' situation. This is of the class of 'circular' problems. Such can only be solved by some injection from outside. What is the least injection? Here it is necessary to study all the dependent problems and risks of the alternative approach routes.

From such an approach, recommendations can be made, but will they be carried into effect?

At this point attention must be directed to the source of resistances which may soak up all the incentives. Most people have difficulties in accommodating new ideas. This has been well covered by Rogers. Resistance to innovation varies with national culture and, in this country, we have a high resistance. Within specific organizations there are resistances also. The most obvious of these is the NIH ('not invented here') factor, which, as Peplow has shown, favours ideas which originate within the organization. But, and this is particularly true of the iron and steel industry, radically new ideas tend to come from outside. The iron and steel industry has, perhaps, the best documented and longest record of resistance to innovation. This may be connected with the very high capital investment needed.

Approaches and Techniques

I have outlined approaches which experience has suggested as valuable for aiding technological forecasting, in connection with the kind of problems which have to be faced in dealing with the iron and steel industry. I should now like to recapitulate briefly, referring to approaches and techniques used.

Technology is a species of problem-solving activity. In this the design method appears to suit best overall. In design, a specification has to be made of the system required to reach a given objective within a specified environment using limited resources. In designing for the future, i.e. technological forecasting in the fullest sense, objectives are suggested, environments predicted, and resources extrapolated, and against these, design is carried through, within the limits and uncertainties prevailing, to provide specifications of likely systems. In addition to the normal factual and imaginative content required for design and the techniques employed, adjustment has to be made for the uncertainties of the future and the extra imagination needed. Most of the techniques listed by Jantsch are, in fact, design techniques, several of them having been notably developed within design.

Within the design method, the systems approach is best suited for dealing with complex situations, at the same time giving assurance of adequate coverage of alternatives and an overall vision.

Historical pattern analysis identifies constant factors in environments and systems capable of existing in such environments and attaining objectives.

Trend analysis indicates, through qualitative and quantitative studies, the kind of change occurring in objectives, environments, systems, and resources, either with time or other variables. The quantitative studies, particularly by economists, tend to assume constant technology.

Biological evolution analogy suggests significance of equivalents for natural selection, breeding, genetic 'shuffling', mutation, admixture, and genetic drift. In addition to genotype equivalents, phenotypes and niches are worth consideration.

Morphological analysis provides the equivalent of genetic shuffling within an identified pattern. This is particularly valuable in generating new process possibilities, but is available also for consideration of alternatives in environments or competitors.

Emergence likelihood analysis deals with the equivalent of mutation. The discovery of new facts, the invention of new techniques, or the development of new situations, are usually beyond the scope of historical pattern analysis or trend analysis. New ideas often occur as an individual response to the challenge of morphological analysis. This is one of the values which come from the use of methodical procedures: the human attempt to outsmart the rules. Emergence likelihood analysis normally depends upon the forming of opinions, either of individuals or of a group, regarding the arrival of such items as new products, or the emergence of new techniques relevant to the field of investigation. In some cases, careful processing of the opinions is necessary; but, for individuals the opinion may represent a challenge to creative fulfilment.

Evaluation deals with viability, with the equivalent of natural selection, and assesses the incentive likely for motivating implementation. Evaluation employs the full range of modern economic tools, with particular emphasis upon capital cost forecasting. The systems approach leads to evaluation at successive levels with adjusted criteria.

Implementation analysis studies ways and means (tree techniques are valuable).

References

W. Adams and J. B. Dirlam, 'Big Steel, Invention, and Innovation'. *Qu. J. of Econ.*, **80** (2) (1966), 167–89.

J. A. Allen, *Studies in Innovation in the Steel and Chemical Industries* (Manchester University Press; 1967).

A. V. Bridgwater, 'A Preliminary Evaluation of New Processes for the Manufacture of Iron by Way of Liquid/Solid Phase Systems' (M.Sc. Thesis, University of Aston in Birmingham, December 1966).

A. V. Bridgwater, 'Long-range Process Design and Morphological Analysis'. *The Chem. Eng.* (1968, April), CE 75–81.

A. V. Bridgwater, 'Chemical Alternatives to the Conventional Manufacture of Iron and Steel' (paper to I. Chem. E., Swansea, March 1968).

M. J. D. Brisby, P. M. Worthington and R. J. Anderson, 'Economics of Process Selection in the Iron and Steel Industry'. *J. I. & S. I.* **202**, (1964), 721–34.

S. A. Gregory, 'Basic Strategies in Process Development', in (ed.) P. A. Rottenburg, *Process Development and Evaluation* (Symposium) (I. Chem. E.; 1967).

S. A. Gregory, 'Opportunities, Technical and Economic, for the Direct Use of Electricity and Allied Forms of Energy for Unit Operations and Processes: Some Reflections'. *The Chem. Eng.* (1966, Dec.), CE 329–35.

S. A. Gregory, 'Chemical Engineering Evaluation in the Iron and Steel Industry: Today and Tomorrow'. Paper to I. Chem. E., Swansea (March 1968).

S. A. Gregory, 'Evaluative Approaches to Gas/Solid System Equipment'. I. Chem. E. – VTG/VDI Joint Meeting Brighton (April 1968). To be published.

S. A. Gregory and A. V. Bridgwater, 'Iron Powder: Prices, Costs and Possibilities'. Paper to be read to Powder Metallurgy Joint Group, Swansea (November 1968).

S. A. Gregory and W. H. Gore, 'Development of a Rapid Method of Evaluating Capital Costs of Process Plants'. Awaiting presentation.

H. W. Grenfell, 'Possible Evolution of Steelmaking Processes of Interest to Chemical Engineers'. Paper to I. Chem. E., Swansea (March 1968).

D. B. Hertz, 'Risk Analysis in Capital Investment'. *Harvard Bus. Rev.* (1964, Jan./Feb.), 95–106.

S. W. Hess and H. A. Quigley, 'Analysis of Risk in Investments using Monte Carlo Techniques'. Chem. Eng. Prog., Symp. Series (1963), No. 42, 55–63.

E. Jantsch, *Technological Forecasting in Perspective* (O.E.E.C., 1967).

J. Jewkes, D. Sawers and R. Stillerman, *The Sources of Invention* (Macmillan; 1958).

A. H. Leckie, 'Technical and Economic Considerations Affecting the Optimum Size of Plant', in *Ironmaking Tomorrow*, I. & S. I. Publication 102, 1967.

A. H. Leckie and A. J. Morris, 'Effect of Plant and Works Scale on Costs in the Iron and Steel Industry'. *J. I. & S. I.* (1968, May), 442–52.

M. E. Peplow, 'Design Acceptance', in (ed.) S. A. Gregory, *The Design Method* (Butterworths; 1966).

E. M. Rogers, *Diffusion of Innovations* (Free Press of Glencoe; 1962).

J. G. Sibakin, P. H. Hookings and G. A. Roeder, 'Electric Arc Steelmaking with Continuously Charged Reduced Pellets'. *J. I. & S. I.* (1967, Aug.), 1005–17.

M. W. Thring, 'Energy Problems of the Iron and Steel Industry'. *J. I. & S. I.* (1967, June), 625–9.

W. Wenzel, 'Using nuclear energy for making iron'. *Euratom*, **6** (4), (1967), 115–20.

(ed.) S. A. Gregory, *The Design Method* (Butterworths; 1966).

Ironmaking Tomorrow. Publication 102, The Iron and Steel Institute (1967).

'Research in the Iron and Steel Industry'. Special Report, Iron and Steel Board (1963).

Appendices

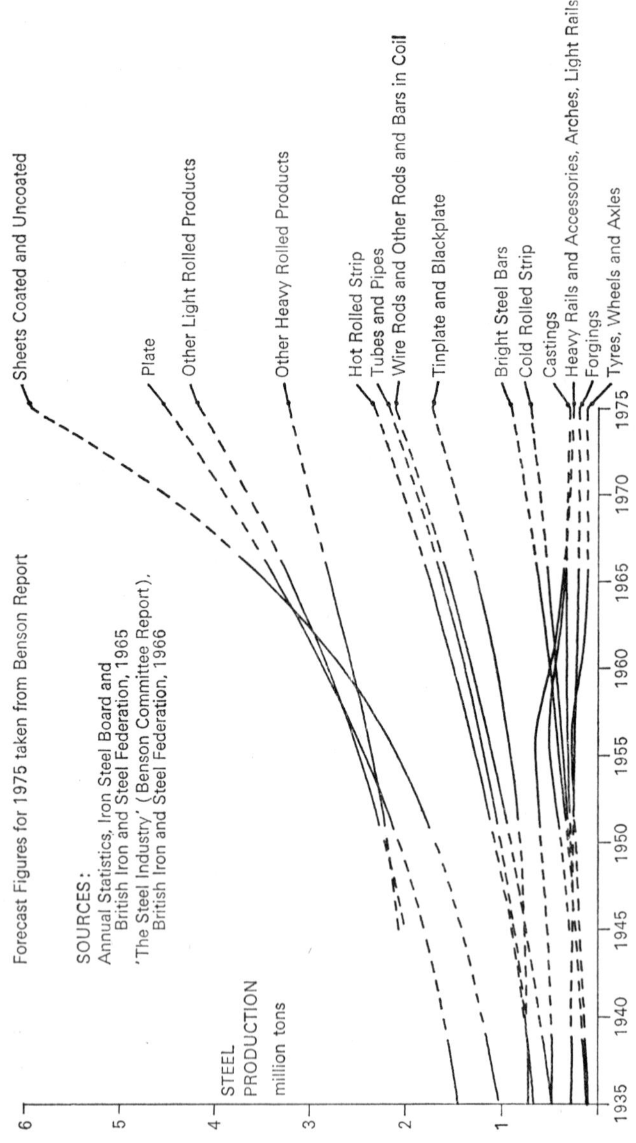

Figure 2. UK steel production—all qualities.

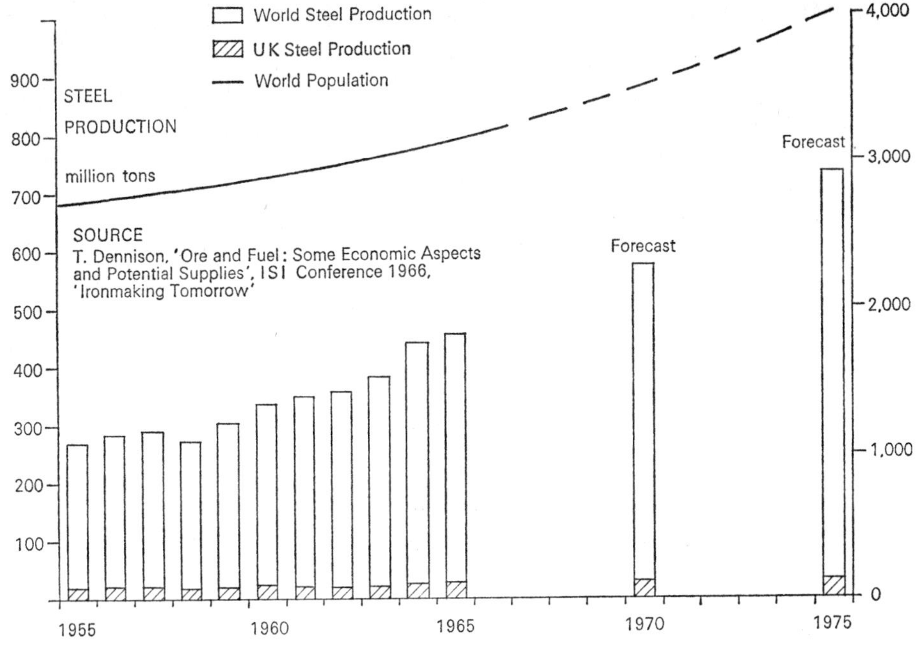

Figure 3. World vs UK steel production to 1975.

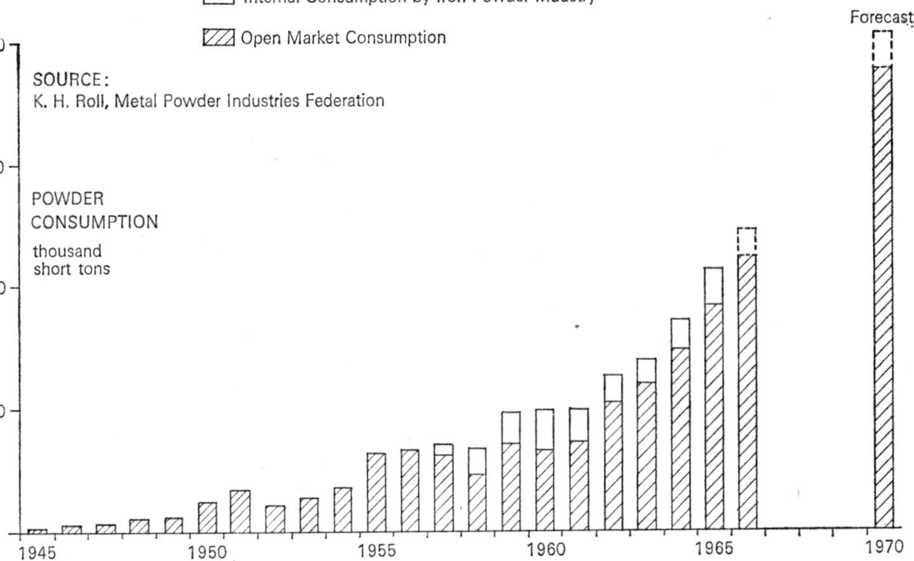

Figure 4. Total US consumption of iron powder.

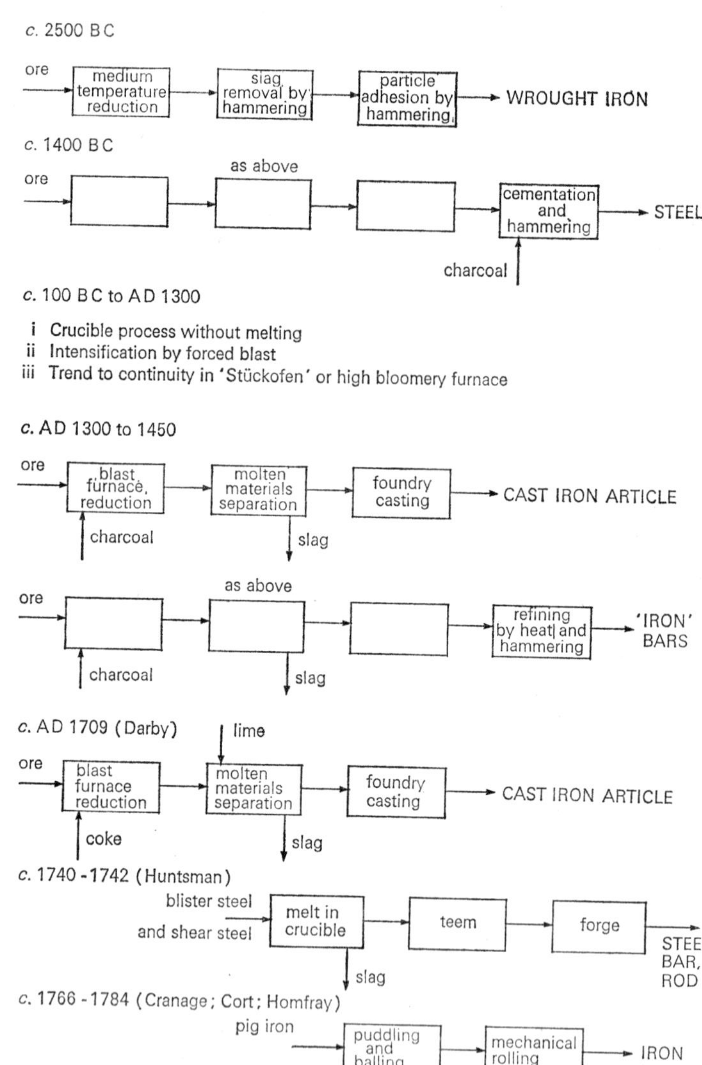

1856: Bessemer (with Musnet) takes carbon from pig directly by oxygen giving high temperature at same time
1865: Simeens introduces checker system for high temperature
1878: Gilchrist Thomas introduces basic process

Figure 5. Past changes in iron and steel making.

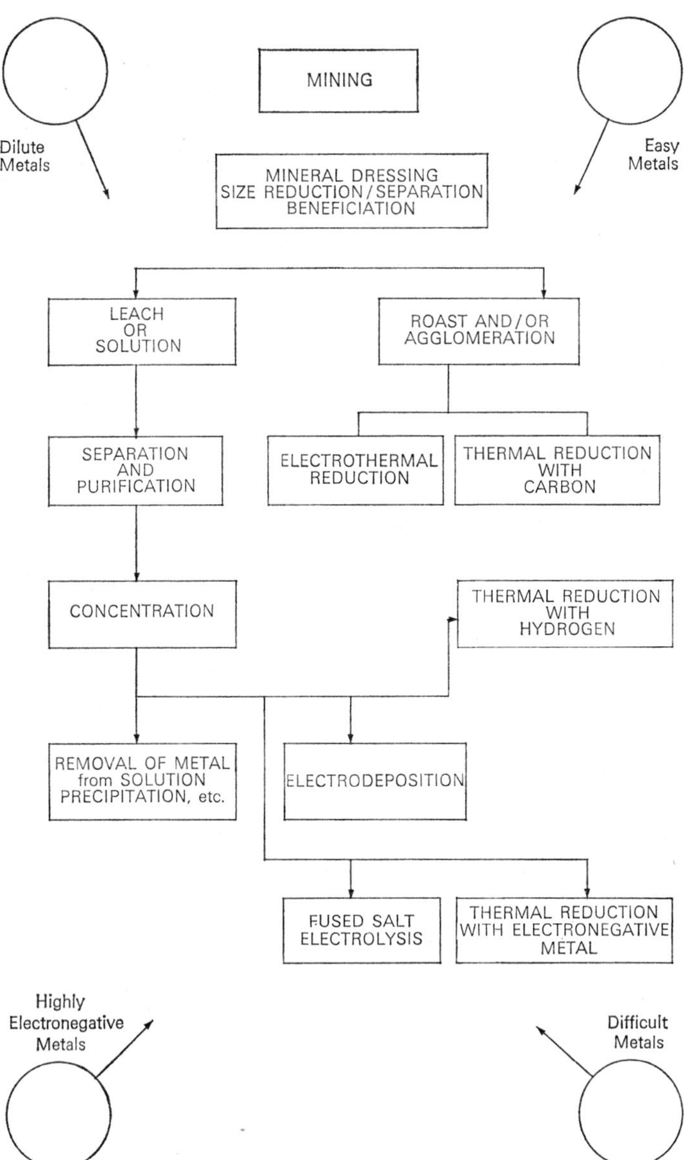

Figure 6. Metal extraction processes.

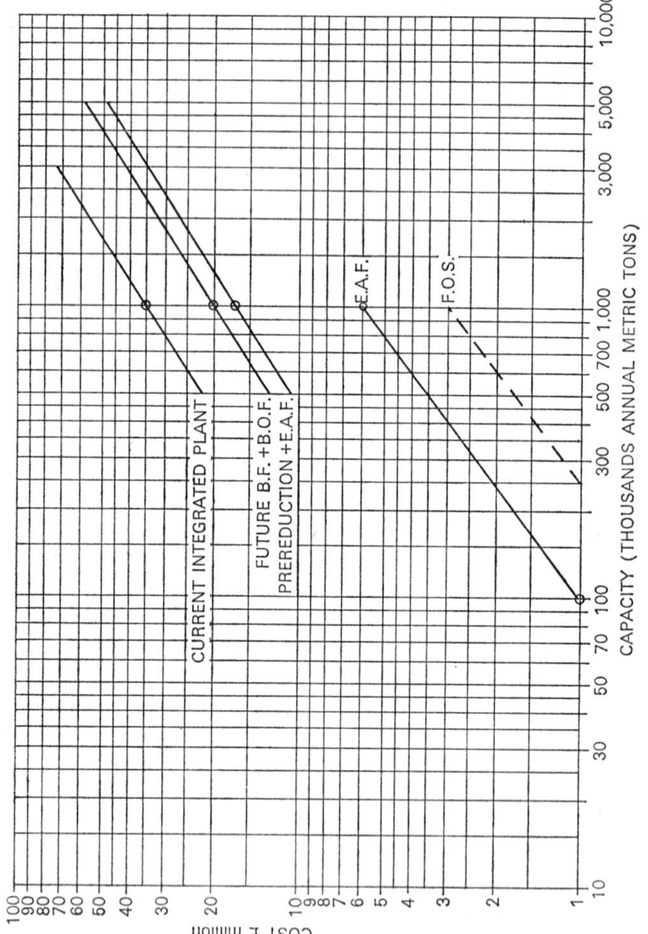

Figure 7. Capital cost—molten steel production.

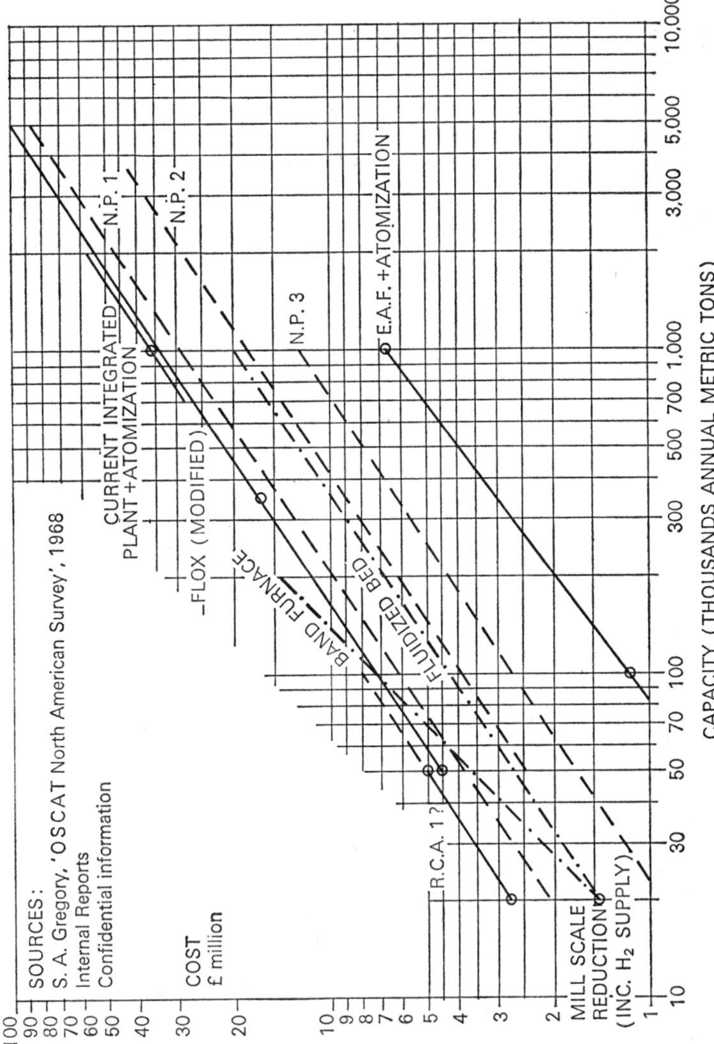

Figure 8. Capital cost—iron powder production.

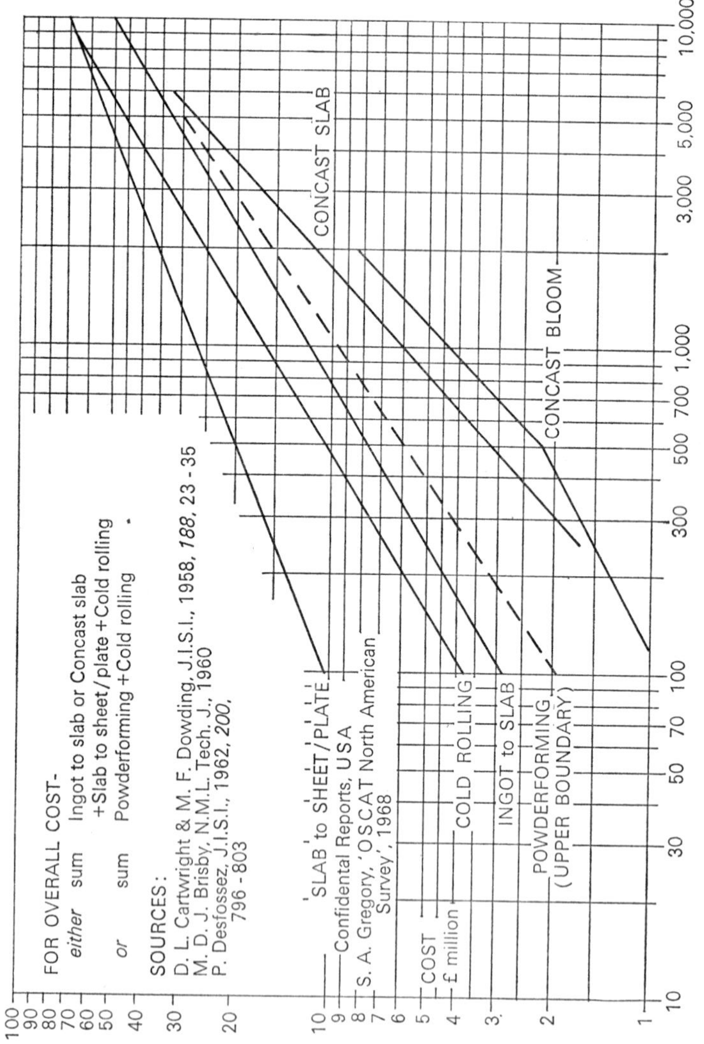

Figure 9. Capital cost—shaping processes.

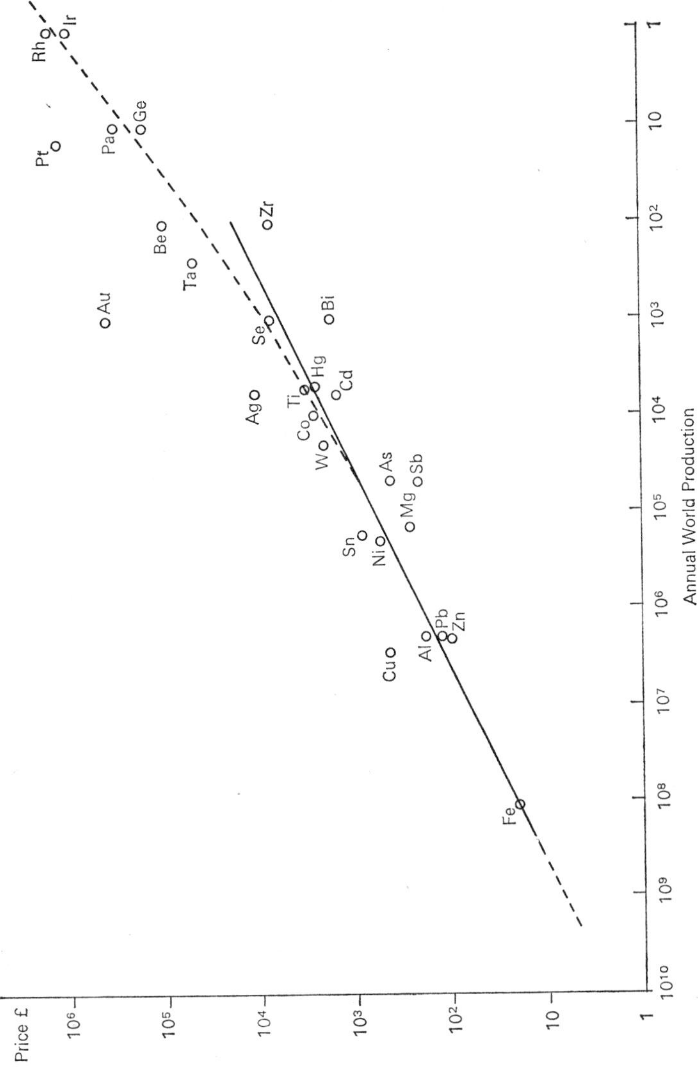

Figure 10. Metal production and cost.

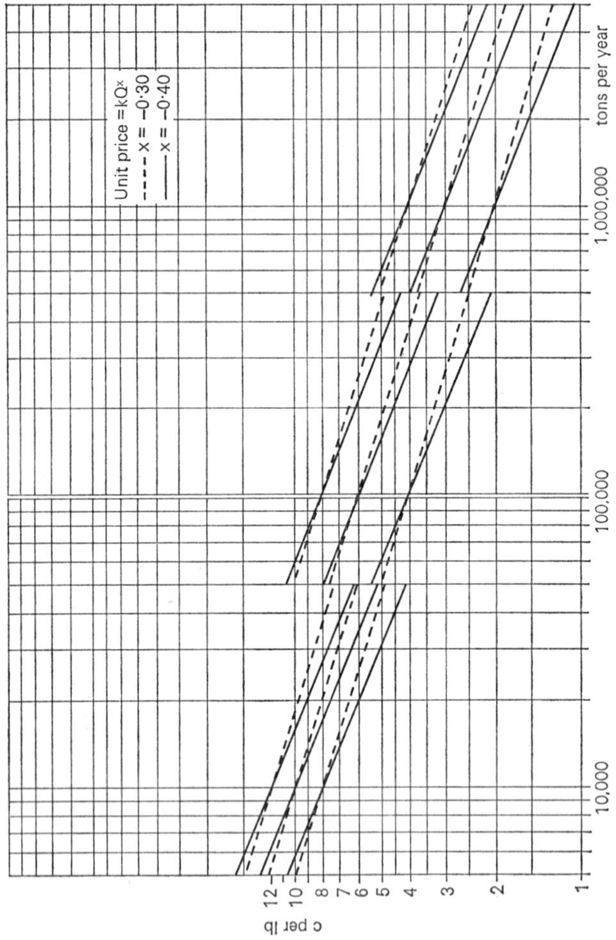

Figure 11. Exploratory curves relating price and quantity.

	Low capital cost	Feedstock 10,000 - 50,000 tpy	Feedstock 50,000 - 300,000 tpy	Feedstock above 500,000 tpy	Suitability for shaping variant	Minimum import disadvantage	Lowest cost reducing agent	Maximum scale - up advantage	Suitability for chromising. etc.	'Common' high purity	Use of least cost thermal energy	Large block nuclear heat energy
A. Mill - scale reduction / band	x	x			x	x						
B. Beneficiated ore reduction / band, etc.	x	x	x		x							
C. Beneficiated ore / other	x	x	x		x			?				
D. Molten metal atomisation	x	x	x	x	x	x	?	?				
E. Molten metal / protected	x	x	x	x		x		?	x			
F. Wet acid / pickle liquor	?	x			x	x		?			x	
G. Wet acid / scrap	?	x	x		x	x	x	?		?	x	
H. Wet acid / ore		x	x	x	x	x	x	?		?	x	x
I. Wet acid / ore (possible)		x	x	x	x	x	x	x		?	x	x
J. Dry acid / scrap (possible)	?	x	x		x	x	x	x	x	x	x	x
K. Dry acid / ore (possible)		x	x	x	x	x	x	x	x	x	x	x

Possible Shaped Products

Rate 50,000 tpy	*Powder preparation process*
1. Engineering compacts:	A, B, C, D, F, G, H, I, J, K.
2. Forging preforms:	D, E(?). F. G. H. I. J.K.
3. Thin strip:	D, E(?). F, G, H, I, J, K.
4. Alloy strip (chromium):	D, E(?). J, K.
Rate 300,000 tpy	
1. Sheet:	E(?). G, H, I, J, K.
2. Tube:	E(?). G, H, I, J, K.
3. Rod:	E(?). G, H, I, J. K.
Rate above 500,000 tpy	
Any product:	only E(?). H, I, K.

Figure 12. Powder processes and values.

TABLE 4A Iron powder production costs at different outputs (Chemical processes only)

All processes, where applicable, are taken as involving comparable requirements. Available information suggests this is not unreasonable.

Scrap is charged at £7·5 per ton of product. This assumes destructor grade or equivalent. Home ore is charged at £4 per ton of product.

Energy is charged at 6·75d per therm, and supplies heat, hydrogen, and motive power. Scrap-fed processes are assumed to need 300 therms per ton and ore-fed processes 400 therms.

Chemical losses are assumed constant and equivalent to 30 lb gaseous hydrochloric acid per ton. Labour requirements, including supervision, are assumed identical at all levels of operation. Round-the-clock manning takes only 150 men and their average cost is £2,000 per year.

Capital costs are read from Figure 8, with particular reference to New Process I and New Process III. Maintenance is 10 per cent of capital cost. Return before tax is 30 per cent.

			COST – d per lb			
Thousand tpy	*20*	*50*	*100*	*500*	*1,000*	*5,000*
Scrap (*a*)	0·81	do.	do.	? do.	—	—
Ore (*b*)	0·43	do.	do.	do.	0·43	0·43
Energy (*a*)	0·90	do.	do.	? do.	—	—
(*b*)	1·21	do.	do.	do.	1·21	1·21
Chemicals	0·05	do.	do.	do.	do.	do.
Labour	1·60	0·64	0·32	0·06	0·03	0·01
Capital charges overall 40 per cent						
New Process I	4·28	3·26	2·42	1·54	1·24	(0·74)
New Process III	2·03	1·46	1·16	0·67	0·53	—
Product cost – Figures in ( ) indicate £ per metric ton						
Highest	7·57	5·59	4·43	3·29	2·96	2·44 ?
	(71)	(52)	(41)	(31)	(28)	
Lowest	5·39	3·86	3·24	2·49	2·32	—
	(50)	(36)	(30)	(23)	(22)	—

COMMENTS. Directed initially at the highest cost process:

1. Since no allowance is made for sales cost these figures suggest that a chemical process without further development, is probably just competitive with existing commercial powder methods, although needing more capital, at the rate of 20,000 tpy.

2. At 50,000 tpy powder by a chemical route drops below 6d per lb at design output. This is the limit of a basis for a radical change in utilization.

3. At 50,000 tpy, or perhaps lower, sheet production becomes attractive, whether by the BISRA technique or according to other steelworks evaluations.

4. At rates above 500,000 tpy the cost of energy becomes dominant. Since energy has been charged in the table as if naphtha, lower costs should be readily possible.

5. Above 1,000,000 tpy it is doubtful whether much economy could be gained in capital investment. On the other hand large output capacity makes possible economy in energy cost by the use, e.g. of nuclear reactors.

6. The advantages to be gained in capital economy by using New Process II or New Process III is substantial. Given adequate development it should become possible with them to make iron powder as cheap as or cheaper than molten steel.

TABLE 4B Shaped steel products – overall capital investment, etc.

Pure iron powder may be made for costs which become lower as the output levels increase. The costs become attractive for the manufacture of different kinds of product at successively lower figures. As far as the steel industry is concerned there is the possibility that, with further process development, it may be economic to make materials such as thin strip at output levels as low as 100,000 tpy.

The opportunity arises because the capital investment for powder forming is only a fraction of that needed for producing the equivalent shape from molten steel. In Figure 3 the investment needed for powder forming to the hot band stage is only one-fifth of that needed using molten steel at an output of 100,000 tpy. At 5,000,000 tpy the investment needed is only one-third. These are upper boundary figures.

Although principal reference is made to flat-rolled products, advantages exist for other shapes, but so little work has been done on them so far that there is inadequate evidence to suggest the kind of advantage which, in some cases, might well be greater, e.g. in the case of tubes.

The substantial saving in capital investment, even the possibility of operating profitably at low capacities, can only be obtained by having supplies of satisfactory powder. For this reason, at the present time, the essential investment must be an overall capital investment for a complete system: powder production + powder forming + finishing. The saving only comes about as the result of system investment.

In addition to capital saving it should be noted that yields will be very high and energy consumption will be substantially less than conventional. In powder-forming the energy consumption is roughly proportional to the capital cost of the forming equipment since the capital cost build-up is strongly related to the amount of power-using equipment involved.

OVERALL SYSTEM CAPITAL INVESTMENT – Cold-rolled sheet

Molten steel system

Thousand tpy	*50*	*100*	*500*	*1,000*	*5,000*
EAF	—	1·0	3·5	6·0	—
Forward BF + BOF	—	—	—	—	58·0
Concast slab	—	?1·0	3·2	6·2	—
Ingot-slab	—	—	—	—	35·0
Slab-sheet	—	?10·0	20·0	27·0	53·0
Cold-rolling	—	3·8	7·7	16·6	46·5
Total £million	—	£15·8	34·4	55·8	192·5
Cost per annual ton	—	£15·8	£68·8	£55·8	£38·5

Pure ironpowder system

Thousand tpy	*50*	*100*	*500*	*1,000*	*5,000*
New Process II	—	—	—	18·0	54·0
New Process III	1·7	2·7	7·8	—	—
Powder forming	1·24	2·0	5·0	9·7	30·0
Cold-rolling	2·45	3·8	7·7	16·6	46·5
Total £million	5·39	8·5	20·5	44·3	130·5
Cost per annual ton	£108	£85	£41	£44	£26

TABLE 5 Iron and steel industry trends

A. *Production-orientated*

1. Cost improvement in existing plant through attacking major items of cost:
   a. iron-bearing feedstock – economies of scale, new source sites
   b. coke – reduction in use, replacement by cheaper fuels and reductants
   c. capital charges – increase in throughput, maintenance review
2. Cost improvement in new installations using existing process:
   a. capital charges – use of scrap, economies of scale
3. Cost improvement in new installations using modifications of existing process:
   a. energy and reductant – materials cheaper than coke, better location
   b. capital charges – elimination of process steps, directly or by getting other people to do them (continuous casting eliminates cogging; coking may be without by-product recovery)

B. *Consumer-orientated*

1. Concentration of effort on growth products, growth areas:
   a. products – sheet, tube, rod
   b. areas – motor cars
2. Concentration of effort on improved quality:
   a. mechanical performance, other function performance
   b. finish, appearance
3. Concentration of effort on new products:
   a. metal only
   b. composites

C. *Overall or System-orientated*

1. Concentration of effort on existing production resources, markets:
   a. operational research
2. Concentration of effort on possible production resources, possible markets:
   a. radical system design

TABLE 6 Preferable characteristics of new system (derived from Rogers). Features aiding innovator acceptance

1. *Relative advantage*: the extent to which a new idea is superior to those which precede it. Although economic profitability may be important, other factors such as reduction in labour needed, ability to withstand crisis conditions, etc. may be important.
2. *Compatibility*: the extent to which the new idea is consistent with existing values and past experiences
3. *Complexity*
4. *Divisibility*: possibility of part-trial
5. *Communicability*

R. CURNOW

A Summing-up

Summing up any conference is not easy; summing up this conference gives an opportunity to make some forecasts too. The facts are that we have had a very large attendance at the first international meeting on technological forecasting. Those attending are a widely disparate group from business, economic or R&D planners, ranging from systems analysts, representatives of the humanities, to those directly involved in the social impact of science and technology. Most of us are directly concerned in working from today out to the future, and because we are aware that this is not a total approach, I believe that we particularly welcomed the address by Professor Jungk which so clearly brought out the social responsibilities of us all.

To the question, is TF a subject or a non-subject? there can only be one answer. We all do it, however imperfectly. It is also clear now that we could all do it better, perhaps even in co-operation. This does not mean that we *should* do it, though I suspect that most of us would rather query just how much we should do of it! What in fact does the pay-off curve look like?

The work published so far does not help us. We need to know more about forecasts which have been made, the technological options discerned, and about the efforts which went into that work, before we can chart strategies for our own approaches.

To the next question, where do we go from here? the answer must be onwards. To my mind, TF at the moment is in a similar state to OR of twenty years ago – we can see some techniques, it's quite clearly a good thing, and quite clearly will offer similar benefits and pitfalls. It also rests on model building or systems analysis. But used to help us improve our future society, it is also clearly more important.

I conclude with a forecast: there will be more conferences on this theme, and the slow emergence of a discipline. As embryonic disciples, I look forward to meeting you all again to discuss the progress you have made, are making, and am confident you will make.